19-1-17

Dear Robin,

Here is a copy of
you find it interesting.
for all of the wonderful care that you gave
me.

I will always be grateful

Regards

On The Toss Of A Coin

Shocking, frightening, brilliantly and finely observed, optimistic, spirited, moving and very funny.

Cherry Mosteshar. Author and Literary Editor.

Irrespective of whether you have personal, hands-on experience of kidney disease, a mere passing association, or no previous link whatsoever, you will find this book, without doubt, an awesome read.

It is eloquent, factual and, in parts, extremely funny. It will have you laughing out loud at the absurdity of some of the situations that Michael finds himself in and also in tears at others.

It is a brutally honest account of life on dialysis. A warts and all insight into the welfare of the sufferer as well as the experience of his loved ones. A no-holds-barred account, which I found emotive and very inspirational.

His family and friends were distraught at being so helpless in his suffering, and yet they created an impenetrable force of love, affection and devotion which saw him through the darkest of days so that he could keep up the fight to see light once more.

I found myself feeling humbled and yet euphoric at the same time. His raw honesty in his use of dialogue, and the beleaguered world that he found himself in (particularly when recounting his time in a coma), was amazing. A complete shock at what it is like to be in a coma - a lesson for us all to make sure that the patient is always considered and included.

Although his story is so dreadfully sad, it is also uplifting. He takes the reader along with him on the journey, experiencing each process as if you were there, sensing and smelling every aspect. I found myself constantly willing him to keep going: Don't give up! Keep going!

Lawrence Keogh, Celebrity Chef, Author and Kidney Transplant Recipient.

There is an arbitrariness to life which can so easily shift us from one life path to a radically different trajectory that is well captured in this compelling memoir of a devastating illness. Disaster strikes in the form of toxic shock, causing acute kidney failure. What follows is an existential battle against the wide range of unexpected challenges that is a daily occurrence for those who have experienced critical illness, and for dialysis patients and their families. The kidneys are fascinating organs to study: they do so much. When they fail, the complications affect every system of the body. This book eloquently describes what it is like to face that daily uncertainty, the importance of family and friends and the inner resolve needed to 'win'.

I have been practising and teaching renal medicine for over a quarter of a century and recognise the struggles of many patients in these pages but I have never before read such an enlightening account. Michael Wise is an expert by experience; he is also a gifted writer whose story provides a deep understanding of what it is like to suffer kidney failure. Doctors and nurses, patients and carers, indeed all of us with an interest in the human condition have much to learn from this expert. The story is ultimately a personal one, that's what makes it a page turner but the message is inclusive. We all celebrate Michael's success and, as importantly, learn a great deal along the way.

Professor Donal O'Donoghue. Professor of Renal Medicine, University of Manchester. President of The Renal Association

Michael Wise has stared into the darkness of uncertainty, indeed worse, possible death. He fought it and with humour, recounts his awful experience.

I watched a close friend go from a shrinking sickly being to his old self, following a kidney transplant. It occurred to me that someone would certainly benefit from one of my kidneys.

Far outweighing any victories of steeplechasing, was the donation of a kidney to a person who I've never met. It is not the smug 'look at me, walking on air' glow, but rather just the satisfaction that part of my battered old body has given someone like Michael the chance to get back to living a life that illness has sapped!

Just ten weeks after the donation surgery, it was superb to return aged 69 to relive that old adrenalin rush, riding in the Legends Flat Race at Aintree on Grand National Day. However, it did not even come within a mile of the effect of the letter that I received from my recipient a week after the swop when he told me I had given him life again! Strong words that made an aged old jockey cry and I am watery eyed again now as I write this as a tribute to Michael's powerful, eloquent and deeply moving book.

Richard Pitman, champion jockey, BBC commentator, author and altruistic kidney donor.

About the Author

Michael Wise was a specialist in both oral surgery and restorative dentistry. He was Visiting Professor at University College London until 2011. In 2007 he was voted second in Dentistry's survey of "The Top 50 Most Influential People in Dentistry". He was the first dentist to to be awarded a Harkness Fellowship from The Commonwealth Fund, for two years of study in the U.S.A., which he completed at Indiana University between 1970 and 1972.

He is on the board of several NHS groups aiming to improve care for patients with acute kidney injury and is invited to lecture to the medical profession about his experience of illness.

He has been married to his wife Priscilla for forty-seven years. They have three sons and five grandchildren.

On The Toss of a Coin

*A memoir of a near-death illness…
and my fight for survival*

Michael Wise

Matador
9 Priory Business Park,
Wistow Road, Kibworth Beauchamp,
Leicestershire. LE8 0RX
Tel: 0116 279 2299
Email: books@troubador.co.uk
Web: www.troubador.co.uk/matador
Twitter: @matadorbooks

ISBN 978 1785899 218

British Library Cataloguing in Publication Data.
A catalogue record for this book is available from the British Library.

Printed and bound in the UK by TJ International, Padstow, Cornwall
Typeset in 11pt Minion Pro by Troubador Publishing Ltd, Leicester, UK

Matador is an imprint of Troubador Publishing Ltd

To Priscilla, the love of my life,
and Lorraine, the saviour of my life.
Without either of them, my world would be
but a pale shadow of what it is now.

Acknowledgements

Many people have enabled me to write my story. In 2012, Dr Chris Laing from the Royal Free Hospital in London first encouraged me to tell it to the medical profession. At his instigation, a presentation at the Wellcome Trust in London resulted in many requests to present to groups of clinicians around the country, and suggestions that I should write about my experience.

I am indebted to the late Professor Aubrey Sheiham, Natasha McInyre, Vivienne Carne, my friends, Larry and Margo Pedlar, Sharon Jacobson, my cousin David Franklin, Rabbi Josh Levy and my remarkable kidney donor, Lorraine Carne, who read all or part of my manuscript at various stages of its development and gave me honest and helpful feedback. My now deceased cousin Ronnie Senator clarified some of the family history.

My sons, Justin, David and Jon gave me invaluable help and advice throughout the process, from conception to fruition. Priscilla, my wife, read, reread and read again, all the time helping me to clarify and hone my writing.

Priscilla, David and Lorraine have written about their experiences which are included as appendices. I am grateful that they were willing to share their feelings.

Dr Mike Jones, Professor Donal O'Donoghue and Dr Chris Laing kindly reviewed some of the medical aspects. Anna Casula from The UK Renal Registry and Lisa Bradbury from the NHS Blood Transfusion Service provided help with statistical data on the number of transplants and transplant patients. Clinical Lead Dietitian, Renal and Diabetes Therapy Team, The Royal Free London NHS Foundation Trust, Sinéad Burke, was very helpful with dietary instructions for dialysis patients. Karen Thomas gave me permission to include material from the NHS Think Kidneys programme. Hilary Stanton Zunin and Leonard Zunin gave permission to reproduce the quote: "The risk of love is loss, and the price of loss is grief". Thanks also go to other sources who gave me permission to quote from them.

Katie Boyles had a profound influence on the manuscript. She stimulated me to convert the book from one that was almost a medical text into an emotional account of my journey. She encouraged me to write in a more autobiographical way and liberated me from previously self-imposed constraints. I am extremely grateful to her for this valuable help.

I am very grateful for the editing of Cherry Mosteshar. She raised some very challenging questions that needed answering and the text has been modified accordingly. She helped me to clarify thoughts on the direction of my narrative, which was very helpful. Lucinda Martin was particularly fastidious in the final editing of grammar and punctuation and I am very grateful to her for the effort, care and professionalism that she demonstrated.

Professor Donal O'Donoghue, Lawrence Keogh and Richard Pitman kindly read the manuscript and wrote endorsements.

Thanks also to my publishers, Matador, who have been extremely professional and helpful, guiding me through the publication process. Thanks also to Ben Cameron for his expert publicity campaign, helping to inform the public about the book.

Many other people played smaller parts with suggestions, information and support, particularly when I was becoming disheartened. I thank you all: you will know who you are.

I also thank all of the remarkably compassionate and professional members of the medical profession and their allied team members. They have provided me with outstanding care; without them I would be dead.

Finally, thanks go to the NHS. It is a remarkable institution, of which we in this country should be immensely proud and should try desperately to protect.

Contents

Introduction   xvi

Part 1: Intensive Care.
21st January 2009 – 4th February 2009
1. Darkness   3
2. Awakening   35

Part 2: Out of Intensive Care.
4th February 2009 – 27th March 2009
3. One step at a time   49
4. Mental distraction   57
5. Dialysis   66
6. Misunderstandings   79
7. Something to live for   83
8. Too weak to walk   85
9. Progress   92
10. Chop off my toes   99
11. Visitors   106
12. Lesson learned   114
13. Financial concerns   121
14. Release   132

Part 3: Home and Outpatient Dialysis.
27th March 2009 – 28th February 2010

15. Much-needed support	137
16. Not a good experience	153
17. An emotional boost	166
18. Back to the same routine	170
19. Setback	173
20. What a difference	181
21. The word gets out	189
22. A heartbeat away from disaster	197

Part 4: The Transplant and Subsequent Recovery.
1st March 2010 – November 2014

23. A part of someone else inside me	207
24. The Olympic pee	213
25. Things that are said	219
26. Regaining what I had lost	225
27. Medication	229
28. The next stage	243
29. Getting on with life	250

Part 5: Reflections

30. What has the effect of the journey been?	271
31. The arts	284
32. Munich	289

Appendices

I. Memories of Intensive Care – Priscilla, my wife	297
II. My son David's memories – aged 35 in January 2009	319
III. The transplant – my donor's experience	330
IV. My Coping Strategies	340

V.   Dietary restrictions for dialysis   342
VI.   History of dialysis   346
VII. Acute Kidney Injury (AKI)   348
VIII. Living kidney donation Questions & Answers   351
IX.   Useful links   359

Notes on Sources   365

Introduction

On the 13th June 1964, my father opened a letter from my mother. She had died the previous day at the age of forty-six.

"My Darling,

If I should have to leave you, please, darling, don't be sad. Just remember (as I am whilst writing) the happiness, and joy we have shared. The contentment of just being together. We had something rare and were blessed. God has been kind to us in us meeting and in the children. So, I'm reflecting, between us we have had a perfect relationship. Thank you, darling, for all your love. You always made me feel like your Queen, and what more can a woman want?

It would take years - no, perhaps it could be said quickly, to reflect on the past and know what real wealth we had between us. Wealth in laughter, love and tears. So I say we have been lucky and good things can't last for ever ..."

On the 27th of January 2009, my wife, Priscilla, could have been in a similar position to my father. I feel a shudder when

I think of how close we were to the precipice. But then I feel joy at the thought that she did not need to open my letter.

I can remember sitting on my mother's lap as a child, snuggling into her warmth, her hands and gentle voice caressing me while she told me stories about her family. One story that particularly intrigued me was about my grandparents. She repeated it many times. In 1902, Leah and Morris Franker fled with their three small children from years of anti-Semitic violence in Poland. In common with countless refugees over the ages they made the agonising decision to leave their home, work, family and friends. They set off afraid into the unknown, with very little money and no security. Leah travelled across Europe on a donkey carrying two-year-old twins. On reaching Belgium with Morris's brother and his family, they decided that one brother should stay there and the other should continue to Britain. They thought that if one of them encountered difficulties, then perhaps the other would be better positioned to help. Their fate was to be decided by tossing a coin. The toss sent my grandfather and his family to Britain and his brother's family initially stayed in Belgium. They then went to Paris and subsequently back to Poland where, during the Second World War, the family was killed in a concentration camp. But for the toss of a coin, that would have been my grandparents who were murdered, I would never have been born. Life can change in an instant and there is no reason why it should work out well.

This family story made me acutely aware of the fragility of life and I have tended to live according to an ancient edict: "Plan as if you will live forever, and live each day as if it were your last." The two concepts in this advice are frequently incompatible. Planning as if you will live forever would require great financial prudence, but living each day as if it were your last may result in the disposal of all financial support. It can also mean that we should plan so that our bigger dreams and intentions, which may take time to come to fruition, can still have a chance to begin. Yet, on the other hand, don't leave what's important (living a full life, a life of goodness, love and integrity) until later, because you may die tomorrow. It highlights the tensions in life and helps me to appraise my behaviour.

Why recount this background? Because I think it had a significant bearing on my attitude, response and fight for survival.

The toss of the coin came for me on Wednesday 21st January 2009.

PART 1

Intensive Care

21st January 2009 – 4th February 2009

1

DARKNESS

On Thursday 15th January 2009, life began to change. How quickly it did so.

I was sixty-two years old and possibly at the peak of my career as a specialist in restorative dentistry, a specialist in oral surgery and Visiting Professor at the Eastman Dental Institute, University College London.

I was jogging six miles three times a week and loving it, which is somewhat strange since I was never particularly good at running as a child. At secondary school, cross-country running at the behest of the somewhat masochistic physical education teacher was quite a torture. Besides running, there was singles tennis for between one and a half and two hours a week and mixed doubles twice a week for two hours, partnering Priscilla. I felt extremely well and vital.

Priscilla and I had a love of life, family, music, reading, piano and guitar playing (for me), theatre, art, jogging, tennis, swimming, skiing, travel and spending time with friends.

Suddenly, I'm nearly dead.

It might help if I describe my account partly as changes to my feeling of how well I felt, which I will describe as a wellness score. For the purposes of description, I will rate myself on Thursday 15th January 2009 as being 100 on my score. This does not imply that I was perfect, but the intention is for it to act as a baseline for future comparison. On Friday 16th January 2009, I visited a friend in a hospice and then began to feel a little bit under the weather, but nothing in particular, and I felt the same the next day. A six-mile run followed by a shower "threw off" the malaise, it's amazing how the endorphins can kick in. Sunday 18th January, feeling fairly well, but not as good as I had been earlier in the week (wellness score 80), my eldest grandson and I went to watch Spurs (an English football team). Those moments of being alone with a grandchild are precious and to be cherished and that I did, marred only by the terrible performance of Spurs. I can still remember that day clearly. What a feeling of continuity; I used to go with my dad, then with one of my sons and now with my grandson, the bonding is amazing and the event transcends age differences. That evening I felt that perhaps I was going down with the flu but it was a very mild sensation and we went out for a Chinese meal with some friends. On Monday 19th of January, I ran a one-day course for a group of dentists and, during the day, gradually began to feel unwell, again nothing serious and I still thought that perhaps I was going down with the flu.

By 4pm, however, I felt decidedly unwell and had to stop the course, something that I had never previously done (perhaps 60 on my wellness score). I sat down in an armchair and, apparently, according to one of my team, started to shake, but that did not last very long. That night I had a temperature and sweated but by the morning, I felt fine and vital, without a raised temperature (wellness score

85). I started work at 8.30 am and for the entire day, I treated a patient with a very complex problem. The treatment went exceedingly well without any complications. However, that night I felt extremely unwell, started vomiting and had diarrhoea as well as shaking. At one stage, I didn't make it to the bathroom while vomiting and I padded bare foot through the vomit. Thinking that perhaps it was food poisoning from the meal we had with our friends a couple of nights previously, I never imagined that it was anything more than that or the flu (wellness score about 40). My temperature was 38 degrees Celsius, nothing to be alarmed about.

The next morning, things went completely topsy-turvy: "the toss of the coin". I just about managed to get out of bed and thought that a bath would help me feel better but, once in, I couldn't get out because I felt so unwell. Although I have no recollection of it, Priscilla managed to get me out of the bath and to bed (wellness score 20). Previously, I had given her a list of things to do in an emergency. Top of the list for a medical emergency, other than an obvious need to phone the emergency services, was to contact a consultant physician from University College Hospital, who was also a specialist in intensive care. He looked after my medically-compromised patients. Priscilla felt that she was bothering him unnecessarily, but she gave an account of what had happened and, apparently, he said, "Dial 999 and get him over to University College Hospital immediately and I will have a team of people ready to meet him." By this stage, I was virtually unconscious (wellness score 0).

During the week, we lived and I practised in a London flat. Priscilla tells me that I was taken down on a stretcher from the fifth floor, into a waiting ambulance. I have absolutely no recollection of this. The memories of the ambulance journey are vague, the sound of sirens mixed with a sensation of swaying and lurching, total disorientation with things coming in and out of vision, nausea, weakness, sweats, shivering, but, fortunately, no anxiety that I can recall. Apparently, my blood pressure dropped to dangerously low levels in the ambulance. I was informed subsequently that on arrival at the hospital, the first stop was Accident and Emergency where the rapid development of a rash across my chest, together with a high temperature, shaking and exaggerated shivering (rigours) indicated that there was an infection in my blood (septicaemia). By this time, although I have no recollection, I was passing into a deeper state of unconsciousness and was taken to the Resuscitation Unit and then to Intensive Care Unit (ICU). Thankfully, there was a bed available. I still can't understand how ICU beds can always be available for the emergencies that require them. Presumably, sometimes they are not; I don't like to think about that. I understand that due to breathing difficulties, a tube was passed into my airway and through my larynx (intubation) to make a clearer passage for air. Subsequently, a diagnosis was made that I had a rare blood infection caused by bacteria, which can give rise to sore throats (Haemolytic Group A Streptococcus). When it invades the blood stream, it can be particularly destructive. In my case, the blood infection rapidly progressed to a condition named toxic shock, in which the bacteria release poisons into the blood and these spread around the body. This resulted in the failure of, or damage to, many of my organs. Although I cannot remember it, I understand that, due to my distress at this stage, I was placed into a drug-induced coma. Severe sepsis is a major cause of illness and death, claiming between 36,000 and 40,000 lives annually in the UK, with a death rate of about 35%. An admission with severe sepsis places the patient at a level of risk of death six to ten times greater than if he were admitted with an acute heart attack and four to five times greater than if he had suffered an acute stroke. I was therefore in a very vulnerable condition.

The origin of my infection remains a mystery. I have no recollection of sticking a local anaesthetic needle or sharp dental instrument into myself. Apparently, a thorough examination of my skin was carried out in ICU and this did not reveal any breach of the surface. Subsequently, I did find out from my hygienist that on the day prior to my beginning to feel a little bit flu-like, the new nurse with whom I had been working had acute tonsillitis, with a large amount of pus pouring out from her tonsils. Had I known this, I would never have allowed her to come to work; it would not have been good for her and would place patients, staff and me at risk. For many years, one of the UK's leading dental microbiologists came to my practice several times a year to run seminars for my study groups and to check our cross infection control procedures. In his view, it is plausible, but obviously not proven, that bacteria from the nurse's throat could have transferred to the aerosol water spray that emerges from a dental hand-piece. Despite wearing a mask, it is possible that inhalation was the way that bacteria entered my body. It is ironic that my team and I have always been meticulous with cross infection control and yet I do not know any other person in my profession who has contracted life-threatening septicaemia.

Memories of the intensive care experience are vivid and

obviously distorted by the illness and the medication, but I believe that some were triggered by what was happening in the room. As an experience (it cannot be described as a nightmare because at no time did it feel like that) most of the time there was a feeling of warmth and calmness, but my brain was working overtime. How was it for my family? I cannot begin to imagine, seeing me deteriorate suddenly from being fit, healthy and vital, to this non-responsive body lying on a bed with tubes everywhere, machines bleeping and total uncertainty. I understand that the medical team was fantastically caring to them, the nurses taking time to explain the meanings of readings and the physicians being realistic about the situation. How our lives must have flashed before them. To further complicate the situation, Jo, one of my daughters-in-law was six weeks from the due date for her second child; how about that for additional stress? Recently, one of my grandsons told me that, when thinking about me, he, his brother, his sister, his mum and dad sat in their parents' bed and all hugged each other and sobbed together.

So how to describe my experience? Weird would be a good word: no appreciation of where I was, what had happened or what was going on. Yet somewhere inside I knew that something had gone wrong and that there were doctors around. I could hear some of what they said, but could not respond to it. That wasn't frightening for most of the time, but it was a very strange position in which to be. Sometimes the meanings of words penetrated my brain and at other times they passed through me without any meaning at all. I can best describe the experience in relationship to smog or a white-out when skiing. I have many recollections of being caught in a "peasouper" in the 1950s on my way to or from school. Smog suddenly descended and was so thick that you could not see beyond your hand and voices appeared to be disembodied and floated in and out of the choking blanket that surrounded you. Due to the lack of visibility, movement felt unreal, almost like floating. In such a situation, your body feels as if it is trapped in strange cotton wool which engulfs you. My intensive care experience felt very much like this. The haze of being unconscious, but with a mind working overtime, the cushioning effect, which I presume was from the drugs and the voices sounding disembodied, penetrating periodically and disturbing my thought processes and adding to my disorientation. I would try to mentally reach out and grab hold of them, but they slipped through me and vanished. I was aware of people giving me their names but it seemed that they disappeared and a new voice with a new name would float in, sometimes causing confusion. It may have helped if the new voice had said, "Hello, I'm … I'll be looking after you now and have taken over from …" Perhaps they did and I don't remember.

In retrospect, I realise that many of my thoughts and hallucinations related to a feeling of being trapped. One in particular is, I think, quite amusing, if anything can be amusing in such a situation. Many years ago, when taking the Fellowship Examination of the Royal College of Surgeons in London, the word was that regardless of the quality of the applicants, only a certain percentage of candidates would pass and therefore small mistakes mattered. The oral examinations took place in an oak-panelled, hexagonal room, the entrance to which was through heavy, double oak doors. I opened the doors and walked in, sat down and answered the questions;

it was almost like being on automatic pilot. The bell went to indicate the end of the session, so I stood up, turned around, walked across the room and through the double oak doors, which I closed behind me in a bit of a dream. I found myself standing in a cupboard! My life seemed to flash before me: What do I do? Should I stay in the cupboard, was there anyone else in here, should I come out? I chose the last, and slunk across the room to the real exit doors that I could now see opposite me. The examiners were peering over the tops of their papers with what looked like smirks on their faces. On exiting the room, realisation set in that this was the mistake, no chance of passing. Candidates were told on the same day whether they had passed and, to my surprise, my result was positive. A ceremony followed immediately during which each successful candidate shook hands with the examiners. On reaching the chief examiner, I can clearly remember that he said: "We couldn't fail you after that could we?" My response: "I can't be the first person to walk into that cupboard." He said: "Never in the history of the Royal College of Surgeons has anyone walked into that cupboard." My family never believed my story until I took them to the room and it became instantly clear how this could have happened although, by that time, the cupboard contained shelves. The cupboard doors were a mirror image of the entrance doors. Why recount the incident? During the intensive care experience, there was a recurring dream/hallucination: I kept walking into that cupboard, but with a variation. After I closed the doors behind me I couldn't get out, surely a feeling of being trapped. I have no idea how, in this hallucination, I exited the cupboard in order to keep re-entering it, but I suppose that is the poetic licence of an hallucination.

Then a period of complete and utter nothingness, not a thought, not a vision, not a sound, nothing. Was this the same as death?

I experienced three states while in the coma: the first was a thinking, but externally unconscious, state; the second, a hallucinatory state; the third, oblivion. How was it possible to be aware of oblivion? It was not the same as sleep, during which there may be subliminally-perceived dreams or bodily movements. It was not darkness or blackness, since there was no awareness of vision, nor its absence. In fact, there was no perception of anything. The explanation lay in this lack of perception. It was an awareness during the thinking states that between the periods of mental activity, there had been a complete and utter void – nothingness.

On numerous occasions, I could see myself lying on a bed surrounded by pointed rocks, which were not as high as the bed. I could see other people on beds around me with masks on their faces. However, in reality, I was in a single room so the other patients were hallucinations, but it indicates a realisation of being in a medical setting. My feelings ebbed and flowed, somewhat like the tide and, as I felt myself sinking, I experienced a very strange sensation. It was the feeling of slowly, slowly, literally falling, uncontained, into some deeper state of oblivion. It was similar to the feeling that I experienced as a child during a recurring dream. That dream was of falling, falling, falling, only to wake up to realise it was a dream, but this time there was no waking. During this experience, the rocks grew higher and higher, surrounding me. Simultaneously, their solid appearance changed into a throbbing, vibrant luminescence. This luminescence was almost overpowering as the light became brighter and brighter, I felt trapped by the rocks, which were engulfing me, but strangely, once again, no fear. The vision then reversed and a feeling of recovery slowly crept over me as the rocks shrank and returned to their solid state; I felt as though I had won some kind of battle. This hallucination returned on numerous occasions and I think that it was related not only to my feeling of being trapped, but also of deteriorating and then recovering. I wonder if this was perhaps the near-death experience that some people describe?

Then a period of complete and utter nothingness, not a thought, not a vision, not a sound, nothing.

There were a few unpleasant experiences and one occurred during one of these rock episodes. I was very aware that I was trying to pull a mask off my face, although I was unaware that I actually had one on it. However, during the struggle, I could hear what I presumed to be a nurse or doctor saying in a very deep voice, "No, Michael, I'm not taking it off." Whether or not I actually said it, I don't know, but I was screaming in my mind, "Just take it off for a minute", but it never happened, it stayed there. It was a very unpleasant experience, feeling as if I was suffocating and it may relate back to my early childhood, when a general anaesthetic was administered for a tooth removal. In those days, a mask was slapped onto your face, accompanied by a feeling of suffocation and a horrible smell of rubber. In retrospect, I appreciate that the nurse or doctor was doing the right thing and I was probably going blue. Perhaps there was panic, or maybe a tube was being passed into my airway, but the memories are vivid; fortunately, they do not haunt me. Apparently, at one stage, I was very restless and tried to pull out the many tubes that had been inserted into my body.

I presume that the mask memory is related to that episode, but there is no memory of anything other than the mask.

Then a period of complete and utter nothingness – not a thought, not a vision, not a sound, nothing.

Another time I was wandering on a very strange seashore. It wasn't large, the sand was very coarse and the grey sea was gently lapping onto a slightly brown-coloured beach which was surrounded by industrial buildings with large chimneys belching black smoke. I kept trying to leave the beach, but couldn't; no matter which way I went, there was no way off: trapped once again. What was the significance of the industrial buildings with large chimneys belching black smoke? Could it be the smoke from a crematorium? Could it be that I was trapped in a concentration camp awaiting the gas chamber and the crematorium, a premonition of my own impending death?

Then a period of complete and utter nothingness – not a thought, not a vision, not a sound, nothing.

There were what seemed to be hours of philosophising about the medical ethics of using the initial cell which results from sexual reproduction (a zygote) but taking a pair from identical twins and using them to heal a sick person. I philosophised about zygotic pairs, don't ask me where that came from, I haven't a clue, although I have read much about evolution and perhaps that stimulated it. So, once again, something was registering that I was in a medical environment. Going through my head was the question of what are the ethics of taking good genes from a healthy human and transferring them to someone else who is ill, perhaps a realisation of my predicament and wish for healing?

Then a period of complete and utter nothingness – not a thought, not a vision, not a sound, nothing.

I revisited my religious journey and that led to considerable philosophising about religion. My journey has been long, starting as a true believer. At one stage in my teens, I seriously considered training to be an orthodox rabbi, but I slowly discarded my beliefs and replaced them with explanations provided by the theory of evolution. From an early age, I was completely absorbed by religious practice, attending religion classes three nights per week and Sunday mornings, in addition to services. My unthinking belief is not surprising, since I now realise that children are "wired" by the evolutionary process. They listen to and trust their parents and significant adults. Of course they do, otherwise in our ancient past their chances of survival would be greatly hampered by the hostile environment. Probably those who had credulity were the ones who were most likely to survive and pass on this behaviour to their offspring.

I clearly remembered my first experience of really feeling the presence of a god. I was ten years old and at school. The French teacher picked on various children to translate a passage from a book. Never being very good at translation I prepared one paragraph and prayed that she would pick me to translate it. As we approached the passage, the teacher called out my name. I felt as if a bolt of lightning had struck me, shivers ran down my spine and I could feel myself offering up thanks. That childhood impression of a god who could answer my prayers stayed with me for a very long time. I never really thought about all of the pleadings that went unanswered. Although I was deeply accepting of the practice and beliefs of my religion,

I cannot ever really remember questioning the existence of a deity until I reached my late teens. When my mother died from a blood clot in the major artery supplying blood to her brain (a stroke), I attended synagogue every day for a year to say memorial prayers during the service. The question of how a benevolent god could allow her to die at an early age never really entered my head, but I was devastated by the loss and by seeing the utter destruction of my father. He was unable to function normally. As I walked along a street with him clutching my hand, his face would suddenly crumple. A deep wail followed, sounding like a wounded animal and then floods of tears. I felt his body shivering with anguish. The feeling of his agony lodged deep inside me and, at the age of seventeen, it was the first time that I had witnessed the grief resulting from the sudden and shocking loss of a loved partner. It was a raw, primitive outpouring of emotion which he could not hide from me. I knew that my parents had experienced a truly happy marriage and realised that the sudden and untimely passing of my mother was almost beyond my father's comprehension.

They met when they were teenagers. My father recounted to me that they had been in love from their first meeting and their passion for each other had survived the years, becoming more meaningful with the passage of time. Apparently, on one occasion, long before they were married, he was saying goodbye to her. She was standing on the platform of a bus and he on the pavement. She plucked up the courage to say to him, "Joe, my brothers won't let me see you anymore." Almost dumbstruck, he stammered a reply, "Why not?" She responded, "They don't think you're good enough for me." So ironic; he was very poor, but they were not so well off themselves, just in a better bad situation. He said, "What do you think, aren't I good enough for you?" She jumped off the bus into his arms and said, "I don't care what they say I love you." I suppose I always had internalised their sharing, caring and loving relationship.

During the year of mourning, I started looking around during the services and, probably as a result of the shock, found myself feeling distanced. For the first time, I was able to observe, watching the repeated behaviours and the repetition of words. It was then that my thoughts began to change. Why would a god require all of this? How could each religion have a direct line to God by their particular practices? Did it mean that the other practices got nowhere, yet each considered theirs to be the correct ones? Why does a god who knows our thoughts and plans have to listen to our prayers? If a god created human beings and then left it up to them to shape their world, why would we need to pray? If there was an omnipotent god, how did it come into existence? If there was a benevolent god, why is there so much evil in the world? Animals struggle to survive and frequently experience a gruesome death, as do many humans, why? Saying that these questions were unanswerable, the response that I frequently received, was not satisfactory for my mind. Early cultures thought that the world was flat, but science disproved this, they thought that the sun revolved around the world, but science disproved this. The belief in many ancient societies was that the spirits and gods made their presence known through disease, but science provided explanations that are more satisfactory. Early societies believed in gods or a god as the creator of the universe and grand designer and many of these beliefs survive, but science has provided the evidence for evolution, the theory of which stands up to rigorous testing and enquiry. Survival of the fittest also provides a good explanation for the presence of evil. Genes do not have morality. Was what I had been taught real or fabricated for a variety of reasons? For example, religious practice keeps a group together and therefore improves its chances of survival through mutual security. A belief covers the otherwise inexplicable, yet with knowledge, the inexplicable becomes explicable. A specific structure and philosophy gives power to certain individuals, which is to their benefit, and it also provides social cohesion, as do the laws and customs of any society.

Many people may say that I doubted because of the loss of my mother, that this was an angry reaction to her death, an attack on the god who should have protected her and me. On the contrary, it cleared my head to think, to free and enlighten me. I wasn't angry, I was accepting of her death. Unbelievably sad, empty, low, lost, but I felt a new inner strength. Her death started me thinking, as opposed to absorbing without thought. This was the beginning of a very long journey of reading and reflection which, by the time of my illness, had led me to the conclusion that I am an animal, I had evolved, and the external god that I had been trained to believe existed was not real for me. It existed inside me as conscience, morality, compassion and many other facets of thought and emotion, all of which are essential for survival of the species. These are for me the product of the evolution of the human brain, which is a very special organ and the centre of my being. Yet its evolutionary process is no different from, for example, the evolution of limbs from fins. The more I thought and read, the more I accepted this view. I was very aware that some theists put forward arguments for the compatibility of religious belief with evolutionary theory. The arguments had not persuaded me of their veracity. My views were subsequently further reinforced by the cogent analysis of Steve Stewart-Williams in his book *Darwin, God and the Meaning of Life*. Drawing on biology, psychology and philosophy, he argued that Darwinian science supports a view of a godless universe devoid of ultimate purpose or moral structure, but that we can still live a good life and a happy life within the confines of this view. He does not, however, argue that evolutionary theory provides a licence for immoral behaviour.

Some may say that my illness was divine retribution for casting off belief. I cannot refute the opinions of others, nor would I wish to challenge them, but I can say that such views do not resonate with me. I never had such thoughts, nor the feelings of guilt that may be associated with them. This does not mean that I rejected the importance of religion for human beings. Certainly not, provided that adherence does not cause persecution, unwanted isolation, conflict, terrible feelings of guilt and despicable crimes to be performed in its name. I can see that, for many people, faith, spirituality and religion help them through their lives and give them structure, purpose, solace, great joy, happiness and a reason for their existence. In common with other human constructs such as nation states, political ideologies and limited companies, it also facilitates the cooperation of large numbers of strangers. However, throughout history, crimes have been perpetrated in the name of religion, but I see similar crimes in the absence of religious belief, such as in Hitler's Nazism, Stalin's Soviet Union and Pol Pot's Cambodia. Perhaps the fundamental problem is that groups of people frequently cannot tolerate differences in others and prejudice arises, particularly at times of economic difficulties. This may be the result of a basic evolutionary drive for survival. But, human beings are social animals and the hope is that development of intellect would suppress the aggressive primordial behaviour. Unfortunately, in too many instances, this does not appear to be the case.

Then a period of complete and utter nothingness – not a thought, not a vision, not a sound, nothing.

I had vivid memories of recognising that my family belonged to a particular group with a long history of persecution. It crystallised when I was returning from religion classes at the age of about eight. Walking home in Stamford Hill (long before it became an area inhabited by a large orthodox Jewish community), I was confronted by youths shouting anti-Semitic and vile comments. They didn't know me, I was not wearing anything distinctive and had never done anything to harm or confront them, yet they wished me harm. I realised that if I did not outrun them I would come to grief. Running the gauntlet became a regular activity and, occasionally, ended with me being caught and assaulted. I wondered why my parents didn't protect me; I really don't know the answer. Perhaps they felt that there was nothing that they could do and that, following the war, they needed to "keep their heads down". This period has lived with me and, if anything, made me proud of my heritage, but it also gave me a desire to integrate with, contribute to, succeed and participate in the wider community in which I live while retaining my identity. I take great delight in the family and community of Reform Judaism which treasures, among other things, Jewish tradition, a vast resource of thought, discussion and philosophy, the ability to evolve in response to the contemporary world, gender equality and the building of a just society. I am very comfortable with my involvement in the absence of a belief in the existence of a god. I appreciate that many people may find this difficult to understand. There may also be those who do understand, those who openly have a similar opinion and those with a similar view, but who are afraid to admit this to themselves or others. I accept the sentiments of others as being personal to them and always hope that they will be as accepting of mine.

In my comatose state, I replayed all of this like a movie in my mind and I found my views tremendously comforting, since why shouldn't bad things have happened to me? There was no reason why they shouldn't. I recalled sections of a book by Steven Pinker, Professor of Psychology at MIT – *How the Mind Works*, a book that greatly influenced me and I was surprised that I could remember the arguments that he put forwards. The concept of being no different from any other animal gave me great peace. However, I also philosophised about what it may be like for people with different views, particularly those who consider that bad things happen as a punishment for sin. It seemed to me that any religion or belief that has a concept of hell must have the concept of punishment for sin. What an awful position to be in, not only being in this unknown situation, but also possibly feeling that this is a punishment. I had been taught that if I followed the religious commandments and lived a moral life, it would give me access to a happy afterlife. Scrutiny of this indoctrination swirled around my mind and, even while gripped by the awful illness, I rejected the concept of an afterlife. Thoughts also occurred about people who were unsure of their beliefs. I philosophised that people with a strong religious conviction may feel comforted by this, but those who were unsure would not be able to draw upon that comfort. I recognised that people with deep religious belief may consider that God had preordained this to be the path for them and I respected that, but it was not the view that I adopted prior to my illness nor during it. Therefore, both the deeply-held religious conviction and the lack of conviction could give comfort, which was an interesting conclusion to come to in my comatose state of total non-responsiveness to the outside world. These thoughts went round and round my head and, in a very strange way, the philosophising was very pleasant. How long it went on for, I haven't a clue, because there was absolutely no concept of time, nor the difference between day and night. Everything just blended into a state of very strange being. I felt content, peaceful, contained, warm and free from anxiety, almost like a brain living freely and detached from my body.

Then a period of complete and utter nothingness – not a thought, not a vision, not a sound, nothing.

The TV programme Star Trek always appealed to me and, at one stage, I believed that I was being transported to another planet where they had medical therapies similar to those available in Star Trek. For any reader who is a "Trekkie" you may recall the doctor holding a gun-like implement over the ill or injured being (not always human) and healing them with some sort of squirt from the gun, without penetrating the skin. In my hallucination, I was transported through corridors with large, silver pipes passing across the ceiling.

This was followed by a long wait in a holding area on a trolley before being placed in a tube-like spacecraft and "beamed up" (by the way, Captain Kirk never said: "Beam me up, Scotty." He said: "Scotty, beam us up."). I wonder if this hallucination related to being taken on a trolley to have a CT scan, the scanner being the spacecraft. Interestingly, in the new University College Hospital there are large silver pipes running along the walkways to prevent beds or trolleys from banging into the sides. Could I have seen these, even though the family said there was absolutely no indication that I was responding to anything?

In my hallucination, it was very clear that on the planet to which I was being transported there would be some form of special sterilisation. Interestingly, new sterilisers had recently been installed in my practice and I was very pleased with them, an obvious trigger. There is not much recollection of what happened to me on this planet after arrival, other than receiving treatment from some form of "super dooper" special globulin, administered through a non-penetrating gun-like device.

Globulins constitute some of the proteins found in the blood. Some of them are associated with the immune response and the fight against invading bacteria. I understand that I did receive immunoglobulin as part of the treatment, and perhaps I had heard this? Apparently, hallucinations are common among intensive care patients. Many have feelings of persecution by doctors and nurses, by alien abductions and from bizarre hallucinations of sea voyages. Fortunately, my alien experience was pleasant, and you probably won't believe this, but it was almost fun! I felt as though I was right in the midst of the programme.

Then a period of complete and utter nothingness – not a thought, not a vision, not a sound, nothing.

Our fortieth wedding anniversary was due three weeks after the toss of the coin. On 24th January, a fourth round FA cup match was scheduled between Spurs and Manchester United at Old Trafford. In my unconscious state, there was a very clear aerial view of the Old Trafford stadium on a beautiful sunlit day; the air was clear and fresh. Crowds were milling around and, just outside the stadium, there was a large open-air restaurant. The restaurant was full, except for one table that I could see in bright sunlight. It was set up for customers who were not there. I clearly remember thinking, "I've brought the family here for the match and for a special lunch to celebrate our fortieth wedding" – going to the match would be about the last thing that Priscilla would want to do – but, obviously for some reason, we were not there. Suddenly, three circular areas appeared in my vision and each seemed like a video. In the one on the right, I could clearly see Priscilla and she was talking to me, saying, "Hello, my lovely," but I could not answer her. Even today, five years later, I can still hear her saying it – how we cling to the words of those we love, but unfortunately, we can do the same to the words of those who hurt us. The latter we should discard and the former we should hold on to and savour. In the central area were my sons, and in the left-hand one were the anaesthetist with whom I worked, the intensive care specialist who Priscilla contacted at the beginning of this saga and a cousin who worked in the hospital. The images were clear, distinct and separate from each other and, subsequently, I found out were actual and took place with them standing around my bed as the sedation was lifted. Warped logic crept in to my thinking.

The fact that I could not communicate with Priscilla was

interpreted not as a problem with me, but as a problem with her. I suddenly realised that she was not at the restaurant table because I had killed her. I "rationalised" that, since two of my sons were in media and the other had a computer science degree, they had put together a video of her to make me think that she was there so as not to distress me. I then realised that I couldn't communicate with my sons and they, too, were absent from the table, so I must have killed them as well, perhaps in a car crash. Slowly but surely, the thoughts and the logic (or non-logic) entered my brain and squirmed around inside. I too was missing from the table and, therefore, I must be dead and everything I was experiencing was death. What was the response to this? Was it fear, trepidation, wonder, resignation, hopelessness, helplessness, awe? It was none of these, the thoughts were very clear and remembered well: "If this is death, then I don't mind it, it's not too bad at all and, anyway, if I've killed the rest of the family I don't want to be alive." The strange workings of the human mind. Was this another near-death experience?

Then a period of complete and utter nothingness – not a thought, not a vision, not a sound, nothing.

At one stage I could clearly see giant rats walking across the wall, they kept coming and coming and then stopped and then came again. Once I was out of the coma, I realised the trigger for this related to the Venetian blinds between my room and the adjacent room. The blinds were half closed. As people walked across the window in the adjacent room, their clothes moved between the slats and I think this initiated the hallucination. Why rodents though? Perhaps rats represented destruction, danger, ruthlessness, voraciousness, decay, devouring everything in their paths – all of which relate to illness and disease – the workings of the subconscious mind. Perhaps I had heard about the gangrene in my feet and legs? It seems feasible that there was an association.

Then a period of complete and utter nothingness – not a thought, not a vision, not a sound, nothing.

One recollection of hearing is embedded deeply in my mind. Remember that I could sometimes hear, but not respond. I heard somebody say over me, "We think he's had a major stroke". My cousin Michael, who is a few years older than I am and is very dear to me, had a major stroke in his early forties. I should add that he has made an amazing recovery, but when I heard those words, I recalled the immediate aftermath of his stroke. The thought went through my mind, "If I'm going to end up like that I don't want to live." I could feel myself giving up the fight, death would be a release. I understand that there was a sudden deterioration around that period. I subsequently heard somebody say, "He hasn't had a stroke," and once again I can clearly remember thinking, "I don't know what's wrong with me, I don't know where I am, but it's not going to get the better of me, I'm going to fight it." That resolution has remained firmly with me ever since, and the recollection is vivid. Apparently, it was around this time that I suddenly started to improve. Of course, I may not have actually heard the words regarding a stroke, it could have been an hallucination, but my son David was with me, and he reports that a doctor used the word stroke. In addition, I have read the intensive care notes, and, while written in medical terms, they also refer to the possibility of a stroke and then to the results of tests showing that this had not occurred. I can imagine that the word stroke was used when describing these events to the family. It is also possible that I heard medical terminology and, because of my training, interpreted this as a stroke.

While I can still remember thinking about my cousin's stroke, I have the feeling that my thoughts of giving up in relation to a stroke went much deeper. It seems cruel that a word, which can have such a gentle meaning in everyday life, can have such a devastating association in illness. My cousin Michael's stroke must have had a significant effect on me. He is four and a half years older than me and was my childhood hero. If he played in goal, I played in goal, if he read a comic, I read the same comic. When he rolled around on the floor with the eleven-year-old girl who lived opposite him, I, at the age of seven, rolled around the floor with her sister, not having a clue why I was doing what I was doing. In addition to my cousin, in my childhood and adolescence I had witnessed the effects of strokes on my mother, my father's brother and my maternal grandmother. I had also heard about my paternal grandmother's stroke. These events all came back to me and I viewed them as if from afar. Sometimes they were like the fragmented pieces of a jigsaw puzzle, but other visions were a coherent whole. Obviously, my mother's stroke affected me deeply, but my grandmother's stroke also left a very deep impression on me. She was a very kind person, who always looked about eighty years old to me. No surprise that she should have aged: she lost her husband in her forties and had given birth to thirteen children, nine of whom survived. She was quite short and had an upright, aristocratic posture. Back absolutely straight, head held high, with long silver hair tied tightly back in a bun. I remembered her holding a handbag when she went out, looking like a precursor to Margaret Thatcher. My mother, father, sister and I lived upstairs to her in a small house of which she occupied three rooms on the ground floor. She did not speak any English, only Polish and Yiddish and so I found it hard to communicate with her, but I knew she loved me. I frequently watched her mannerisms and can clearly recall her scraping the inside of an apple with her lower dentures. If she tried to bite it, they would fall out. I often reflect upon how my grandchildren may observe and interpret my mannerisms, and particularly those which they observed when I was desperately unwell, but out of the Intensive Care Unit.

During the Festival of Passover, four small cups of wine are drunk during a recounting of the story of the Exodus from Egypt and this is followed by a meal. My grandmother (Bubba) used to make wine for all the family. She had a large zinc bathtub into which she placed grapes, a large piece of pure white muslin was positioned over them, and then I was invited to climb in and tread the grapes. I can remember doing this from about the age of four. Oh, the delight of having grape juice squirt up my legs and onto my face; with Bubba leaning over the bath with her crinkled, angular, pasty face curled up in a smile while she hummed a tune to accompany my trampling. I can remember my shock when, on one occasion, her full dentures dropped out into the bathtub and her face instantly transformed from an eighty-year-old to that of a corpse. I had many happy times with her, and loved her very much; although sometimes, I must admit, her appearance frightened me. I can clearly remember one incident when she was babysitting me. She had a nine-inch EMI black and white television. The picture was viewed through a thick magnifying glass, which was permanently fixed to the front. We were watching what I knew to be a film, but she thought that it was the news. An atomic bomb was dropped on London. She picked me up, rushed under the kitchen table and sat there pulling me close to her until my parents arrived home. I can still feel the trembling of her bony frame as she held me so tightly, but I was pleased that she had misunderstood, it felt so good to be cuddled up to her. In her living room, there was a coal fire which had a water boiler in the back of it. This fireplace, together with an Ascot heater in our bathroom, provided the hot water for all of us. I used to love watching the coal man delivering sacks of coal from his horse and cart. His coalman's hat, cocked nonchalantly to one side, protected his wrinkled, weathered forehead and a leather sheet placed over his right shoulder protected him from the rubbing of the coal sack. He poured the coal through an opening into an underground bunker. I would shovel up the coal and bring it to Bubba for her to put on the fire. One day, when I was about nine, my sister Trisha came home from school at lunchtime. She knocked on the door and, after a considerable wait, Bubba opened it for her. I cannot imagine the devastation for Trisha when she saw our beloved Bubba standing there, one side of her face and hair completely and severely burned; her description is seared into my mind. Bubba had a stroke, fell into the fire, somehow managed to get herself up and struggle to the door. She died shortly after that. This and other memories of strokes were deeply embedded in my subconscious, no wonder I wanted to die.

Then a period of complete and utter nothingness – not a thought, not a vision, not a sound, nothing.

There was a time when the family were called in to say goodbye to me and, whether or not it was at the stroke episode, I would not know. I was not aware of their ordeal. The intensive care record on 24th January 2009 states, "Discussion with multiple family members, explained: Michael is critically ill, he has multi-organ failure, he may not survive, but some people do."

My mother's family are all fighters, not in the physical sense, but in the sense of making good out of bad situations and I think that attitude passed on to me, whether genetically or behaviourally or both I would not know, but thankfully it did since I had resolved to fight. There was a report from one clinician subsequently that said, "This patient was succumbing and miraculously there was a turnaround." I have no doubt that this was a result of good medicine, but my mental state must have greatly influenced the outcome. What can be learned from this? Primarily, even when clinicians think that a patient is completely non-responsive, they should never talk across them other than to say encouraging things. If I had heard the first part of the stroke diagnosis, but not the second, I can only guess as to what the outcome would have been. Certainly, on hearing the first part, I had given up and willed myself to die. The power of the human mind should not be underestimated and can perhaps be utilised to help a patient's recovery. In my journey, I have come across clinicians who are excellent but seem only to be concerned about the figures in results and the readings of machines, not the person, and I have also come across clinicians who gave me hope, encouragement, compassion and empowerment.

Apparently, my feet and legs were going black from the toxic shock, the drug used in large doses to raise my blood pressure (noradrenaline) or a combination of both. I understand that at one time, a registrar said over me, "We'll probably have to amputate his legs." My son David asked him not to talk like that across me and his response was, "He can't hear anything so it doesn't matter." David said, "You don't know that, stop it," but he didn't and it was necessary to call in the consultant to prevent him from continuing with this. Fortunately, I only had to have nine toes almost totally amputated, my legs recovered. If I had heard him, I do not know what my response would have been, but I have a feeling that I would have given up. So much can depend upon so little.

After talking about my experience to a group of clinicians, an intensive care specialist clearly told me that everything was hallucination and nothing related to the room at all. My response to that is how can a clinician claim to know what's going on in your head and what triggers it? After the experience with this particular clinician, somebody came up to me and said, "I know exactly what you're talking about, my son was in the Army in Afghanistan and was caught in an explosion, and he was then unconscious in intensive care. Over his bed was a red flashing light and he hallucinated that he had been captured by the Taliban and was being tortured by a laser beam and couldn't move." For me, this is another example of how something in the room can trigger an hallucination and how a patient feels trapped. He was less fortunate than I was, since I could imagine that his hallucination was excruciating. I do not know what can be done about these things, but I am sure that with more thought, new ideas could be forthcoming.

On the subject of hearing, the sounds of my family were very comforting. In retrospect, I would advise that the family should talk to the patient, keep them informed of the world, tell him/her where they are and give comfort and love. It is very lonely being trapped in this strange world and any small realisation of the ones you love penetrating it gives tremendous comfort. Hearing Bach and Mozart that my family played was also comforting, but I have explained how the voices of the medical team could have a negative effect. Interestingly, some clinicians say that there are patients who have an intense dislike of music during this period, but music is part of my being. Fortunately, I was not aware of hearing any alarms from equipment. I can imagine that these could be very distressing to some patients, particularly if the nurse leaves them ringing for a long time because they are routine and of no particular consequence. To a patient, all alarms are potentially "alarming".

There is growing evidence of poor mental health and quality of life among survivors of intensive care. Particularly those whose breathing was maintained mechanically by a machine for more than 24 hours or those who had two or more organs supported by a machine, (I had both). As clinicians become more aware of this, perhaps they will become more aware of how the patient's environment, physically, visually and audibly, can have a long-term effect. Fortunately, I do not seem to have succumbed to many of these psychological outcomes; although my emotions are now very fragile, as I will describe later in my story.

In my late teens, I had started to think about the possibilities of determining whether what I experienced is real or if it is a dream. How did I know that I wasn't seriously ill in a hospital bed and everything that I thought was real was in fact an hallucination? I grappled with this conundrum for many years, never to resolve it, but was reassured to find that it is a very human question, which dates back to time immemorial. Plato had posed the same problem in which Socrates is in discussion with Theaetus and the question was, "What proof you could give if anyone should ask us now, at the present moment, whether we are asleep and our thoughts are a dream, or whether we are awake." I had now lived my thoughts, I had been in a hospital bed unconscious, living in an hallucination that I thought was real, but the reality was the coma. That irony was not lost on me when I thought about it later in my recovery.

From my experience, it would be wrong to assume that all patients who are in a coma are unaware of everything. I am sure that the medical teams do not make that assumption. I could hear, not all of the time, but certainly some of the time, occasionally see, and certainly my brain was working overtime on multiple philosophical concepts, which I know intrigued me. Being locked in my own little world was strange, but not unpleasant. My brain seemed to be divorced from the destruction of the body that it normally controlled. Similar perhaps to a military command centre buried deep in the ground, but unaware of the destruction above it. According to my family, I made no response to vocal or visual stimuli, although there was the occasional flicker of an eyelid. They had absolutely no idea of what, if anything, was going on in my mind.

Surviving this phase raises a major question for me, namely how and when is a decision made to turn off life support because a patient is not responding? How do the doctors really know what's going on inside that amazing organ we call the brain? What are the differences between someone who shows no response and somebody who is locked into their body, but somehow can't transmit to others that they want to be released from their torment? I was not responding, a machine assisted my breathing, my heart had sustained damage, my lungs were collecting fluid, a machine replaced my kidneys, and I was developing gangrene. The tests to show that I was alive were presumably positive. My brain was very far from dead, yet my family could not see that I made any obvious response to outside stimuli. While I support the concept of assisted death in appropriate circumstances, I have some niggling thoughts. Will the registrar who so blatantly talked across me about amputating my legs or the individual who spoke about the stroke change their attitudes about their respect for the patient with the passage of time? Or will they retain their attitudes and be the ones to make the life and death decisions? While I appreciate that one individual never makes these final decisions, the whole experience does give rise to concerns and questions which are perhaps almost unanswerable since the answers will undoubtedly change with time, knowledge and technology, but hopefully not under the influence of political views.

As I came out of my coma, it must have been incredibly difficult for my family. They didn't know whether I would actually wake and if I did whether it would be me, some grossly incapacitated person, a gibbering wreck of a human being, paralysed, partly paralysed, unable to process thought, blind, deaf or mute. This was not a part of life that anyone would want to experience. I understand that their mutual love and support helped them enormously, but for unsupported individuals, this situation may be even more excruciating. While it was not my fault, I do have a lingering grief that can eat away at me, causing my gut to knot; due to me, they had to endure this awful ordeal. It was for real, not a dream.

2

AWAKENING

"Fucking hell, where am I?" Were my first words on waking, which is a little strange because I have never sworn around my family nor, for that matter, very much around anyone. David then explained what had happened and I am told that an expletive was once again the order of the day since I replied, "I don't fucking well believe you" – maybe this broke the tension for the family, I don't know. I recall seeing a nephrologist standing at the end of the bed, he had bright braces to hold his trousers up and I recognised him subsequently in another location. Severe pain developed in my right leg, which was controlled by the strong opioid painkiller tramadol, combined with endless massage from my son Jon and daughters-in-law, Jo and Davina. This was the first time that I had experienced real discomfort and perhaps some distress at not being able to escape from it. As I slowly re-entered the world, the realisation of surroundings became more obvious, as did that of the state of my body. Weakness, emaciation, stubble, black toes, blackish legs, hands and legs that I could not move. It didn't feel as though I was paralysed, more that I was restricted and then, on looking, I could see that I was. There was a layer of thick, unyielding skin covering my legs, feet, hands and arms. A surgeon came with a big pair of scissors and with glee cut through this skin layer, as if he was cutting through a piece of cardboard, opening a present. Once he had cut all the way along he peeled it off very much like a snake's skin, what a relief to be able to move. My brain was scrambled and I could not concentrate on anything. I knew that I was being extremely short-tempered with Priscilla, totally out of character but I couldn't stop myself, it was excruciating. It felt as if my brain was separate from me and was taking control, making me into something and someone that I disliked intensely, as though a monster had taken over my body. The pain of being like this when she was trying so hard to care for me still lives with me. I know that it was not intentional, but that was how I was acting while I lay weak and emaciated in my bed (wellness score 5).

Now that I was conscious, I experienced another hallucination. Butterflies appeared everywhere, on the ceiling, on the walls, on people's faces and their clothes. There were pink ones, blue ones, purple ones; butterflies with spotted wings, butterflies with triangles on their wings and many more shapes. Butterflies are not something that I had any particular attraction to, so where they came from I do not know, other than probably the effect of the drugs. I can remember saying to Priscilla, "What's wrong with you, you've got butterflies all over you, can't you brush them off?" I did find this quite disconcerting because it was impossible to remove them from my visual field and I began to wonder whether they would ever go away, but fortunately they slowly "flew away" never to return.

The weather had turned very cold, with masses of snow and, when my bed was wheeled to a window, I was amazed to see the transformed landscape. There was a blanket of blazingly white snow covering the buildings and roads. The sky was blue and the sun shone. People walked almost as if in slow motion, leaning forwards with slightly hesitant footsteps, leaving clear imprints of their shoes or boots in the pristine surface of the snow. It looked so quiet and peaceful as if the world had changed, without me being part of that change. Public transport was in great disarray, yet the nurses either stayed with friends to ensure that they could be at work on time or made other arrangements to ensure that they would be there to care for the patients. It was truly amazing to see the dedication and lack of self-concern these people had. Many of the nurses had obvious, deep religious faith and felt that God had given them a calling to care for the sick. Despite my own views on the existence of a god, their belief, faith, sincerity, gentleness and goodness were quite overpowering, and frequently, when they expressed their views, these initiated waves of emotion that exploded with sobs of gratitude, respect and indeed some awe.

There was now a dramatic change in my response to music, it became excruciating, I could not bear to listen to it; it pained, it jolted, it jarred, it stimulated horrible sensations, and I felt lost. There was a realisation that I was experiencing a massive bereavement. What would my world be like without music?

A life devoid of music was unimaginable to me. The thrill of feeling music enter my body, frequently sending tingles down my spine, was remarkable. It demonstrated to me that being a receptacle of music is not just about hearing, since music has the incredible ability to affect the whole body and mind. It can pass into and out of you in a flash, it can linger, it can disappear only to later reappear in your mind, it can alter your mood, reaffirm life, generate feelings of spirituality and sometimes it can get into your head, driving you crazy with repetition yet it is such a life-enhancing medium. It can teach us about life, since as in life it can build to periods of beauty and ecstasy, but these cannot be sustained for its entire duration. Realistically, they will fade. Similarly, with periods of sadness, grief or sorrow. There are of course many, many other effects of music on the human being, but to go into all of these would mean writing a book just on that.

Making music with other people has been a great source of happiness, as has listening to it. I have had wonderful times at family singsongs, my niece playing the piano and my sons, nephew and me playing guitars while we, my sister Trisha and the rest of the family, sang. It was a privilege to be part of rock group during my university years and we travelled around the country playing in numerous locations. It allowed me to see very different parts of the UK, meet and interact with people from vastly different social backgrounds. We played in community halls, on council estates, glitzy hotels in London's West End, pubs, dance halls and a regular venue in Portsmouth in which there was always a fight between various sailors at about 11 pm. We also had a regular gig once a month performing for the evening at the very popular Whisky a Go Go club in London's Soho, and were contracted to the American air force bases, travelling around to entertain their personnel. How I loved playing lead guitar in that group. I organised the rehearsals, venues, travel and the other administrative tasks, all of which were incredibly valuable in later life when I led a professional team. It gave me excellent training as a team leader and a keen eye to be able to assess the functioning of other teams. Observing how teams functioned became an interesting and important diversion when I was admitted to hospital and became part of my strategy to remain focused outside myself, otherwise the effect of my illness could have mercilessly devoured me. When I was at university, I had a split life, studying in the day and evenings, rehearsing and travelling around the country at weekends making music. Priscilla became a groupie and came along whenever possible. My friend, who was to be our best man, often looked after her. We were young, carefree and happy. However, as I became older, classical music predominated my musical tastes. My mother was the instigator of this. She ensured that our home was constantly filled with music of all types, but predominantly classical, which she provided either from an ancient radio, by singing or from vinyl discs played initially on a wind-up HMV gramophone which was subsequently replaced by an electrically operated player. I distinctly remember singing along with her at an early age to the famous tenor Beniamino Gigli while he performed Your Tiny Hand Is Frozen (Che gelida manina), from Puccini's opera La Bohème. Or she would wheel out a bronze-coloured food trolley and place some music on it. She would then encourage me to pretend to conduct to Tchaikovsky's violin concerto played by Jascha Heifetz. Piano lessons were mandatory. She taught me that music could bring me more happiness than anything money could buy. How bereft I was now.

There are vague recollections of two very helpful physiotherapists coming to assist me in getting up from the bed; what an ordeal that was. "Slowly, slowly, turn, slowly put your legs over the side, slowly stand-up while we support you," and then rapidly feeling my emaciated, weakened legs collapse beneath me. Back on the bed, try again, same again, exhausted back on the bed. However, after returning for several attempts, we were successful. I felt a great sense of achievement and could feel the love, excitement, and feeling of encouragement from my family who surrounded me. There were wonderful photographs of my grandchildren placed within my immediate visual field as well as drawings and paintings that they had produced for me. I spent hours just looking at them and feeling a sort of energy coming towards me from them. It must have been good therapy for them to while away anxious times feeling that they were doing something to aid my recovery and, indeed, now that I could take in their creations they did just that.

During this period, something started to happen that I realised was amusing but didn't really register at this stage. However, it continued throughout the various hospitalisations that I experienced. The something was nurses, doctors and occasionally a cleaner asking for a dental opinion from me. To this day, I don't know whether it was just to make conversation, whether they were testing my ability to think and communicate or whether it was truly seeking an opinion. I have a feeling that much of the time, it was the latter because there were so many fingers placed into mouths pulling lips back for me to look, that it would be hard for it to be just conversational. I was always very happy to give an opinion if I could, for what it would be worth in my disorientated state, but I suppose it was good that I wasn't in some other speciality!

The intensive care experience lasted for two weeks, out of which I understand ten days were spent in a coma.

Throughout this whole experience, other than the mask on my face, I had absolutely no sensation of tubes being inserted into my veins, arteries, nose or throat. Nor did I have any soreness from needles, tubes or any other device – quite remarkable. At the end of the intensive care stay however, I did experience a very unpleasant procedure. It was necessary for a plastic tube to be inserted into my jugular vein. At that time, I didn't know the reason for this. An obviously inexperienced clinician carried out the procedure and even though some mild sedation had been administered, I have vivid memories of somebody struggling and taking what seemed to be an inordinate amount of time to carry out the procedure, pushing, pulling and a feeling of panic from him. I am not complaining, just recounting. Despite this incident, I am left with an enormous feeling of gratitude for the care, dedication, kindness and professionalism of the staff in that Intensive Care Unit and also a relief that I was so fit when struck down. I and the clinicians doubt that I would have survived had I not been so.

I was sufficiently aware now to realise that I had nearly died and my future survival was still in the balance.

Death has been no stranger to Priscilla and me. My mother died unexpectedly from a stroke, at the age of forty-six, two weeks after a hysterectomy. She had come home, gone to the toilet and suddenly there was an enormous thump. Rushing into the toilet, I found her lying unconscious on the floor in a pool of vomit. I was seventeen at the time and it was the day before my A-level exams. She was the baby of her eight siblings and the family was completely devastated. I can clearly recall seeing her lying on a bed in the Whittington Hospital, with a sheet pulled up to her neck, but with her deathly white feet poking out from the end of the sheet. At the corner of her mouth was a dribble of bubbly saliva and her face was contorted. It seemed that all of the family surrounded the bed and the anguish was palpable. Then shortly afterwards she died. It took me years to be able to drive down the road past the entrance to the hospital through which she went on her final journey.

For the remainder of his life, my father never came to terms with my mother's death. He would frequently break into sobs when thinking about her and he spoke to her every day. Many years after my parents' deaths, Priscilla and I went to see Antony Sher in a play about Sir Stanley Spencer, a British artist. My mother's birthday was on 5th March and my father's on the 7th. We saw the play on 6th March. At the end of the play, Spencer's wife had died and he was painting and started talking to her in the same way that my father had to my mother following her death. I was hit by what felt like a bombshell of emotion, bringing out deep sobs. The impact of art on my emotions was apparent, and it has become more profound since my illness. The pain of death and the pain that it caused my bereaved father have never left me and the thought of causing such pain to my loved ones is a deep concern to me.

My father died at the age of seventy-eight from a heart attack, shortly after surgery for cancer of the colon. It was 1994, he was staying at our house and I was very excited to come home and tell him that the publishers had agreed to publish my dental textbook, only to find an ambulance outside the house, he had died suddenly with Priscilla by his side.

My closest friend, who was to be my best man and who

looked after Priscilla while I played rock music, died on the operating table three weeks before our wedding. Priscilla's mother died at the age of thirty-nine when Priscilla was nine years old and her father at the age of forty-eight when she was sixteen.

A session in the sauna with a very dear friend always followed my singles tennis. While baking in the heat, we solved all the problems of the world, only to find that they came back the next week and so we started again. Sadly, in September 2011, he unexpectedly had a massive heart attack and dropped dead on a path in Snowdonia. What a tragedy to have to come to terms with the loss of one so dear at a time when my life wasn't that great, as will become clear later. We had a common childhood background and both became dentists, studying at the same university. He was incredibly insightful, caring, generous and well read. There were no barriers between us and we could discuss our inner feelings and fears without any concern of crossing a boundary and getting into something that would be too sensitive or would erect barriers between us. He was my friend and I loved him, so his death was devastating. While I write this, I can feel the pain of that loss rising up inside me. Death is never easy, but is as real as birth and is as much an act of living as is being born. He told me that his mother never cuddled him. Not being cuddled by his mother was a major difference between us. My mother and father, numerous aunts and uncles and great cousin Kate cuddled me constantly. Great cousin Kate was my mother's cousin. She was great in many respects: tall, with beefy arms, bulging bright red cheeks, enormous lips painted with post-box red lipstick and, with what seemed to me as a child, to be gigantic, pendulous breasts. When she

43

saw me, she would make a beeline across the room, grab both of my cheeks between her thumb and forefinger, squeeze my cheeks and ask, "Mikala, how are you?" – I was petrified, but I recognised that this was an expression of love. The love, warmth and caring of family and close friends, expressed by physical contact, has been enormously important to me but has probably led me to have wrong expectations of some people. I find it difficult when I am in need of this physical contact and overt expression of care and concern, to be with people who are unable to express or give it. I realise that this is a fault of mine, not of theirs, but it is a deep-seated feeling. When my body was being ravaged by illness, that need for warmth in relationships became extremely important and haunted me when I felt a distance.

However, these experiences of the finite nature of mortality have helped me to be realistic and not shy away from the fact that my death is inevitable. This inevitability is best accepted as part of life, and that is a healthy attitude to have. Both my parents taught me that the only certainties in life are birth and death. This does not mean that death does not cause unbelievable pain and anguish to those left behind, but life will not continue forever. There is a price to pay for taking it for granted because it can slip by like a dream, never really being grasped, wasting precious minutes, days, weeks and years as if there is a limitless supply of them in a bank of time.

I was alive and, if I had anything to do with it, I was going to stay alive for as long as possible.

And so I finish the first and in many respects the easiest part of my journey, but perhaps the most difficult part for my family (wellness score 3-5). I had been locked away in my own world, without distress, feeling cosy and warm and the only pain of which I was aware came as the sedation was lifted. Interestingly, however, on reviewing the intensive care records, there were many entries stating how agitated I was at times, trying to pull out the tubes and climb from the bed, yet I have absolutely no recollection of that. I had the freedom to philosophise, frequently I am sure with ridiculous outcomes, such as my zygotic pairs' episode, but nevertheless my mind had total freedom. I was insulated from the outside world, other than for the intrusions of voices, which for most of the time didn't bother me, except for the stroke incident, which had a major impact. If I had not survived, then I would have slipped into the same nothingness that existed for all of those millions of years before I was born and I would have known nothing of it, so no fear of that outcome. I do not believe in an afterlife so no fear of hell nor an expectation of a promise of paradise. Of course, for my family the loss would have been enormous and perhaps that is a form of hell that we subject our loved ones to by prematurely exiting this world. This is so beautifully described by Hilary Stanton Zunin and her husband Leonard: "The risk of love is loss, and the price of loss is grief."

PART 2

Out of Intensive Care
4th February 2009 – 27th March 2009

3

ONE STEP AT A TIME

One, two, three, lift. That was me they were talking about as I was slid from the bed onto a trolley, like a large, inert sack of potatoes. There was just time to say one final thank you to everyone around me before being wheeled down the corridor, lights on the ceiling passing by one after the other. I wasn't sure if it was them or me moving. Faces seemed to be flashing by, voices coming and going. The calmness of Priscilla's voice floated over it all, through the doors up the ramp and into the ambulance. Why was the blue light flashing, why was the siren screaming, this couldn't be for me, was it real? The ambulance started, swaying as before and I had strange recollections of my previous almost unremembered ambulance trip. Then I saw Priscilla and Jon's faces over me, Jon is my youngest son; they were smiling, obviously trying to reassure me. Since I have insurance, I was being taken to a private hospital for what would hopefully be a recovery period. The thought of having my own facilities rather than being on a ward was a good one (wellness score 5).

Through a somewhat hazy consciousness, the decision firmly made in ICU was reinforced, "I don't know what's wrong with me, but I'm not going to let it get the better of me and I'm going to fight it." I resolved to observe my reactions, what was going on around me, what was done to me, the way doctors and their teams worked, the reactions of people around. I tried to think about all of this as a project. I was both a patient and a clinician, which may have given me a unique insight. Challenges have always attracted me and that is probably why my practising career revolved around treatment of very difficult and complex problems. Once again, I realised that I had challenges before me and almost felt excited at the thought of facing them and trying to overcome them if I could. During Priscilla's first pregnancy, she was helped enormously by Betty Parsons, who counselled women with sound advice. I have always remembered some of the words of wisdom from this very charismatic woman. She instilled the message that "labour can be viewed as something that may get out of control or it can be viewed as climbing a mountain, where the challenge is to get to the top, but each step must be taken one at a time and only that step thought about. Some steps are more difficult than others, but once taken they never need to be taken again, they are behind you, one step closer to your goal." This analogy has served me well for many challenges in life and would serve me well again during this most momentous of challenges.

Deep inside, I had internalised my mother's often-repeated message to me. She said, "When you do something, you will have to deal with the consequences whatever they are, but always ensure that you can be satisfied that you have done your best." My parents didn't bribe me with promises of presents for passing exams, they wanted me to feel that I had tried my best, and that was good enough. I realised that I was not in a competition and that, however hard I tried, I may not be able to overcome my illness but, on the other hand, I was determined to try my best in my fight.

As said earlier, my mother's family are fighters and two of my cousins and their families stand out; they have always had my love, admiration and deep respect. One is Michael who had the stroke and he, like me, was not expected to survive. But, while having disabilities from his stroke, he has lived life to the full and has always been positive. Eddie, who is now in his seventies, had a car accident at the age of twenty-one and has been a paraplegic ever since. He and his wife Sue have lived remarkable and inspiring lives, doing amazing things, always with a positive outlook however hard life has been for them. What incredible role models these people are for me, if they can do it so can I. I started repeating a personal mantra to myself, which has remained deep in my psyche, "I can and I will do it, maybe not immediately, but I will do it." The fighting spirit of my mother's family and their ability always to look on the bright side of situations were very helpful to me.

Another thought went through my mind during the ambulance journey. A good friend of mine frequently quoted a saying to me, which possibly emanated from Confucius, "Our greatest glory is not in never falling, but in rising every time we fall." He interpreted this as "we should never be afraid to go after something that we want for fear of failure. We all need the courage to try. We may not get there straight away and sometimes we may never get there, but we must not be afraid to give all that we can to go after our goals and dreams. Unless you put yourself on the line and give it your best shot, you'll never know what you could achieve". This concept has helped me in many situations both in life in general and in my professional life, now I would need to put it to its ultimate test. I had certainly fallen and that was a fact, I needed to pick myself up and give it my best shot.

So on the journey in that ambulance I made further resolutions, which were to become my template for the next four years and beyond. I would not give up, I would face the challenges and, bizarrely, try to enjoy and learn from them. So strange that so many thoughts and so many conclusions could be drawn on that journey, but perhaps it was the knowledge of a transition, a new stage in my life, even though I was feeling so rotten. Sometimes the movement from one situation in life to another is a time for reflection; I was now starting on the next climb up the mountain. Perhaps I would only ever remain in the foothills, but I would take each step one at a time and give it my best shot trying to get the most out of the experience. I appreciate that many people may say how could you possibly think that way in such a situation, but that's the way my mind works and in retrospect it seems to be a very good strategy. Possibly, I had already climbed the steepest part of the mountain; I didn't know what lay ahead of me.

Out of the ambulance, into a lift and up to a rather nice room, but to my surprise it was carpeted. I had thought that hospital rooms would have hard floors for cleaning purposes. (wellness score 5). Prior to my illness, I had developed substantial allergies to dust, beech trees, pollen and the hair of some dogs. Many years ago, I tried a course of desensitisation injections which, after the third injection, resulted in my sinuses feeling completely blocked within thirty seconds of the injection and some breathing difficulties. Amazingly, at the time the clinician told me that it was nothing to do with the treatment, but to me that seemed ridiculous. I felt that I was well on the way to a massive, possibly life threatening, allergic reaction (anaphylactic shock) so I stopped. The treatment actually made me even more sensitised to allergens and Spring was always a difficult period. On entering this room, when I inhaled, there was a feeling of allergen passing into my airway, which perhaps was coming from the carpet. That night was a difficult one with substantial breathing difficulties, only alleviated by an oxygen mask. Of course, the breathing difficulties could have been due to problems with my heart and fluid on my left lung, but the recollection of feeling allergen pass into me during breathing is still crystal clear. Perhaps the oxygen mask provided a double benefit, namely oxygen and clean air. I asked to be moved the next day.

The manager was very obliging and moved me to a non-carpeted room, but as I entered it on a trolley, I breathed in and could feel allergen passing into my airway once again. Breathing suddenly became extremely difficult and I did have a feeling of panic. I called for help and said, probably quite forcefully, although I did not have much energy in my voice, "I have to get out of this room I can't breathe, get me out." Perhaps I was being a difficult, confused patient, I do not know. What transpired next was possibly one of my worst experiences. It still lingers with me, coming back from time to time to haunt me. A male nurse leaned over me and placing his face about two inches above mine said in what seemed to be an incredibly menacing voice, "I've met people like you before and I know how to deal with you," and with that, he walked away. Talk about abusing a patient. The feeling I had was quite overwhelming, not only was I feeling desperately ill, but also I felt totally at the mercy of this individual. In writing this now I feel such empathy for the people we read about whom care workers have abused, it is appalling. Fortunately, my family arrived very shortly after this episode and, having told them what happened, they were able to have me moved to another room which had an air-conditioning unit. This seemed to clean the air and I was able to breathe without difficulty. I asked the ward supervisor not to allocate that nurse to me again yet to my horror, two days later he was. In no uncertain language one of my sons arranged for a change of nurse. However, I did feel a total lack of compassion and sensitivity towards the patient's needs. How do vulnerable people without advocates survive in such scenarios?

It was now much clearer that my sensations had altered. I had indeed become hypersensitive to some allergens; exposure to them precipitated breathing difficulties. The inability to listen to music tormented me. I couldn't focus on it, it literally hurt my brain, it agitated me, made me crave for a return of the pleasure I previously gained from it and the feelings and emotions it evoked, but it had gone, left me, leaving a mental pain behind. This loss made my situation seem spiritually bereft. I wondered what else had changed. I soon discovered the answer. I found myself mentally counting. It would go on and on, impossible to stop, sometimes almost driving me to distraction. "Fight to stop it," I would say to myself, but to no avail, the incessant counting would persist. Sometimes it was clearly at the forefront of my thinking and at other times like a metronome clicking away beneath the sound of music. Was it brain damage? I didn't know, but it did concern me. I suspected that it might be the inception of an obsessive-compulsive disorder, possibly related to anxiety. I did not report this to the clinicians, feeling that I had enough on my plate already. This mental counting lasted on and off for about a year. I was slowly able to force myself to reduce it by initially setting a limit of one thousand on the counting, and then nine hundred and so on. It gradually diminished until, to my great relief, it faded completely.

The nurses who had now been assigned to me were very empathetic, compassionate and caring, but I did have the feeling that the hospital was geared more to acute care pre-and post-surgically than to patients who were severely debilitated and, in this case, one who was to remain there for forty-nine days. I understand that, at the early stage, I was still on the critical list and my survival was in the balance.

There seemed to be a marked difference between the day and night nurses. The night sister was delightful, made me feel secure and cared for, but there was a range of night nurses. Some were excellent, but some seemed very uncaring. During the night when you are on your own, having difficulty sleeping, wondering, mind racing and then becoming tangled up in stray thoughts, gentle, compassionate care would be welcomed. This was always available from the day nurses when they came into the room but not always so forthcoming from the night nurses. Every night, I gave myself the same challenges. How will I react tonight? On a score of 1 to 10 (1 being good, 10 being awful) how would I score the night? Will I need oxygen? Will it be from a mask or nasal cannula? How does that compare to last night? Will the night be long or short? How quickly will the nurse come if I need to call her? If I can't sleep, will she make me a cup of tea and a slice of toast, which I found very soothing?

This may all sound very simplistic but the conversion from being a passive recipient to somehow being actively involved made a tremendous difference and helped me through the sometimes long and lonely nights. Even though sleeping pills assisted my sleep, I woke early in the morning and my mind instantly started to race.

4

MENTAL DISTRACTION

What do you do with a brain that was doing mental gymnastics and a body that felt as if it hated you? I tried hard to make my mind seek out episodes in my life which were in some way associated with what I was experiencing. Sometimes, these scenarios popped into my head without me thinking. I found that this strategy helped me to detach myself from the bulk of my anatomy, which felt as if it harboured an alien, invading and displacing the real me.

When I found myself in a difficult situation or had unpleasant or painful symptoms, I forced myself to think of amusing events that had occurred in my life which were in some way associated. I realised that, with practice, I could partly change my response to what was happening in the here and now by using it to trigger something from the past that made me smile. I will give examples of these events as my story unfolds, but here is one now as an example.

On many occasions, I succumbed to a terrible sleepiness, which became overpowering and was not pleasant. However, I recalled an episode which occurred in the 1970s when I was a young dentist. I attended an all-day course in America, given by one of the towering figures of gum disease (periodontology). He had the reputation of being a man with whom you would not want to argue. After lunch, he started a lecture to an audience of about a thousand people. Lunch and a darkened auditorium were not conducive to staying awake. He suddenly stopped and pointed to a young dentist in the audience who had a very large lower jaw. He shouted, "You, you with the horse face, him next to you, wake him up." The young dentist slowly stood and to my amazement, he said, "Dr … I have two things to say to you. Firstly, I take great offence at anyone making derogatory comments about my facial morphology and secondly, you put him to sleep, you come down and wake him up!" Stunned silence. He went on to become a leader in the same speciality, but I'm not sure that the two men ever had a good relationship after that. How could it fail to bring a smile to my face when I thought of it when sleepiness was engulfing me? It didn't remove the horrible feelings, but raised my mood and helped me to cope just a little bit better. At least I could succumb with a smile on my face. With practice, I became much better at bringing stories to the forefront of my mind and playing the game of finding one that related to what I was feeling. A good coping strategy.

On numerous occasions when circumstances threatened to overwhelm me I fought hard to to think of Priscilla, reflecting on how much I loved her and the enormously happy and fulfilling times that we had had together and with our family. It was extremely difficult to come to terms with the absence of a sexual relationship and I tried desperately to put thoughts of the potential permanency of this out of my mind. No one in the medical team raised this as a possible concern for me. I find it hard to imagine that some other patients would not have similar feelings combined with a deep sense of loss.

I was unable to listen to music because of my illness, but some crazy DJ seemed to be working in my head and frequently switched on two pieces. One was by Cole Porter, *Every time we say goodbye*, I could hear Ella Fitzgerald singing it. The other was *Songbird* composed by Christine McVie of Fleetwood Mac. I could hear Eva Cassidy singing it. I frequently listened to her album *Songbird*, which was released two years after her premature death at thirty-three. The connotations of the first song in relation to Priscilla are obvious; the lyrics of the second describe loving someone in a new way, which I had always interpreted to mean with greater intensity and passion. Both songs resonated so much with me and I felt an outpouring of emotion through the music in my brain. On reading this, I realise how cheesy it may sound. On the other hand, who is in the position to criticise the thoughts and emotions of a seriously ill human being?

I met Priscilla when we were teenagers, we have been together ever since and have found enormous happiness and fulfillment in our mutual love and support. It started with the early infatuation and discovery of teenage years, but moved gently towards a much profounder love, with a sense of deep oneness, intertwining lives, respect, and mental and physical knowledge of each other. While remaining individuals, we have flourished by having the concerns and needs of the other as central to everything that we do. We delight in the other's well-being and happiness and feel pain in the other's traumas, wanting to relieve their hurt, putting the other before self. We recognise that selfishness is a destructive force and it has not been a part of our mutual development. The only problem is that in a situation such as the one in which we now found ourselves, each of us felt so much for the other that was hard to live with. Priscilla is an extremely caring, gentle, insightful, moral, ethical, thoughtful and selfless person, attributes which have made her a wonderful wife, mother, grandmother and psychodynamic counsellor. Having to cut her education short by the premature death of her parents, I have great admiration for her determination in her late thirties to obtain a degree in psychology, as our three sons became more independent. A Master's degree in health psychology followed and then further psychotherapy training. She loved her work, and I loved seeing the satisfaction that she obtained from helping others. I felt extremely sad that she felt so overwhelmed by my illness that she could not continue with her career. However, because of her training, she was well positioned to help me in the face of devastating illness. Some people may say that fate had a hand in this. I do not consider this to be the case, nor do I think that it is luck. Certainly, she was incredibly well placed to help me but it seems to me that in most situations we create our own luck by positioning ourselves in such a way (usually unconsciously) so that what may seem like luck can actually occur. It is luck that your lottery ticket is picked but it is necessary to buy a lottery ticket in order to have a chance of winning.

We have had wonderful times together, enjoying family, two years in America, horse riding, skiing, tennis, theatre and music, among many other things. She encouraged me to start horse riding and jogging. If she had not encouraged me to become so fit, I doubt that I would be writing this book;

I would have died. She unflinchingly supported me in my work and I appreciate how difficult that must have been for her when I perhaps became overly immersed in it. I can truly say that, through our shared lives, I frequently would look at her and think, I don't know how this is possible but I love you more than ever before. When I heard Songbird for the first time, it was a very emotional experience. Now in my hospital bed, we were denied physical love, but her absolute devotion to me was an unquantifiable source of support and love. As I have said previously, I was not afraid of dying for my own sake but, throughout my illness, I did not intend to leave my loved ones behind without a fight. Some years later, my then nine-year-old grandson said to me, "Poppa, if you had died, my life would never have been the same again." A poignant reminder for me.

What I have not said is that I have experienced the horror of nearly losing Priscilla. When she was eight months pregnant with Jon, she suddenly developed severe abdominal pain. I was at work and she drove herself to the doctor and described almost crawling up the path because she couldn't stand upright. He examined her and effectively said to her, "Go home, you silly woman, pregnancy has pain." Bewildered, she returned home and phoned me. I said that I would come home immediately and meanwhile my sister went round to sit with her. When home, I took one look at her and phoned the consultant (you could get through to them in those days) and told him what had happened. He said, "Get her into hospital immediately." I did so. He examined her, put her on a drip to delay labour and reported to me that there was a problem with the placenta. He doubted that both she and the baby would survive, possibly neither would. The horror of the situation didn't take long to sink in, compounded by the fact that I needed to care for two young boys, Justin and David. The drip was continuous for a month. I arranged for help at home and split my time between a limited amount of work, the boys and the hospital. During that month, the fear of losing Priscilla and/or the baby was an enormous burden to carry. I tried to adopt a positive view but seeing her looking so ill made that difficult. Fortunately, she was unaware of her predicament and placed her trust firmly in the hands of the medics. At the end of the month, she was induced and, to my great relief, the consultant was wrong, they both survived. Jon was whisked away to an incubator for five days. This was a period when we were uncertain as to how it would turn out for him. When he did survive, our relief was enormous. So now with my predicament, Priscilla and my roles were reversed and I remembered that with serious illness, doctors don't always know what the outcome will be, regardless of what they say.

In the long, lonely nights, I often replayed my father's grief at the loss of my mother. Anguish never left him. For the remainder of his life when he came to our house alone or when he took out a photograph of her from a filing cabinet in his shop, he would dissolve into heart-wrenching sobs and talk about his despair and unhappiness. We tried to encourage him to seek help, but he said, "I'm not going to see any trick cyclist (psychiatrist)," and that was the end of that discussion. His only sources of joy were in being with his family (his beloved grandchildren in particular), his customers and a few old friends, but the latter died before him. I suppose I only really began to know him after the death of my mother, when we lived together for many years in the flat above his shop. He was such a kind, generous and caring man who had the ability to get on so well with everyone. He instilled in his family the importance of family and he lives on in his children and our spouses and very much in his grandchildren. One aspect of his love for me, which in adult life I realised was not helpful, was his over-protectiveness. If my athletic cousins dived into a swimming pool and I was about to do so, "Be careful". If they rode a bike and I wanted to, "Be careful". If they climbed a tree and I followed, "Be careful." I think that subconsciously it made me think there was something wrong with me, I needed to be protected whereas they didn't, I was vulnerable. It seems to me that infantilising a child is not to their benefit. I am not saying that at the age of thirteen they should be left with no clothes in the middle of the wilderness to fend for themselves. I am saying that they should be encouraged to participate in normal childhood activities without too much caution. I think that my white coat syndrome, my blood pressure going up at the sight of a doctor or being in a doctor's surgery related to that underlying feeling of vulnerability. This affected my life in many other ways, such as nervousness before lecturing in my early career. How strange that with all of his warnings of "Be careful", I should have nearly died from something that being careful would not have prevented. I was always careful about infection.

I am comforted to think that he died when he was with Priscilla. She loved him and he loved her. I do not relish the thought of dying without being with my loved ones. He was a small shopkeeper, but when, at his funeral, I turned around and looked back, there was a line of people at least a quarter of a mile long following his coffin to the grave. He certainly left behind a good name, which is a truly meaningful and aspirational legacy for my family and me. I loved him and I knew that he took great delight in my career, although he never seemed to understand what I really did. He loved Priscilla like a daughter. For several years, before we were married, she lived in a rented room close to us. One day, he said this is ridiculous, we have a spare bedroom here she should come and live with us. So she did. Me in one bedroom, her in another and my father snoring in the room between us. I think that youngsters today would not understand the sexual restraint that we exercised at that time. The fact that my father loved her so much, made her even more precious to me and now, I loved her in a deeper, more tender and passionate way than ever before. Illness evokes new emotions.

Our three sons have been a joy to both of us. We have delighted in their individualism and in their connections to each other and to us. They have in common highly ethical, moral and caring attitudes to other people and society in general; they have good friends and care about family. We feel very proud to see these virtues in them. They have worked very hard at obtaining good educations and then moved on to each of their chosen fields of work. They are good sons, our daughters-in-law are good daughters-in-law, and Jon's more recently arrived partner Jon, has similar virtues. We feel that we have shared quality time with them and learned so much from them. We are enormously grateful to have such a caring and supportive family around us, especially in our time of difficulty. They have a genuine desire to be there for us, which we feel emanates from love and not from guilt or duty. How could thinking about them fail to boost my spirits?

Of course, there were also thoughts of the grandchildren. What a source of happiness, and so many good times to play over in my mind. There is so much reciprocal unconditional love. Enormous pleasure is derived from the trust that they place in you, the fun you have with them, the ability to be a child with them, the ability to relive a part of your life, the part that was spent with your own young children, but now without parental concerns. I tried to imagine what it might be like for them seeing me in my severely compromised condition. There is actually no way of second-guessing their thoughts. This was brought home to me some years later. I had a problem with one eye, for which I needed an ophthalmic surgeon's opinion. After the consultation, one of my then eight-year-old granddaughters asked me whether it would get better. I explained that it probably wouldn't unless I had an operation, but it wasn't bad enough for that. She said, "Oh well you're old so you won't have to live with it for very long" – out of the mouths of babes!

I focused on the thoughts of family and reminisced on the good times and the love that I felt for all of them. I frequently found myself thinking that you reap what you sow and now would not be a good time to be feeling remorse for damaged relationships. Sometimes my thinking would make me sad and triggered thoughts of what had been, but most of the time it triggered good feelings and took my mind away from myself.

5

DIALYSIS

It's strange how institutionalisation creeps up on you and you almost welcome the routines, listening out for footsteps, food trolleys, the changing of bed linen, washing and other daily routines. In particular, I recognised Priscilla's footsteps along the corridor. The emphasis on one shoe followed rapidly by the other and then a slight gap before returning to the first one. It had a particular rhythm that was unique to her. I tried to find melodies in my head that fitted the timing, but never did. It was, however, a very welcome sound to hear at 7.30 every morning, departing only at 10 pm, sometimes at eleven, when she knew that the night sister had safely tucked me up in bed. Being shut off in your own room has the great advantage of privacy. However, it has the disadvantage of nurses not generally moving around and observing you as they would in an open ward. I suppose it's not possible to have it both ways.

While on the critical list and severely debilitated, a nursing assistant was assigned to sleep in my room for about a week. I felt so sorry for him sleeping in a chair at the end of my bed, but it was tremendously reassuring to have him there. He was very compassionate and caring, and to start with he washed and shaved me in my bed. There was no way that I could shave myself, I was too weak even to hold a razor in one hand and to sit up unaided. As the week went by, I was able, with assistance, to get out of bed to the bathroom and shaved and washed at the sink, but had to use the commode as the toilet seat was too low. There was one unfortunate episode with him, which perhaps was related to his tiredness and/or inexperience. The commode has a pan, which slides along two grooves to position it beneath you. On this occasion he had forgotten to insert the pan before I sat on the commode and being male inevitably parts of my anatomy, which I remember my father calling "his jewellery", hung through the opening in the commode. He realised the pan was not in position and slid it violently into place, performing almost, I'm happy to say, an instant castration. The pain was horrendous, not a good experience at the best of times. Despite this, I am very grateful to this person who disappeared from my life, never to be seen or thanked again. That is one of the strange things, so many people helping just one person and frequently the inability to say thank you in a meaningful way. I had the luxury of this personalised care because of private insurance. I wonder now what it would have been like in an NHS hospital. While my nursing experiences in an NHS hospital were excellent, frequently there just wasn't the nursing capacity to offer that type of care.

On the morning following the breathing and allergen problem, I was lying on my back waiting for some breakfast. Sitting up unaided was impossible. I simply did not have the energy. Looking down at my arms, where two weeks ago there had been muscle, all I could see was emaciated, yellow skin, flesh and bones. Pulling the covers and sheets back gingerly, I peered at my legs and saw the same pattern, but noticed slight blackening and a soggy looking, fluid filled, grossly enlarged swelling towards the lower part of my limbs. As I looked further down my legs to my feet, I could see black stumps hanging off the ends with gnarled yellowing toenails. This was on all my toes except for the big toe on my left foot. For some reason it had pretty well escaped the ravages of bacteria and noradrenaline (the drug that had been used in intensive care to keep my blood pressure at an acceptable level). However, there was a big patch of black gangrenous tissue on the under surface of my left heel. What a change in two weeks. Forcing myself to look again, there was a wave of nausea and sadness, it wasn't a pretty sight.

Two nurses came into the room and placing their arms under my arms, hoisted me up in the bed to a semi-sitting position. They gave me a bed bath and instead of the moist cloths feeling good on my skin they felt irritating, very much like the feeling of skin sensitivity at the height of the flu infection, another altered sensation. One of the nurses said that breakfast would be coming and I should eat it quickly because I had to go to dialysis. At first I did not comprehend what she was saying, no one had mentioned dialysis (or if they had, I didn't remember) and my mind was racing as to the implications. I asked what was happening and noticed that people had to lean close to hear me. My voice was hardly loud enough to exit from my mouth. Priscilla was with me and she explained that there had been kidney damage in intensive care. I was very aware that in the presence of severe kidney damage, it would be necessary to have waste products cleared from my blood by a machine otherwise

I would die. I ate a small breakfast and then the bedpan and bottle arrived. Getting onto a bedpan is undignified, difficult, particularly when there is no muscle strength, and uncomfortable. Furthermore, nothing functioned and that was a waste of time (interesting that I automatically used the word "waste"?). There was absolutely no urge to pass urine and that's understandable now since there was no kidney function, but a realisation of the implications began to filter through my brain. What a massive change to a normal bodily function. A function that is deeply ingrained. It has so many connotations and memories. There's the early potty training by one's parents and teachers, the need to request permission at school to go to the toilet, the occasional feeling of warm fluid trickling down your leg as a child, crossing swords when having a communal pee with other little boys. Standing in a line in a wood as children, seeing whose stream would go the furthest. Ensuring that your bladder is empty before taking an exam or going into the theatre. Hiding behind a tree so that no one can see you doing what they all do. Standing at so many undignified urinals with strangers, lined up like animals. Being intrigued as a child, watching men shake their penises of various shapes and sizes, in a variety of ways to remove the last vestiges of urine. Observing how for some old men it seemed to take forever before they produced a small stream of urine, compared to young men, who took great delight in hitting the back of the urinal in an instant. Observing men carrying out an almost choreographed ritual as they bent one knee, usually the left, tilted slightly to the side and replaced their penises in their underpants. Then rapidly standing upright while zipping up their flies. Very funny to see when there was a row of them doing it almost in time with one another. How very strange. And all those words and phrases derived from this basic function, presumably trying to avoid taboo words: to go and spend a penny; answer the call of nature; do a wee; go peepee; going for a number one; pass water; siphon the python; taking a leak. Coarse phrases such as: piss off; don't take the piss; piss poor; piss on you; he's a pisser, getting pissed and many more. So, it was more than not producing urine, there was a lifetime of connotations associated with it and the mental gyrations of accepting the situation were very complicated.

I was not under any illusion that dialysis was a treatment to resolve the outcomes of illness, more another life support system. With less severe kidney damage, dialysis may be used while the kidney recovers, but not in my case. I met patients subsequently who had been convinced that dialysis was a treatment and were shattered when they discovered that for them this wasn't the case, perhaps indicating a real need for better patient information and possibly psychological help.

Now dialysis started, and what a change this made to Priscilla's life and to mine. I must admit that prior to experiencing it myself I had never given much thought to dialysis, nor to what it may be like for the people receiving it. I cannot describe the experience, lasting from 4th February 2009 to 3rd March 2010, as being particularly pleasant; once again, there was a feeling of being trapped. Of course, there were good parts and bad parts but the overall experience was not great. I don't know how much of this was due to the dialysis per se, but it was probably influenced by the greatly debilitating after-effects of the toxic shock and, in the early stages, following discharge from hospital, by the absence of a caring environment at an NHS/Corporate dialysis centre.

When I was subsequently transferred to another NHS unit, which provided a far more caring environment, my experience vastly improved. I am aware that some dialysis patients have been angry with me when I have voiced my feelings of being trapped like a prisoner. Of course, I recognise that dialysis kept me alive, but I could not separate out the other feelings and put them away. I never developed a negative attitude to it, which would have been debilitating. To focus my mind and turn the experience into a project, I forced myself to see it as another challenge, making a study of observing what was going on, how I reacted to it and how the dialysis teams worked. I will give more details of dialysis later on, however, being tied to a machine for four and a half hours three times a week, with approximately half an hour getting attached to it and half an hour getting off it took a very large chunk out of my life, most of the time feeling pretty awful. Of course, dialysis was better than being dead, but denying the downside would be untruthful. I don't know how other patients felt.

As I slowly recovered, some of the unpleasant symptoms subsided and I could use the dialysis time fruitfully, which was, I think, an important coping strategy. I had no idea as to how long I might be on dialysis – six months, a year, forever? How long was forever likely to be?

At this stage, I was so out of it that the details of dialysis were not of concern. It had the maximum effect on Priscilla and me following discharge from hospital, but I was so debilitated (wellness score 8) that it was just something else that had to be tolerated. If both the medical profession and non-medical people have a better understanding of the difficulties presented to patients on dialysis and to their families, perhaps they may be in a better position to empathise and help. It is often difficult to appreciate that, when kidney failure requires dialysis, this does not simply mean that a patient is connected to a dialysis machine, the blood is cleaned and everything is "hunky dory", it is far removed from that. Many people said to me unthinkingly, "So the dialysis cleans out your blood and you're fine." This is not the reality and quite upsetting to hear.

There are two types of dialysis available to outpatients, haemodialysis and peritoneal dialysis; I'll only discuss the haemodialysis since that is my experience. I was connected to the machine via a tube in my neck, which went into my jugular vein. Blood was pumped out of my body and circulated in an artificial kidney machine. This mimicked the kidneys and washed waste and toxins out of my bloodstream. Blood was returned to my body through another tube inserted into my jugular vein.

Unfortunately, the dialysis process is nowhere near as efficient as kidneys that function twenty-four hours per day, seven days per week. I understand from Professor Donal O'Donoghue, the former National Clinical Director for Kidney Care England, that "good quality standard haemodialysis, three times per week will provide on average only about 10-12% of normal kidney function".

Kidneys are bean-shaped organs, each about the size of a fist. They are located just below the ribcage, one on each side of the spine. Presumably, their location protects them from accidents. They are extremely important organs and it is not possible to live without them or without some form of replacement treatment. They make urine, remove wastes and extra fluid and control the body's chemical balance.

They help to control blood pressure, keep bones healthy and make red blood cells. If dialysis is required, it means that the kidneys are damaged and urine production is impaired. During a dialysis session, there is a limit to how much fluid can be removed from the blood. However, if excess fluid is retained, it can lead to an increase in blood volume and heart failure. So that a reasonable balance could be maintained, my fluid intake was limited to one litre per day including fluids in foods such as vegetables. Maintaining this control can be quite difficult, particularly during hot weather and exercise. Furthermore, careful restriction of dietary salt is needed, since it can give rise to thirst and then more fluid intake. Salt is found not only in the salt cellar but also in most processed foods, it can be difficult to avoid it.

Dietary and fluid intake instructions are extremely restrictive. As Priscilla and I found out more about them, we realised that if I survived, they would have an enormous impact on our lives. Perhaps you decided to put this book down for a while and have a small glass of wine. You may have followed this with a delicious slice of honeydew melon, followed by a bowl of tomato soup. Maybe you then had another small glass of wine with the main course of chicken, vegetables and baked potato, onto which you sprinkled a little salt. A glass of water may have helped the meal to slip down and, for dessert, you had a bowl of yoghurt with a sliced banana.

I hope you enjoyed it, but spare a thought for the dialysis patient. The fluid that you have swallowed will have exceeded my daily fluid intake allowance by about 250ml. Melons are high in potassium and should be avoided, and tomatoes in the soup should be avoided or limited for the same reason.

Vegetables are also high in potassium, so the ones in your meal would have needed to be boiled for about ten minutes, soggy to say the least. However, water soluble vitamins such as vitamins B and C may then be reduced and need to be supplemented. Baked potatoes must be avoided completely and the salt was bad news. The dessert sounds good, but due to their phosphorus content, milk, yoghurt and cheeses need to be limited to two thirds of a cup of milk or yoghurt per day and three to four ounces of cheese per day. To top it all, bananas contain very high quantities of potassium and need to be avoided. For the interested reader, you can find out more about these dietary restrictions in Appendix V.

My mind wandered to the rationing that I experienced following the Second World War, which seemed relatively trivial when compared to the dialysis dietary regime. In the post war period, I can clearly remember my mother taking me to the local grocer's shop clutching our book of ration coupons which entitled us to limited amounts of food. For example, children were limited to three eggs per week and adults to one. Each person was allowed a maximum of 224 grams of cheese per week. Rationing did not end until 1954. Every day at school, in order to supplement the diets of the children, malt was given to them to give them more bulk. I distinctly remember lining up at primary school for our teaspoonful of malt. The only problem was that, with the surname Wise, I was at the back of the line and there was only one spoon. This was used for each child without any washing. I wondered how current Health and Safety legislation would deal with that! Certainly a thought to bring a smile.

The dietary regime may severely inhibit socialising. It's interesting to observe how many people think, "You're over the top with your diet," which is not at all helpful. I am not a frequent pub-goer, but I can imagine the social implications for somebody whose "previous life" was centred on drinking with friends at the pub or some other establishment. "Have another pint, Mike," would not be a phrase that I would welcome. While alcohol within the recommended limits is not totally advised against, it will come out of the fluid allowance. Furthermore, alcohol may also affect blood sugars. Therefore, careful consideration is needed for people with diabetes, especially those who are on medication to lower blood glucose levels.

Once the hospital was no longer controlling my diet, I found three books very informative, all published by Class publishing. There were two books by Stein A. and Wilde J. and one by Auer J. . Patients and their carers may want to look at these. More recently, there has been a new publication, Dialysis: making the right choices for you. It is certainly worth a read.

My emaciated, debilitated state must have been problematic for the clinicians, how to rebuild body mass with the dialysis dietary restrictions. I was prescribed Pro-Cal, a fluid food supplement, which adversely increased my fluid intake. After a short while, I was encouraged to eat high fat, high carbohydrate containing foods but that was difficult since one of the symptoms of kidney failure is loss or reduction of appetite. Dialysis helped, but didn't return me to a good appetite.

The history related to the development of dialysis may be of interest to some readers and so I have included it in Appendix VI.

It is some decades since the elderly or patients with

additional medical conditions were automatically refused dialysis, or simply not referred to renal units. I find this interesting and thought-provoking, since history frequently gives a different perspective to life today. In the light of the past, today, even with its flaws, may be remarkable, yet today will in turn, become history. Perhaps, not that long ago, I could have been refused treatment. What an awful thought. It was only in the 1970s that one of my nurse's mother was refused haemodialysis because she was over fifty-five years old. I felt so grateful that this life saving treatment was available to me, in my sixties.

Despite representing just 0.1% of the population, 2% of the English NHS budget is spent on services for dialysis and transplantation patients. The cause of my failure to produce urine was a condition known as acute kidney injury (AKI). The degree of damage in AKI is graded as levels I, II or III. I had the severest form, AKI III, which resulted in a rapid and complete cessation of kidney function.

The following section is reproduced with permission of the NHS Think Kidneys programme. "AKI, previously known as acute renal failure, is an emerging global healthcare issue. It is characterised by a sudden decline in kidney function and is rarely caused by physical injury or trauma to the kidneys. AKI can occur without symptoms and is detected through a routine blood test. It has many different causes and usually occurs alongside other serious illnesses, such as infection or dehydration and is common in patients in hospital. In some cases, certain medications can also affect the kidneys adversely and this can lead to AKI or add to the severity of AKI. AKI is linked to an increased risk of death or prolonged illness as toxins and fluid collect in the body.

There is a complex link between the long-term medical conditions' (for example, diabetes, heart disease and cancer), medication and acute illness, which can be complicated by AKI. It is estimated that one in five emergency admissions into hospital are associated with AKI, up to 100,000 deaths in hospitals are associated with AKI and that a quarter to a third could potentially be prevented.

This is not just an issue for kidney specialists. Kidney doctors and those working in intensive care may look after the most severe cases, but the majority of cases arise and/or are managed in the community or across specialities within hospitals.

The older person with complex health issues and associated illnesses is most at risk. The complication of AKI to ongoing illness prolongs hospital stays and increases mortality even when the severity of AKI seems mild. The long-term outcomes of AKI are especially poor for people in this situation."

The financial burden on the NHS is large. It has been estimated that the in-patient cost of AKI to the NHS in England for the year 2010-2011, was £1.02 billion. As a comparison, for the same period, the combined expenditure, including community care, on breast cancer (£580 million), lung cancer (£183 million) and skin cancer (£122 million) was £885 million. Based on the 2010-2011 figures, it has been calculated that if 20% of AKI cases were prevented, it would produce a saving of £200 million a year to the NHS. Professor Donald O'Donoghue stated in 2013 that "… thousands of deaths could be avoided through the provision of basic medical care, including reviewing medication, ensuring that patients are hydrated, treating infections promptly and ensuring consultant review within twelve hours. Ensuring that health care professionals think of the kidney as a marker of good quality care, and consider the risks of AKI as a matter of course, will drive exactly the care needed to make certain that patients are treated with dignity and respect". How I wish that all patients received the care that they require, particularly when simple procedures can make such an enormous difference, save lives and expense.

Anyone interested in finding out more about AKI should turn to Appendix VII.

6

MISUNDERSTANDINGS

My friend Ed was a very gentle man and he had a very interesting misunderstanding. He wore thick glasses, was not a tall man and would never become angry nor confront someone. One day, he was late for work and rushed out of his New York apartment. As he made his way along a crowded street, a large man jostled him. Ed stopped and felt into his pocket, his wallet had gone. Totally out of character, he turned to the man, who was towering above him, pushed him and said, "Give me the wallet." The man then very slowly put his hand into his inside jacket pocket and started to withdraw it. A very frightened and trembling Ed realised that he could be withdrawing a gun. To his surprise, the man took out a wallet. Ed rapidly put it into his pocket and dashed off to work. On arrival, he sat down at his desk and took out the wallet. He looked at it and gasped. It was not his. He immediately returned home only to find his wallet on the kitchen table. In his hurry to leave, he had forgotten it. Ed was the mugger not the other man. He did return the wallet. How it made me smile to think of it when I needed a boost.

I first became aware of the possibility of misunderstandings in language when I was studying in the

USA. We lived in the Midwest and it seemed as if the British accent was not commonly heard. Frequently, people would say, "I just love your accent, say anything; I just want to hear you speak." We had taken a supply of Enid Blyton's Noddy books with us to the States, to read to Justin, when he was two years old. Having exhausted our supply, Priscilla went to the local library and in her British accent asked the librarian, "Do you have any Noddy books?" The librarian gave her a very quizzical look and said with a very Midwestern accent, "What kind of nawdee books do you want ma'am?" Priscilla replied, "The ones about the little boy with the blue hat and his friend with big ears." The librarian looked at her even more strangely and said, "We don't have any of those ma'am, but if you go to the bookshop around the corner, they have all kinds of nawdee (translation: naughty) books." Much to Priscilla's amusement and embarrassment, she suddenly realised that her words had been misunderstood. We never did get more Noddy books!

Acute kidney injury is a medical term, and when I talk about it I usually find that people think it means that a blow of some sort or penetration by a knife has damaged the kidney. It is a poor term from the patient's perspective because of this potential misunderstanding. Does the public even know what the kidneys do? If they don't, then when a doctor informs them that they have a problem, they may not understand the implications. An Ipsos Mori survey in 2015 found that only 51% of the population knew that the kidneys make urine and, of those people, 59% were graduates. Only 12% of participants thought that the kidney had a role to play in processing medicines. More people believed that the kidneys help to remove waste from the body (60%) than thought they made urine (51%) and more people thought that the kidneys made urine rather than removing excess fluid from the body. Sixty-eight per cent of the sample had not heard of Acute Kidney Injury. The possibility of a misunderstanding occurring about Acute Kidney Injury is substantial.

During my many visits to waiting rooms, I found it very interesting to listen to patients talking either to each other or to their carers. It became clear that frequently a clinician used a medical term which was misunderstood by the patient. Perhaps this could have occurred because the patient simply did not understand, or did not hear it correctly. This may be due to anxiety, a hearing disability, a poor explanation, English not being their first language or because of an accent in the clinician's speech.

Commonly, the word acute, which in medical terminology means a condition with rapid onset, often with short duration, was misunderstood by patients to mean severe disease, perhaps life threatening. I overheard anguished conversations between patients and their relatives, the patient thinking they had been given a death sentence because they had been told that they had an acute condition. There was one instance in which a patient had been informed that she had chronic kidney disease. Chronic, in medical terminology, means a condition which develops and may worsen over an extended period and can be applied to any disease. Since the patient's father had chronic back pain, somehow or other she mistakenly thought that the word chronic always described a type of back pain. The doctor's use of the word in relation to her kidney disease was misinterpreted. She thought that for some reason he was talking about her back and since she didn't have a back problem, she was utterly confused.

End-stage renal disease is a total and irreversible failure of the kidneys, it cannot be fixed. It is impossible to live without dialysis or a transplant. On hearing this term, the wife of one patient thought that end stage referred to her husband's life and not the kidney. She was devastated. There were patients who thought that antibiotics were painkillers. They are not, they are used to kill bacteria in infections. There were those who thought that the instruction to take medication orally meant taking it regularly or at certain times as opposed to taking it by mouth. There were a few who thought the word hypertension meant that they were highly stressed or tense (not unreasonable: hyper tension) as opposed to having raised blood pressure. One patient had read about full-blown AKI in a patient information leaflet. He was worried that he had it and his kidney would "blow" like an oil well and release urine inside his body. A full-blown illness is one that is fully developed. Some diabetic patients were concerned that, since they were injecting themselves with insulin, they were becoming drug addicts.

As a clinician and teacher I frequently recalled a pertinent saying which is related to miscommunication, "I know you think you understand what you thought I said, but I'm not sure you realise that what you heard is not what I meant." Recognising this, I always felt that it was important to check that the patient had understood what I said by asking them to repeat important information to me. Rarely did I experience this as a patient. A simple word, a minor body movement, a look, a gesture can all create misunderstanding if used unwisely, creating anguish and anxiety in the patient. In the busy environment of the medical world, it is easy to forget this. Patients may not really grasp what is meant.

7

SOMETHING TO LIVE FOR

Sometimes there are situations in life which we are unable to alter significantly. But, we can alter our reaction to them, taking responsibility for our own lives and thoughts, rather than blaming others, a supernatural power or the situation itself. Of course, in a seriously ill state, it is necessary to give yourself over to professional care, but I was determined to take control of my mind and my responses. This view was reinforced for me some time ago when I came across the writings of Victor Frankl, a renowned Austrian psychotherapist and Holocaust concentration camp survivor.

Even in the degradation, torture and abject misery of a concentration camp, Frankl was able to exercise the most important freedom of all: the freedom to determine one's own attitude and spiritual well-being. No sadistic Nazi SS guard was able to take that away from him or control the inner life of Frankl's soul. One of the ways he found the strength to fight to stay alive and not lose hope was to think of his wife. Ironically, he was not aware that she was already dead. Frankl clearly saw that those who died the quickest in the concentration camp had nothing to live for. He also realised that to recognise there is a meaning in one's life is the most effective way to survive even the worst conditions. My thoughts and love of my wife, children, their wives/partners and grandchildren, certainly gave me something to live for, as did my desire to return to my profession.

I was truly not afraid of the possibility of my death. I felt fulfilment in what I had achieved, my deeply reciprocated love for Priscilla and my family, the special relationships with friends and the acquisition of a good name and reputation. I considered that I had always lived an ethical and moral life and, professionally, put the interests of my patients before my own. I tried to adhere to the precepts of Frederick Douglas, an author who was one of the key architects of the movement that ended slavery in America. He said, "I prefer to be true to myself, even at the hazard of incurring the ridicule of others, rather than to be false, and to incur my own abhorrence." In many respects, this paraphrases a quote from Hamlet in which Polonius states, "… this above all: to thine own self be true, And it must follow, as the night the day, Thou canst not then be false to any man." So there was a feeling of closure without major regrets, I could look at myself in a mirror and be satisfied and at peace. However, the thought of leaving those people whom I love so much with grief and loss was not something that I was going to succumb to without a fight. For me there would be the nothingness, but for them there would be loss. I certainly had something to live for.

It is difficult if not impossible to pinpoint chronologically the awareness of these concepts during the long recovery period, but there is no doubt in my mind that, as with my resolution to fight in intensive care, they helped me enormously.

8

TOO WEAK TO WALK

Returning to my initiation into dialysis: I was wheeled to the dialysis unit in my bed, being too weak to get out of it. The nurses in the unit were very caring and with the ratio of one nurse for two patients, always available. The purpose of the tube in my jugular vein now became obvious. Additional tubes were connected to it and these were then connected to the machine, which was a little bit like a Dalek sitting by the bed.

At the start of each session, I needed to have a painless injection of a drug to stop my blood from clotting in the tubes (heparin). This was given under the skin in my abdomen. There was also a regular injection of a drug, which was given to try to prevent anaemia from developing (erythropoietin), colloquially and somewhat lovingly called epo by the nurses (pronounced eeepo). This occasionally sounded like hippo and I chuckled to think of having an injection of a hippo. I was also aware of the need to have blood transfusions on several occasions. Blood donation is an altruistic human act that is so life sustaining, thankfully there are people who are willing to do this.

At this early stage, my sessions on dialysis consisted of lying there, in a semi-daze, doing nothing in particular.

Dozing on and off because of a profound sleepiness which could not be shaken off, nor which improved with sleep, this was an outcome of kidney failure. Eyelids became heavier and heavier, regardless of how hard I tried to fight it. My body felt leaden and completely de-energised and sleep would engulf me. I talked sporadically to my family, one of whom was reassuringly with me all of the time. Priscilla came every day for much of the session, Justin sat quietly and reassuringly by my bed doing his work, tap, tap, tapping away on his computer. David and Jon would somehow find time in their busy work schedules to pop in with bright smiles (for David this was subsequently made harder by the birth of a new baby), news of the outside world and words of encouragement, all tremendously helpful. Occasionally, I tried to watch the television screen hanging over the bed but invariably my eyes glazed over, it was almost impossible to concentrate and, in fact, it was quite irritating.

Now there was an overwhelming feeling of nausea. It started just above my stomach and periodically slowly worked its way up into my throat. Great effort and concentration were required to control the feeling that this would lead to vomit exploding from my mouth. Wave after wave of this ascending nausea would sweep over me and take control of my being. This was accentuated during the whole dialysis experience while connected to the machine, but was present at varying levels of intensity even when I was not connected to it. Medication was given to control the nausea, this helped, but never eliminated the feeling. There were many times over the next few years when Priscilla would think that I was not participating in conversation and cutting myself off when, in fact, I was meditating, focusing on a distant spot in an attempt to control the nausea. It is hard to describe just how debilitating nausea can be, it is not the same as pain but it drags you down and causes you to focus on it at the expense of the outside world. To try to lighten my mood and refocus my mind, I frequently fought hard to recall an amusing incident associated with vomiting.

We have come a long way since barbers were surgeons and blacksmiths pulled teeth! However, when I was a dental student, we did not wear gloves, no one thought about that in those days, how filthy for both patients and dentists. I was treating a fourteen year-old boy. I placed a mould into his mouth and within about ten seconds he started to retch and then this turned into violent vomiting. What was my reaction? I rapidly removed the mould, cupped my hands and held them beneath his mouth, collecting a handful of foul smelling, incredibly sticky, lumpy vomit. I looked down at it, couldn't believe what I had done, started retching myself and tried to deposit it in a sink. As it fell into the sink, it seemed to stretch out like bands of treacle (maybe that's what he had eaten!). I never repeated the experience, but now it made me smile and helped me to control my nausea.

Combined with the nausea was an ever-increasing itchiness of the skin, as if there was a relentless flea jumping from one part of my body to another. Scratching did little to relieve the itching, yet it felt imperative to scratch. The damned flea was merciless; it would desist from its relentless tormenting for short periods only to start up again somewhere else. Nausea and itchiness are common symptoms in kidney failure, they don't sound like very much, but to be on the receiving end is very debilitating. My lips started to dry out and crack and, throughout the dialysis period, Priscilla would apply lip salve at every opportunity which helped to relieve the cracking. It became a bit of a joke between us, as to how she would sneak up on me with the tube and make for my lips, nice to be able to laugh. That was so therapeutic.

As I slowly, slowly, over the days and weeks, began to take small steps up the mountain, awareness of surroundings and my body became more obvious. Once again, this was similar to the feeling of slowly penetrating thick fog, vision and awareness of surroundings increasing as the fog thins. By about the fifth day, with considerable help, I was able to be taken to dialysis in a wheelchair, not on my bed and, after about two weeks, could walk with assistance to the unit. During the long hours of dialysis, it gradually became possible to watch some television to pass the time, but reading was impossible. Concentration on the text just didn't work and made me feel very irritable.

Common occurrences during dialysis, besides the nausea and itching, were periods of severe low blood pressure (hypotension) and leg cramps. From a patient's perspective the hypotension can perhaps be best described in three categories, one being non-postural, one being postural and the third a gradual-onset, prolonged hypotension.

The non-postural was experienced during dialysis while lying on the dialysis couch. It ranged from a mild sensation of losing concentration, suddenly and very briefly, to a sudden loss of consciousness without warning.

The postural hypotension was experienced when moving from a lying or sitting position to an upright, standing position. I found that it usually occurred when standing from a low seated position. It was similar to the non-postural experience, but frequently accompanied by a longer period of detachment and a feeling of the world retreating with a loss of control. This was accompanied by a sensation of a band tightening around my head and confusion. As I slowly recovered and became more mobile, I experienced even more severe effects, too many times for my liking, with loss of consciousness. On one occasion, I was taking just a few steps from the dialysis couch to a wheelchair when the next thing I was aware of, was lying on the floor with an oxygen mask on my face. I was viewing the somewhat anxious-looking nurses from a completely different angle to usual as they peered over me, what nice nostrils I thought.

The gradual-onset, prolonged form of hypotension, started much later in my story. It is, I think, primarily related to drug therapy. It tends to creep over me later in the day (not every day), particularly if I am tired. It feels like a band around my head, vision becomes a little difficult and poorly defined. There is a feeling of detachment and inability to concentrate and, frequently, a feeling of mild nausea. It is always associated with a postural change, usually from a low sitting or supine position to an upright one, it never occurs while I am just standing, sitting or lying. There is a rapid onset of dizziness with a need to lower my head or sit down, otherwise I would fall or lose consciousness. Normal blood pressure is about 120 (systolic) and 80 (diastolic), described as 120 over 80, but there is a normal range up to 140 over 90. When I take my blood pressure during these episodes, systolic is usually around 80 and diastolic around 50-60, which are outside the normal range.

Muscle cramps could suddenly come during the dialysis session or hit me during the night, and they could be very severe. Massage and stretching by one of my family or the nurses helped during the day, but at night, there is no one around to do this. A trick that helped, which I had shown to one of my daughters-in-law when she was suffering from cramps during pregnancy, was to have a necktie available. The tie is placed around the sole of the foot and both ends of the tie pulled to stretch the calf muscles. In the early days, 100 mgs of the opioid painkiller tramadol were prescribed at night because I still had considerable pain in my right leg. It controlled the leg pain and fortunately relieved the pain from muscle cramp. I must admit that tramadol is a drug that I find very pleasant to take: it controls pain and gives me a very warm and slightly detached and pleasurable feeling. There is a risk of becoming addicted to it and the need to save it for special circumstances but, for me, it is a remarkably effective painkiller. However, it's not for everyone; it seems that about 5% of people have very unpleasant "spaced-out" feelings on it. I did prescribe it for my patients, for a few nights following possibly painful surgery and always found it effective. It was interesting to be on the receiving end and experience the benefit without side effects.

I cannot deny that I found dialysis unpleasant: needing to attend three times a week and being tied to the machine for a large part of the day. However, I resolved to utilise that time to my best advantage. As my health slowly improved, I was able to understand more about dialysis and take better control of the procedure, which I think was important. There were periods of pleasurable entertainment, periods spent expanding my mind, periods spent sleeping and periods spent in preparing lectures. There were quiet times and conversational times with Priscilla, my family and visitors. There were also sad times, when symptoms overwhelmed me and the reality of my loss sank in although, fortunately, these were not frequent. My mental meanderings in intensive care frequently came back to me. My view that I am just an animal and things happen to animals helped me to accept my situation.

9

PROGRESS

I certainly needed the skill and knowledge of the two clinicians who were controlling and guiding my care. One was a general physician and was the intensive care specialist whom Priscilla first contacted. The other was a kidney specialist (nephrologist). Both instilled great confidence in me and I looked forward to their visits. They had very amiable dispositions, were compassionate, empathetic and highly professional. However, it did strike me that, sometimes, one or the other could look somewhat tired, anxious and stressed. Perhaps this was not surprising, since a visit would be very early in the morning or at the end of a long day at an NHS hospital. I don't know how they work the hours they do and continue to make correct decisions. I must admit that on occasions my mind did wander to the possibility that exhaustion may influence their judgement, not that anything ever happened to support those thoughts. It was intriguing to recognise the effects of minor alterations in a clinician's demeanour (physicians, nurses, physiotherapists) on Priscilla and me, probably disproportionate to the alteration, but very real for us. As Priscilla, who amazingly and lovingly hardly ever left my side, except to sleep, became more tired, I think she responded more to body cues, which unsettled her. I became aware of this and it made me feel even sadder about her predicament. However, her presence had and still has a remarkably positive effect on me. Major illness can make you feel very lonely. The illness is yours and no one else's but when surrounded by people whom you love and who love you, there is a feeling of sharing the burden. To be so ill and alone must be excruciating.

Another observation regarding the physicians was the difference that it made when they sat at the bedside to be on a level with me, rather than standing and peering down from what seemed to be a great height. I appreciate that on a busy ward round in an NHS hospital there is little opportunity for a consultant to do this. Indeed, there is the risk of cross infection, but for the seriously ill the difference between a clinician standing at the end of bed teaching a group of students as if you are an object provided for their pleasure and convenience, compared to somebody who sits by your side, is enormous. I always remember my paraplegic cousin Eddie telling me how difficult it is to be in a wheelchair and have people carry out conversations over your head or talk "down at me". For this reason, I always try to sit level with him, feeling that this is best for him and as an expression of respect. Now I was experiencing this for myself and could verify and further empathise with this part of his life experience.

As I slowly recovered my ability to concentrate for short periods, I became aware of the numerous get-well cards which surrounded me. I found that reading them was a very emotional experience. It brought tears to my eyes. The tears slowly welled up, rolled over my eyelids and trickled down my face. It wasn't a feeling of sadness, but a feeling of human tenderness and the ability of people to reach out and touch each other in times of need. In fact, that feeling has heightened with recovery. I have always been an emotionally sensitive person, but now, on seeing acts of human kindness, frequently an emotion wells up inside which can lead to at the least tears, but I often burst out with deep uncontrollable sobs. This can happen in actual human contact, but also during a play, opera, film or while reading a book. It even happened once when sitting watching Tinkerbell with one of my granddaughters! Besides cards, numerous letters were sent by patients, friends, colleagues and family, and there were letters from distant contacts, some of whom were long ago placed into the recesses of my mind. In some respects it was a little like reading my obituary before dying, a privilege that is not extended to everybody. This was amazingly supportive and satisfying but very emotional.

During this period, we had the bizarre experience of celebrating our fortieth wedding anniversary in the hospital room with our family, and the medical staff popping in for a glass of champagne. It certainly was not what either of us had planned for this occasion. Nonetheless, it was a celebration of so many truly happy years spent together and of my being alive and here with Priscilla on this day. I could only manage a tiny sip of champagne and sat in a chair feeling dazed; happy but sad, elated but dejected, numb but slightly alive, engulfed in a warm feeling of surrounding love. I still remember that day with clarity and deep emotion.

My Aunt Rose and Uncle Joe were admitted together to the Royal Free Hospital in their eighties, he to the men's ward and she to the women's. One morning, at the six o'clock observation round, the nurse found Uncle Joe in Aunt Rose's bed, the two of them cuddled up close to each other. They could not bear to be apart and he had found his way to her during the night. I can empathise with this. It is possibly difficult for people to understand what it feels like to be without the physical contact of your loved one when you are feeling weak, disorientated, lonely and a little bit frightened. I was in a private room and one day Priscilla lay next to me on the bed and we held each other tightly. I can remember looking into her face and it felt as though I was watching one of those movies where the facial features of a lover become soft, caught in the spotlight and the eyes become misty. The moment was magical and I wanted to be engulfed by it, held by it, never to let it go. The door suddenly opened and one of the consultants walked in, he looked, smiled and said, "Don't worry, that's fine." I felt like a naughty teenager caught by a parent and so the moment ended and reality rapidly returned with the feel of a stethoscope.

Priscilla told me that prayers had been and were being said for me by numerous people in churches, synagogues, mosques, temples and other places of worship. One acquaintance, who is an atheist, subsequently told her that he even found himself praying in an attempt to do something. I didn't believe that the prayers per se would do me any good, but was deeply moved by the fact that people would care sufficiently to do this for me. That feeling of their caring and desire to help was extremely beneficial; definitely one of the benefits of prayer, but only if the one prayed for is informed. Of course, there may be a counter-effect. If they are praying for you, you're probably close to being on the "way out" and that may be a very difficult realisation for some people. I think there is another element to the prayer and that is for the benefit of the person praying, feeling that, in an almost hopeless situation, they are in some way helping and there is nothing wrong with that.

Gradually, but very gradually, I made improvements. The nurses, with humour, tenderness, compassion and care helped me out of bed into an armchair by a window. Just the feeling of being out of bed, sitting in a chair made a tremendous psychological difference. To start with, I could only manage about an hour in the chair because I felt so exhausted and needed to get back into bed. There was absolutely no way that my wasted legs could propel me to an upright position let alone climb into a bed unaided. An incredibly motivational physiotherapist started to help me. Initially, she focused on my coughing and breathing because there was fluid on my right lung. For several weeks, I required an oxygen mask at night to help with my breathing. Without it, I was quite short of breath. The mask was then replaced for about three weeks by a tube placed in each nostril (a nasal cannula) that provided the oxygen. The feeling of not being able to breathe properly is horrifying. I have never had a drowning experience, but I imagine it might feel like this, although here the breathlessness continued (unless oxygen was administered). No succumbing to the water as in drowning, it just went on and on. One minute, I would try to take control of it by breathing slowly and deeply and then an overwhelming feeling of near panic would take over, the oxygen was essential. Now when I see people walking around with a nasal cannula, carrying a bottle of oxygen, or being wheeled around in a wheelchair in a similar state, or gasping for breaths between words, my heart goes out to them. I can begin to imagine what life must be like for them. Perhaps only by experiencing something can you truly empathise rather than just sympathise.

The physiotherapist pushed me, but was gentle when I really didn't have the energy to do as she requested. Stand by the bed, hold on, bend your knees, stand up – could do that twice to start with, hold on, stand on one leg, close your eyes, let go, fall over, but caught by her, lie on your back, lift your legs, hold it – two seconds maximum to start with and so on. "I can and I will." I realised that no one could do it for me, I had to do it myself, but the motivational impetus of others was invaluable. Slowly, I progressed to walking to the door of the room aided by her, then out of the door and down the corridor. It seemed essential to have points to measure against so that the slow progress could be internalised and progress assessed. The day that I reached the end of the corridor and turned right, turning an important corner, to look out of a window at the streaming traffic below felt like bursting into a new life. This may seem crazy to the reader but that milestone was amazing. Gradually, walking became unaided, the initial feeling of insecurity is hard to describe. It's similar to the first time you swim unaided, building up courage and letting go of the side. With perseverance, I was able to do more and more myself and to establish an exercise regime of getting up in the morning, doing the bedside exercises and then setting off down the corridor, chin thrust forwards. I now realise that I was trying to stride faster and faster past the nurses desk to gain and value their approval. Round the corner, look at the view, back to the room. A bit different to jogging the six miles that I did not so long ago, but far harder. The physiotherapist started me walking up a few stairs and then down, how hard the down bit was, something that previously I had done without thinking now became a mammoth task. I actually had to think about moving muscles, how do I do this, which foot first? A feeling of no control, will I tumble? Will I gain uncontrollable momentum? It reminded me of the feeling that I often had when listening to some of the compositions of J.S. Bach and I know that may seem strange. I frequently had the feeling that the natural impetus of this music was almost like somebody running downstairs, leaning forwards almost, but not quite losing control. I thought that I was now devoid of that control (wellness score 5-8). Would it ever return?

10

CHOP OFF MY TOES

The word amputation is not a pleasant one to hear when it's referring to a bit of your body as opposed to someone else's. However, blood tests showed that I still had a source of infection somewhere in my body and the clinicians thought that my gangrenous toes were a possible cause. Amputations were required. It came as no surprise to me since they were in such an awful state, black, smelly and virtually hanging from my feet. To minimise the duration of the general anaesthetic, preparations were made for two vascular surgeons to work together, one on each foot. Before the surgery I was concerned by being told that the toes would be amputated and a flap of skin would not be closed over the wounds to protect them, leaving bare bone exposed. During the night prior to the surgery my mind raced, bare bone, chopped off and exposed – what about the pain? Would I be able to play tennis again? How would I walk? What would my feet look like? What would it be like to have a disability? How would my grandchildren view me when they saw my feet? No one had spent time with me to address these fears and concerns. For the surgeons, I am sure that this was routine. Presumably, they had treated many patients with gangrenous toes, particularly those who suffered from diabetes. However, for me it was a first. That's a bit ridiculous to say. Of course it was a first, how many times can you have your toes chopped off? Some counselling would have been appreciated. As my mind raced, I drifted back many years to an episode with our son Jon. He was two years old and Priscilla had left him in the care of an au pair. When she arrived home, the au pair was hysterical and there was blood splattered on the walls and kitchen worktop. When trying to calm her down failed to stop the hysterics, in desperation, Priscilla resorted to the classic movie act. A couple of light slaps to the cheeks, totally out of character. It had the desired effect. The au pair had sat Jon on the worktop. He managed to open a liquidiser, put his hand in it and turned it on. In those days, they didn't have security switches. His tiny little fingers could have been liquidised in an instant. Fortunately, he was only cut superficially, but it was a very narrow escape. Some months later, a new patient attended my surgery. I noticed that she kept her hands in her coat pockets. After taking a history, she sat in the dental chair and I examined her. I wanted to show her something in her mouth, so I tried to give her a mirror. She said she couldn't hold it. I asked why. She removed both hands from her pockets, but they were missing all of the fingers. She explained that when she was two, she had put her hands into a liquidiser after her mother had sat her on a kitchen worktop. Jon was so nearly like this. The toss of a coin for him. The thought of the closeness of that incident to a horrific outcome went round and round in my mind and heightened my anxiety. However, after the surgery, there were no ill effects from the general anaesthetic. In fact, it was quite pleasant to have my feelings of malaise removed by sleep and, much to my surprise, no post-operative pain – nine toes reduced to stumps, the gangrenous lesion on my heel cleaned, but not removed. After a week, the dressings were replaced and I found it very difficult to look at my stumps. I forced myself to do it and slowly became used to what I saw, but I think it took about six months before I could truly look at them without a feeling of loss. The fact that my family on many occasions asked to see them and did not show any signs of disgust was very helpful.

Not too long after the amputations, the doctors gave permission for Priscilla to take me out of the hospital, initially just to sit in a courtyard, breathing outside air and watching normal life. Another step towards normality of some sort. My feet needed to be protected by bandages and some "funny shoes" to reduce the risk of infection. I was not permitted to put the shoes on to any outside surface other than a wheelchair. Jon and Priscilla took me out for tea, wheeling me along the street in the wheelchair, the sun was shining and people in short-sleeved tops buzzed around me. This was life happening, normal, flowing, no one knew of my predicament, and that felt good; life carries on. I'm certainly no butterfly, but the thought went through my mind that this is like a butterfly emerging from a cocoon. The institutionalised environment of the hospital being the latter. We went to a very nice café and the odours of food hit me in a way that I have never previously experienced. They seemed to penetrate my nostrils in rapid succession. I could discern one odour after another, some of which I had never previously been conscious of. They were crystal clear, distinct and very strong, almost painful. Everything around me seemed to be bursting with life and bright colours, seen with an amazing clarity. However, I realised that I had normal three-dimensional vision for objects close to me, but everything about three metres away and beyond seemed flat, uni-dimensional and surrealistic. I looked around and wished for, hoped for, almost pleaded for, three-dimensional vision, to no avail. I had not lost the vision in either eye, so something else was going on. Another sense had been altered, but this time, causing a depletion not an enhancement. This surrealistic perception lasted for a long time (several years) but after about six months, it mainly occurred when I was tired. It was not a loss of accuracy of vision, it was a loss of the perception of what I saw beyond the clarity of a few metres. So if I went to a football match, for example, as I did later in my recovery, it was more like seeing it on a 2-D television screen and not with the depth of three dimensions. I do think that considering the various sensory changes that I experienced, I probably suffered some brain damage during the toxic shock/intensive care phase.

The physiotherapy took on a new dimension as the physiotherapist helped me to walk, difficult at first with bandaged feet, but essential after a general anaesthetic. She took me to the gym and that was another stage up the mountain. Another release from the institutionalised environment of a hospital, doing normal things in a gym, which could have been anywhere. My first try on an exercise bike lasted for three minutes before I became exhausted, but the time slowly improved. As I reached a slightly new level of ability, it felt greatly encouraging, as it did for my family, who looked on like proud parents.

I was seen by a cardiologist, who struck me as having very little bedside manner and no empathy. That may have been my perception and not reality, but I don't think so. He made no reference to what I had been through or what I was experiencing now. An echocardiogram was prescribed, presumably to see if there were any collections of blood products (vegetations) on my heart valves. If there were, they could harbour organisms and cause bacterial endocarditis (a very serious condition), fortunately that was negative. The echocardiogram could also identify any areas of damaged heart muscle. My view of the cardiologist was confirmed when he phoned me later to say, "There was evidence of left ventricular damage," (one of the major chambers of the heart) not something you really want to hear. I asked, "What was the significance of that?" and he said, "I am too busy to explain and will see you tomorrow." Being on the receiving end, I think that that was cruel. It wasn't as if I'd had a minor illness and he was giving me an insignificant test result. How did he view me? Was I just a heart in a bed with no emotions or sensitivities? Maybe he'd had a bad day, but I don't think that justifies his behaviour. Maybe he had no emotional intelligence and simply could not appreciate what it may be like to be a patient but then again, he was a doctor and doctors should care. I played over the possibilities of my ventricular damage in the night when all was quiet, I was alone and the demons were out relentlessly hammering away at my brain. Only a good dose of a sleeping pill (zopiclone) finally put me to sleep. The straightforward, empathetic and compassionate physician, not the cardiologist, subsequently reassured me, but that was on the following day. Needless to say, after discharge from hospital, I didn't stay with the cardiologist, but why and how can some clinicians be like that? Maybe they distance themselves to retain objectivity

103

and enable them to cope with the array of personal tragedies that they encounter, but by so doing they remove compassion.

Unfortunately, the blood markers of infection did not reduce and the physicians were puzzled as to the source. A thorough clinical examination, a whole body CT scan and a gallium scan revealed nothing. I recall how difficult it was to lie absolutely still for each of the three successive gallium scans, which I think each lasted for twenty minutes, or it might have been one scan for forty minutes, my memory is hazy on that point, but either way it was not easy. I wasn't very happy about the amount of radiation that I was receiving and the future potential consequences of that but there seemed to be no other choice. No site of infection could be located. Antibiotics were prescribed and slowly my infection markers decreased, but the cause of the raised level was never revealed.

There were numerous ultrasounds of my kidneys and the radiologist said that their size was normal and there was no evidence of the shrinkage associated with degeneration. That gave some hope regarding their recovery, as did the head of intensive care at University College Hospital who had told my family that the kidneys are "the cowardly ones": they are the first to shut down and the last to recover. He also said that eight out of nine recovered within six months, so I thought, let's give it six months and see, although I did note that the nephrologist seemed sceptical of that view. I requested that the small amount of urine I produced (50ml per day) be measured to see if there was any trend for an increase but, alas, there was none. In retrospect I realise how ridiculous that exercise was. The fluid output didn't need measuring since it was so low; any return to normal would have been obvious. However, much to their credit, the physicians and nurses humoured me and in no way ridiculed me. How did I feel about the lack of change? Sanguine is the word that came to mind at the time and still does: "I will have to face and deal with whatever the outcome may be and I will try and give it my best shot."

11

VISITORS

In the early stages, I really didn't want to see visitors other than my immediate family. Their presence was incredibly helpful, but I simply didn't have the energy for anyone else. Priscilla came early every morning and stayed all day. My sons, Justin, David and Jon also came virtually every day, as did my daughters-in-law, Davina and Jo, even though Jo was heavily pregnant. I relished the thought of them all being with me. It was interesting to observe their different responses to me and the way in which they helped. They all gave psychological support and Jon, Davina and Jo helped physically with virtually daily massages of my aching legs. Most important of all, they were all calm, accepting of the situation, supportive and loving. The parent/child relationship changed, they definitely became the parents to me the child. This actually felt good; I trusted them implicitly and knew that they would not make important decisions without consulting me but also knew that they would try to relieve as much pressure as possible from Priscilla and myself. There was definitely a warm glow inside me which rose up over the nausea and fatigue, a feeling, in a very basic, primitive sort of way, of love and of protection. Slowly, as I improved (wellness score 5-10), I welcomed visitors, they energised me and my nephew's wife, who is a physiotherapist, joined in the leg massage regime, which was greatly appreciated. I loved seeing my grandchildren and on some occasions managed to watch Spurs on television with them, again a feeling of pseudo normality. My son David came to watch every televised Spurs match with me, giving up his season ticket for these matches. It felt very therapeutic to be sharing something from my previous life, although it was very difficult to concentrate on the television. I can clearly remember one day when I was lying in bed, everything seemed to be in a bit of a haze. Objects were coming in and out of focus, nothing was clear in my mind, concentration was impossible, the bed-clothes felt so, so heavy as did my eyelids. Sounds were fragmented and then I realised that my grandsons, Noam and Lior were standing by my bed. Noam, my eldest was holding my hand tightly. I struggled to throw off the fog in my brain, looked at them and felt myself saying inside my head, "I love you so much, I want to live for you and see you grow and be here for you." My head sank back on the pillow and my body relaxed, their energy had perfused my being – it was better than any drug.

As I regained a little strength, Priscilla and I were taken for walks (me in the wheelchair) and for lunch by friends. I couldn't participate much in conversation, but just feeling that they cared for both of us made such an enormous difference. It was interesting and uplifting to see them. I appreciate that it is impossible for people in good health to see the world through the eyes of one so ill or for them to understand and truly appreciate the impact of their visit. That must influence their feelings about the value of their presence. There were those who came to see me who were incredibly helpful and supportive, these were people whom I would expect to visit – not expect in the sense of "I expect you to be here", but in the sense of I think it is probable that you will come. There were those whom I never imagined would be so helpful and seemed to come from nowhere, I never realised the strength of the bonds that we had developed. This was so reinforcing and energising.

There were also some whom I thought I was close to but they only made the perfunctory visit or didn't visit at all. Maybe because they couldn't bear to see me like this, didn't care, were too busy, had an aversion to hospitals, would not want visitors themselves if the tables were turned or felt that they would be imposing and in the way. Perhaps they didn't know what to say to me and to avoid the challenge and the awkwardness, they gave themselves the excuse that I probably wanted to be on my own with my family. It is possible that they didn't appreciate the importance of them being there (maybe the result of low self-esteem) or because it would have brought them face to face with their own mortality. Irvin Yalom addresses the inevitability of, and difficulties associated with, confronting one's own death in his beautiful book *Momma and the Meaning of Life*. He quotes a Babylonian story to illustrate that these feelings are part of human history. In this tale, which dates back four thousand years, Gilgamesh realised that the death of his friend Enkidu was a precursor to his own death and that part of his grief was a fear of his own death, "Enkidu has become dark and cannot hear me. When I die, shall I not be like unto Enkidu? Sorrow enters my heart. I am afraid of death." I appreciate all of these possibilities but it was very painful being on the receiving end and regarding some of those individuals, the pain lingered no matter how much I analysed the reasons. It irrationally played on my mind, taking on a disproportionately debilitating focus which really dragged me down. What helped to mitigate it was that later in my journey, on two occasions, friends from Canada came over especially to be with us and support us – to find a friendship like that even once in a lifetime is a glorious experience.

There were also visitors who I wanted to see but the only times that they could come to the hospital were inconvenient. A prime example of that was my cousin David who lives abroad. He was constantly in touch with Priscilla and he tried to see me on each of his frequent visits to London. Each time I was either too ill to see anyone, or about to undergo a procedure. It made me feel guilty, he was trying so hard. I wanted to see him, but I couldn't. The interpersonal dynamics of illness can be difficult to cope with. On the one hand, I could be logical, I simply could not see him, on the other hand, there were emotions from which debilitation had removed the lid. When I experienced kindness, it didn't take much to bring tears to my eyes, not crying as such, but great big tears and a sob. I hated myself for feeling critical of people who I would have loved to see but who didn't visit. When people did visit, I was delighted to see them but then if they overstayed their visit, I felt a resentment.

I do not have strong memories of my upbringing with my sister, Trisha. She is four and a half years older than I am and a girl and so she played with her friends and my older cousins, rather than with me. However, she did look out for me even though it must have been difficult for her having me around, displacing her as the only child. She was and is a far superior pianist than me and I recall her playing the piano for hours, once again filling our home with music. I do know how much she loves me and think that my illness was an incredibly difficult thing for her to accept. I can imagine that seeing me in intensive care brought back memories of the time just before her wedding when she saw our mother on that hospital bed, dying. I think Trisha found the replay with me intolerable. I was aware of this, very difficult for both of us. Once again, illness played horrible games with my emotions. How did she express her love and concern? Like any good Jewish matriarch, by cooking. She has the ability to produce a meal for ten people at the drop of a hat. An ability probably inherited from our mother. So, she brought food round for our freezer, her way of showing her love. It was interesting for me to observe how different people expressed their concern, anxiety and love.

Focusing on visitors led me back to thinking about my father's elder sister Auntie Dora. She did not speak to him for twenty-five years. What precipitated that? It was the failure of me at the age of fourteen and my sister at the age of eighteen to visit her husband in hospital after he had suffered a heart attack. Fortunately, my father did ultimately get back together with her and she became like a grandmother to my children. Priscilla, in particular, gave her tremendous care and support until her dying day. I could now understand how hurt my aunt must have been by our inaction and how wrong we had been. Not that it justified twenty-five years of anger. I wanted to resurrect her and say, "Auntie Dora, I was wrong so very wrong, please accept my apologies." But it was too late for that. A lesson that important conversations should not go unsaid and left until it is too late and they are no longer possible.

Trying to assess the way in which visitors responded to me occupied and stretched my often very fuzzy brain throughout my illness. I created a personal game, putting them into categories. There were those, such as my immediate family who came in to the hospital room and then, later in my story, into the ward, with confidence and a beaming smile. They were genuinely interested in how I was feeling and explored those feelings, before giving me news of their lives and the wider world. There were those who I could see hesitating before entering. Frequently, their faces changed from very grave to an artificial smile when they saw me. Others would ask how I was but it was obvious that they didn't want to know. Some were very relaxed and matter of fact which felt very comforting, while others looked as if they were at a funeral and talked in hushed tones. Then there were the visitors who just didn't know what to say and stood there grinning but without real words coming out of their mouths. It felt as though they were suffering from some form of mental disability or minor brain damage, and it was they and not I who was ill. There was a feeling that I had to make the conversation, not something I had the energy to do. Some visitors tried to reassure me by telling me that they knew my kidneys would come back to normality – how would they know that? I am sure they were trying to help me, or maybe help themselves, but I was far more realistic about my situation. Lastly, there was the visitor who would ask me how I was and without waiting for an answer start a conversation with Priscilla without any further direct reference to me. I appreciate that Priscilla needed support but I felt as though

I was a corpse in the bed, already past communication. I am not trying to be cruel, because all of these people made the effort to come and visit me. That was hugely appreciated. It's just that, once again, I was able to focus on aspects of my situation and help to prevent myself from dwelling on my own predicament. In fact, I spent many hours working out a research project in my mind, in which patients would assess the effect of different types of visitor responses. I thought that maybe there was a place for a book, A Guide to Visiting the Sick. Maybe it exists, but the mental process took me out of myself.

Another interesting observation was that, while I was very grateful for visitors, I couldn't deny the occasional feeling of envy that raised its ugly head. Visitors could feel concerned or sorry for us, but rightly be able walk out of the hospital and carry on with their lives, while I was left with my illness and with Priscilla, who carried her anxieties and feelings of potential loss. Envy is a destructive force and one that has rarely consciously visited me and so I suppose that illness can bring out many unwanted and unexpected emotions which perhaps are unaddressed by the medical profession. I searched for one of my coping strategies, trying to recall a humorous experience related to envy. One came to mind. It was humorous but also had pathos. When I was a child, living above my Bubba, there was not much money to go around but sharing with the wider family and the fun generated by my vivacious uncles and aunts mitigated this. Many happy days were spent at the house of one of my mother's brothers, Uncle Arthur. I played endlessly with my cousin Tony. I never felt any envy for his material comforts, except for his electric train set. I must admit that my eyes almost popped out of my head every time I saw it. My father was very aware of this. He spent much of the week travelling around the country trying to obtain orders for dresses. One night, he came home and said to me, "I've got a present for you." With great excitement and anticipation, I opened it. It was, I'm sorry to say, a pathetic, battery-operated electric train which ran around a single, small track. I was about seven years-old and very sensitive to my father's expectation. I feigned great excitement and gratitude, not wanting to spoil the moment for him but, underneath it, I felt even greater envy for my cousin's train set. On recalling this, I could see the funny side of it, how ridiculous to have envy regarding material things, nothing is as important as health.

12

LESSON LEARNED

As I slowly improved, I became aware of a change. I started to have sexual thoughts about the nurses. I suppose the close proximity to them combined with their caring attitudes helped to precipitate this and I found it interesting that I should have these thoughts and feelings. While I have always been monogamous, I did not see it as a bad thing because I had wondered if I had lost my sexuality. I didn't make any comments, but found myself fantasising. On the one hand, it felt potent, my normal functions were reappearing but, on the other hand, it felt very sad. Here I was, an ageing male with a body that felt as if it belonged to a parasite that was taking it over. I was like the many pot-bellied, sallow-skinned or over-suntanned ageing men, who often have enormous, anachronistic piano-key white teeth which wouldn't even look right on piano, let alone an ageing face. They delude themselves into thinking that their advances to young women will be perceived as attractive and well received. At least I did not fall into that trap.

When I was a child, one of the exciting programmes on television was the London to Brighton train journey in four minutes. The train journey was filmed from the driving cab and then speeded up when shown. In the light of modern technology, it is remarkable to think how exciting that was. I now felt as if my life had been accelerated and replayed. I started in intensive care with my every bodily need cared for by maternal and paternal figures. I learned to stand, and then take a few steps, then walk, then climb stairs. I had to be fed, then could feed myself with help, and then without it. I needed to be washed and have my teeth cleaned and then learned to do this for myself. Now I seem to have reached adolescence again, with sexual fantasies. I just hoped that it would not be accelerated through the next stages to further infirmity and death. I remembered the words of a very dear mentor of mine who lived in Amsterdam, he said, "Life is like the water running out of the bath. To start with, it goes very slowly, but then it goes faster and faster, and finally it suddenly disappears down the plug hole."

It would be dishonest of me to say that I never had or have lows of mood and feelings of sadness. Of course I did and occasionally do now but, at no time, would I classify it as depression (nor did the clinicians). With sadness, sometimes other people can help to lift you out of it, and it often doesn't take much to do so. One of the benefits of visitors. Your carer can be a tremendous help in recognising your drift into one of these low moods, being sensitive to it and giving support to lift you. However, with serious and persistent illness they, too, have lows and need help. As a baby needs its back rubbed, when life feels too difficult to cope with, the parents need their backs rubbed. With depression, you erect a wall between yourself and the outside world. You are a prisoner of your mind, building a barrier to all of those things that affect you and nothing simple can penetrate that. In a way, it could be considered to be self-protective, although it is extremely destructive. My feelings towards my situation were very realistic and I believe that I was and am very accepting, but it is inevitable that low episodes will occur. It is important that I recognise them, understand that these feelings are not abnormal, knew and know that I will always come out of them. At no time did I, or do I, require any form of medication to deal with this. Laughter is incredibly therapeutic and is a wonderful releaser of tension. When sleep is difficult, a very low dose of the sleeping pill, zopiclone (less than 3.75mg) is very helpful. However, I do find that even this very low dose can sometimes lower my mood the next day and so I try to limit its use.

Two songs almost continually repeated themselves in my head. I couldn't shake them off. One was *Yesterday*, composed by Paul McCartney. It's pretty obvious why those words were so profound: my world and I had certainly changed.

This seemed so meaningful and, even to this day, particularly if I don't feel well, the melody and lyrics come back and play repeatedly in my brain, not a welcome feeling, but almost impossible to shake off. So my conscious acceptance of my situation obviously has underlying rumblings that quite reasonably surface from time to time.

The other song that came back to me was from a tape that Priscilla and I used to play in our twenties when driving along open roads in the sunshine feeling carefree, young and perhaps a little invincible. It was a track from Nashville sung by Henry Gibson and called *Keep a Goin'*. He adapted the lyrics from a poem written by Frank L. Stanton. The last verse of the poem is:

When it looks like all is up,
Keep a-goin'!
Drain the sweetness from the cup,
Keep a-goin'!
See the wild birds on the wing,
Hear the bells that sweetly ring,
When you feel like singin', sing—
Keep a-goin'!

I knew that it was only a song, but the words seemed very poignant and the melody upbeat. Every time that I replayed it in my mind I found myself revitalised, it's strange how little things can make a big difference when you're vulnerable.

A large soft fluid-filled swelling (a bursa) suddenly developed on my left elbow, which looked very unsightly and felt like a big squashy ball hanging from me. It's amazing how many times you lean on your elbow! The physicians had no explanation for the cause and did not prescribe anything for it. It slowly subsided (over two weeks) and then reappeared and subsided, not to return. In the third week, I tried to sign my name, but my writing was so shaky that neither I nor anyone else could read it because it was so squiggly. It was emotionally very painful for my hand not to be able to do what my brain was telling it to do, particularly since my profession requires extremely precise manual skills. With more and more practice my control slowly improved but it was a very slow process, requiring much dedication and support from my family. I remember the great sense of achievement in the early days when the consultant asked me to do up my shirt buttons. Having just come out of the Intensive Care Unit, been scanned by computed tomography and gallium scanners, it made me smile to think that in this day of high-tech medicine such a simple everyday skill still comes up trumps as a test. I wondered what its diagnostic accuracy was!

Perhaps, sometimes, simple is good and that shouldn't be forgotten. Certainly, in dentistry, I see a move which implies that the fancier and more technologically-advanced the equipment or test, the better it must be. That is not always the case and there is a real danger that a clinician's ineptitude hides behind the technology. Diagnostic acumen, experience, ability and with diagnostic tests, the validity, the benefit/risk ratios are all of profound importance.

A ridiculous yearning for chopped liver developed and friends started shipping it in by the ton load. On thinking about it, perhaps one of the reasons for this yearning was that my now long deceased mother made delicious chopped liver which I loved when I was a child. Perhaps I found it to be a comfort food. At a time of such debilitation, there is an almost desperate desire for a mother to pick you up in her arms and comfort you. This doesn't diminish the relationship with your wife but it is a more childlike, primitive innate response. The chopped liver was good for a while but obviously never replaced my mother, and furthermore it was bad for me, liver contains high potassium levels – not a good idea when on dialysis. In fact, one evening, the physician came in and checked me, left, returned and said, I think we should check your potassium – not sure what triggered that. The result came back quickly and it was very high – immediate transfer to intensive care. This time the experience was very different. It was an overnight stay, during which I was conscious and found it hard to sleep because of the bright lights. There were very ill patients around me (I was pretty ill myself, but they looked worse than me – well, that's how I saw it) and the thought did occur to me, from time to time, as to whether or not I was going to end up like them. This was quite disconcerting but I was able to dismiss it and think positively and observe. The quiet, calm efficiency of the nurses going about their work was intriguing and very reassuring, these people are remarkable. Looking around and seeing the resuscitation equipment took me back to 29th September 2001: an incredibly exciting match at Spurs. They were a mediocre team, playing Manchester United who seemed invincible. However, Spurs were winning 2-0 and then, against all the odds, they scored again. The crowd went wild, as did the man to the right of me. He jumped up, shouted and promptly collapsed between the rows of seats. I went over to him, no pulse. Started resuscitation. It seemed forever before the St John's ambulance came. I sat down. What did they do? Nothing.

I asked, "What are you doing?"

They said, "Waiting for the paramedics."

I said, "You can't wait," and went back to resuscitation.

Then the police came and said, "Everyone back to your seats," so I did and they stood there.

I asked, "What are you doing?"

One policeman replied, "Waiting for the paramedics."

I said, "You can't wait."

He said, "Back in your seat, sir."

I said, "You can arrest me if you like, but I'm not leaving him," and went back to continue.

Fortunately, they didn't arrest me. Finally, the paramedics arrived. They applied a defibrillator to him and ultimately carried him out and I understood that they were taking him to intensive care. I suppose that's why, lying conscious this time in intensive care and viewing the equipment, my mind wandered to this incident. The sequel to the story is that two weeks later at Spurs, I saw the niece of the man and asked her how her uncle was. She said, "He died." I said, "I'm really sorry to hear that." She said, "Don't be sorry, he was eighty seven years old, he lived for Spurs and he saw them beating Manchester United three nil and then he dropped down dead. A perfect ending for him." I suppose it was, because had he remained, he would have seen Manchester United go on to beat them 5-3! He certainly knew when to leave the party! This was black humour, but it did distract me from my predicament.

Fortunately, nothing untoward happened during the night and, in the morning, I was returned to my room.

I subsequently told Priscilla what had happened and we reached a pact. This had been the first time that she had not been informed of something to do with my care. I didn't want her to be worried in the night but, as she rightly pointed out, "If I ever withheld anything from her, she would never truly know what I was feeling or what was going on. We had always been absolutely honest and transparent with each other in our relationship and now was not a time to be changing that." – lesson learned!

13

FINANCIAL CONCERNS

Thinking slowly became clearer and with that came complications. I had a single-handed dental practice operating with a very high overhead. This overhead was necessary in order to provide the quality of care that was so important to me. A large part of the expense resulted from the salaries of the team who worked with me. A decision had to be made as to whether or not to try and dispose of the practice, keep all of the team employed, make some redundant or try and keep everything together.

Priscilla and I have never had a legacy to fall back on in a time of financial difficulty and we were acutely aware of that. What we have achieved therefore has been of our own making and our histories have highlighted the fragility of life to us. We now had enormous decisions to make. They would be hard in good times, let alone when faced with such debilitating illness and no knowledge of what the future held for me. The feeling of being forced to give up my life's work now, when in a few months I might regret that decision, bore down very heavily on me. There was also one patient in particular who had experienced many debilitating failures of extensive reconstructions of her mouth. Treatment to date had taken two years and we were entering the final stages when my illness started. I was sure that, as far as is possible, even with such a severe debilitation of the mouth, I could resolve most of her difficulties, concerns and problems. The final stage entailed using procedures developed in my practice, and my desire to return to complete the treatment became a driving force. Could someone else have completed it? I'm sure that was possible, but I felt that it would be best for the patient if I was able to do so. She was asked and she said that she wanted to wait, in the hope that I could complete it for her. The sense of purpose was an enormous motivator for me. I made a decision to try to keep the practice and my team intact. That meant large outgoings with virtually no income for two six-month periods over two years. I did have insurance to help towards practice overheads but could never obtain sufficient cover. There was also critical illness cover but in retrospect that was not nearly as much as I should have taken out, so this period ate significantly into our savings. My family was very helpful to me in analysing the situation, but only I could really make the decisions. They did not want to be the ones to finally take the practice away from me and saw my desire to return as an excellent motivator. No one on the medical side even acknowledged that these concerns were a problem. I appreciate that they do not have training in this area but it is such an important part of the response to serious illness, it seems prudent that someone should at least raise and acknowledge it. It's interesting to note that financial concerns are common in patients who have been in critical care. In addition, 44% had significant anxiety or depression. I am extremely fortunate to be in the 56% without it. Is it luck or attitude and family support, both or neither?

Financial concerns did weigh heavily on my mind but good things often come out of bad. Three dentist friends, two from the UK and one from Canada, made offers of substantial sums of money to help see us through these difficult times. None of them were people who could afford not to think about the personal implications of what they were doing. I didn't accept the offers but the feeling of gratitude, love and support made a tremendous difference and still lives with me, as does the fact that they should care so much.

Was the decision to keep the practice going the right one? From the financial perspective, definitely not, but from the psychological perspective, definitely yes. It motivated me to fight to return to functional health and to feel that I had retained a very important part of my life.

My view has always been that money is important but it cannot buy happiness. The psychological importance of keeping my options open outweighed the financial considerations. That was true, but the reality of the situation needed to be kept under constant review. My father's precarious childhood came back to me and made the decision-making even harder. His father died prematurely, leaving him with a mother who had a severe stroke and was completely bedridden. There was a younger brother, an older sister and two older brothers with families of their own to support. Other than from a Jewish charity, there was virtually no social care and the small amount of support they received from that charity did not provide enough for them to live on. There was no NHS at the time and the family could not afford fees for doctor's visits, and so my father had to leave school at the age of fourteen and work to help provide for the family. In 1930, working seven hours per day, five days per week, he earned two shillings and sixpence (thirty pence) per week at the Houndsditch warehouse. A doctor's visit in 1930 would have cost thirty pence (my father's weekly wage), and that was without the additional cost of medication. What a contrast to the Britain of today with social care and an NHS. I repeatedly dreamed about him as a struggling teenager, which made me very sad when I woke up. I think that the underlying processing of these dreams related to our own financial instability. I also repeatedly replayed a period in my life when I witnessed financial and psychological instability in him. For many years, he had run a small wholesale dress company with his partner. I understand that they made a relatively small income from this. My father spent a substantial amount of his time travelling around the country selling and finally he obtained the biggest order of his life, in the North of England. This order was for several thousand dresses. He sent the order to his partner who, unfortunately, was on the golf course for the next few days, something that he frequently did. When he returned from his golf and finally placed the order with the manufacturer, he found that the material was no longer in stock. Without checking, he ordered the dresses in a different material. When they were delivered to the retailer, they were rejected. The cost of manufacturing had to be paid for and my father and his partner were bankrupted. He was devastated but true to his gentle nature, he never fell out with his partner. He took a job as a manager in a menswear shop and, after two weeks, I overheard a conversation between him and my mother, "Cissie, I can't do it, I can't work for somebody else, I have to control my own destiny." Sobbing … "Joe you don't have to, we will sort it out, we can do it, we can and we will." Then she stopped and gently started singing the words from the song *Smile*, written in 1936 by Charlie Chaplin, John Turner and Geoffrey Parsons. She was the strong one in the relationship and I know that my will to fight came from her and her family, as did my mantra, "I can and I will." I watched through a partly opened doorway, as she sang, his sobs changed to a smile. He took her into his arms and they swayed in time to her singing. How, as a teenager, could that fail to impress on me the unquantifiable value of love between two people? I was so fortunate that in my time of need, it was there for me.

These thoughts led me on to thinking about my mother and her siblings, sadly all now long dead. I had the feeling that I was being supported by the cumulative experiences of a loving, caring, fun family. Frequently when I was lying alone in my hospital bed, I reflected on this. I thought about the benefits of having internalised not only a good mother figure, but also a good father and wider family figures. I speculated on how much a society loses when families become fragmented by the lack of a stabilising parental factor. The developing child may lose the internal security and feeling of self-worth. Both are so important and needed in the journey through life, to provide support in difficult situations. My mother's brothers and sisters were larger-than-life characters. All but one of them were determined to get the most out of life. My mother was the baby. Besides being strong-willed, she was caring and compassionate, with a tremendous sense of fun and of the importance of family. She was a great cook, could produce food at a moment's notice to entertain people, always had a shoulder on which others could cry and was never judgmental. She didn't push me beyond my capabilities but always encouraged me to do my best. Nor did she ever reveal any sign of defeat to me and that is because I think she looked at every potential defeat as a challenge. I have obviously inherited that view. My Uncle Alf had flashing eyes, a big moustache and always seemed to be painting his toilet. He courted his wife-to-be when they were both in hospital during the war. She was on the women's floor below him and constantly played classical music on the balcony. He would lower messages to her on a fishing line and so they developed a relationship which blossomed when they finally met. Most importantly, Uncle Alf could sense any distress in me and would sit me down with him and say, "Michael, you're unhappy, what's wrong, tell me about it," and then he would first listen and then proceed to give me sound advice. Uncle Alf was the person who first taught me to play the guitar. Uncle Arthur became a successful hairdresser and he and his wife Lila always had an open house for us. I almost felt as though it was my second home. He was an extremely good-looking man, always dapper, even in his nineties. His piercing blue eyes burned into me and his amazing head of hair was always perfectly in place. He had an infectious laugh and deep wisdom. My cousins and I would chuckle over old photographs of him accompanied by beautiful young women. One day, when I was six, my Auntie Fay's husband Sid came into a room wearing a bright new tie. He swept Auntie Fay up in his arms and started dancing around the room, singing "tonight's the night we're going to have some fun". He had just come back from a post-operative checkup following a prostate operation. I didn't have a clue about the meaning of what was going on. Uncle Arthur stood up and said to Sid, "I don't like that tie," and he took out a pair of scissors from his top pocket (he was after all a hairdresser) and cut it off below the knot. You can imagine the shock for a six year-old, not to mention for Uncle Sid. End result, the family burst into hysterical laughter, as did Uncle Sid. Always look on the bright side. Uncle Dick was a very gentle man and a very accomplished violinist but he had to leave the Royal Academy of Music when he developed tinnitus. He was the family expert in classical music. Then there was Auntie Anne, poor Auntie Anne. By the time I knew her, she was the only one who did not have a zest for life. Early in her adult life, she had been deeply in love with a man. As was common practice in Jewish families, since her elder sisters were not married, her older brother and my Bubba, her mother, forbade her to marry him. Finally, she did marry, but not for love, and she ended up in a psychiatric hospital with deep depression. Uncle Harry was kind and gentle and had a wonderful tenor voice, once again bringing music into my life. I would delight in the sound of it when he sang to us. Aunts Fay and Rose were the twins, always laughing, having fun and working extremely hard in their dress shop. They were diminutive in size but enormous in character. I remember them well at family celebrations with what looked to me as a small boy like complete foxes hanging around their necks, tail and head included. These whirled and twirled as they hurled themselves across the dance floor in time to the music, with their husbands hanging on to their spouses for dear life. Auntie Kitty was the eldest and seemed to live a very affluent life since her husband was very successful in business. I did not know her very well. These people and their respective families helped shape me into who I am and how I react. Thoughts of them and my father entered my mind and they seemed to encircle me and be saying, "Michael, we all came from absolutely nothing, but we made it and lived lives full of challenge, excitement fun and (except for Auntie Anne) love. You can do it, you can make it."

Another person who kept popping up in my mind's eye, urging me on but also making me smile, was Bubba. I remembered her varicose veins. These were severe and she wore thick, elasticated, pink, waterproof stockings to try to control them. As a small child, there were many times when I watched her lying on her back with her leg in the air while my mother or her sons rushed around her, one of them applying pressure to a burst and profusely bleeding vein, the others trying to calm her. It was terrifying. However, she had another use for the stockings. Whenever I was ill with any kind of fever, but particularly with a sore throat, she would fill a stocking with hot porridge, tie the top closed and put it around my neck, insisting by sign language that it would cure me. I could see her now marching into the hospital clutching her handbag, back straight, head held high, wielding a stocking filled with porridge and saying, "Where's my Mikala?" It did me the world of good just to think of it, but I didn't think the medics would have approved of its use.

At one time, most of the family lived together in one large house in Leslie Street in the East End of London. There were the brothers, sisters, husbands, wives, children and Bubba. Times were very harsh, with little money, no bath and an outside toilet, but the only stories that came out of this were good ones, about how much fun they all had together. Some years before my cousin Michael's stroke, he went back to see the house that held so many family memories. He stood outside and looked up at the windows, thinking of the family stories. After a while, his reverie was broken by a woman throwing her head out of the window and shouting down to him, "Hang on a minute love, if you're waiting for Rosie, she's with another fella, and it'll be your turn in five minutes." Maybe a lesson that, as I have discovered, our perceptions and dreams may change or be changed for us very rapidly.

These thoughts provided a helpful distraction but it was necessary to try to focus on the problem of my practice. My dreams for this had certainly changed very suddenly and dramatically. In reality, my brain was so confused that decision-making was probably much more a "gut instinct", part of the process of dealing with loss and grief, than a clear analysis of the possibilities. How many patients are left alone and tormented by financial difficulties when perhaps professional help could be of assistance, but is not forthcoming?

After six months, I did return part-time to my practice, completed the treatment for that patient and finally passed the practice on to a colleague in December 2011, two years and eleven months after entering the Intensive Care Unit. The process of divesting myself of the practice was a very difficult one emotionally, practically and legally. While it came at the right time in terms of my illness, the illness forced it upon me, as did the need for a lease renewal. The effect of separation from an adult lifetime project should not be underestimated. On one hand, there was the relief of not having the responsibilities that are associated with the work. On the other hand, there was the giving up of something that I loved, the loss of potency associated with leading a team, making important and challenging decisions, helping people, the actual provision of complex treatment and the loss of an income. The passing up of all of that is something of a mental castration.

Establishing my practice had not been an easy task and that made giving it up more difficult. I was determined to practise the way that I had been taught. On my first day, I had only one patient. I promptly referred her to a specialist, knowing he would provide better treatment than I would. I also had taken out a three-year lease, had loans on my equipment and received a £10,000 tax demand for unpaid tax from the previous two years (a substantial sum in 1974). I must say I nearly died. Subsequently, an accountant pointed out to me that this was an estimated tax demand. I had not completed a tax return for two years; I had been in America as a student without income. It took about three years for me to feel that my finances were not on a knife-edge but seven years before I began to feel relatively secure. During that period, many in my profession laughed at me and said I was crazy for what I was trying to do and the way that I was doing it. That was very hard to accept but I never doubted the validity of my approach. I was subsequently vindicated when critics came seeking treatment and colleagues around the world requested that I teach them. The emotion associated with divesting myself of the practice was made far worse by the machinations of the legal profession. It seemed that a process that should have been simple and straightforward was escalated into a very stressful and long-winded one by the lawyers. It certainly did not enhance my health, and Priscilla and I felt an enormous relief when it was finally concluded. Fortunately, when it actually came to it, recognising that I had fulfilled my objectives in respect of my clinical life gave me a feeling of satisfaction, closure and few regrets. However, it is important to realise that serious illness is complicated by far wider concerns than just the illness itself.

Four weeks after being admitted to the private hospital, my fifth grandchild was born, a boy. Financial concerns left me for a while. This new life was far more important. It is hard to describe the feelings I had when this tiny, living, breathing, warm, alert human being was brought in for me to hold. Me, who had been vital, fit and mentally strong, now an emaciated, weak, confused person holding this little being with his whole life ahead of him. Would I be able to support him, have fun with him, love him, get to know him, share with him, advise him and be there for him? Neither I nor anyone else could know the answer to these questions. It made me elated and made me feel low, but I certainly had another person to live for, I would try not to let him down.

14

RELEASE

Bad news arrived forty-six days after admission. The consultant physician came in to see me and said that my private medical insurance had contacted him. They informed him that "as from the next day" they would pull the plug on my care, considering dialysis to be the treatment of a chronic disease, which is not covered! After forty-five years of being a subscriber, they decided without compassion or a decent warning period to cease cover. What kind of morality is that? However, I am probably being very naïve to consider that morality, money, healthcare and insurance go together. With much wrangling, my consultant managed to obtain a three-day reprieve for me. No dialysis means death and so a place had to be found for me in an NHS facility. During the wait, an interventional radiologist removed the plastic tube that was in my jugular vein. With local anaesthesia, he inserted a Permacath, a more stable entry into the vein for connection to the dialysis machine. Relatively little discomfort occurred, which was very different to the first experience of having a tube inserted at the end of my stay in intensive care. During this three-day period, I noticed another altered sense that had been slowly creeping up on me. Water drunk from a glass was taking on a more and bitter distastefulness, whereas drinking from a plastic "glass" was not a problem. Why should that happen? In fact, I could only drink water from plastic and not glass from then until March 2010, when the situation reverted.

Three days later a dialysis slot was found on the NHS and I was discharged on a Friday. Wonderful friends came to help us home. They packed up everything for Priscilla who drove me, while they followed closely behind to ensure that she was all right. They helped us into the house and then left so that we could be by ourselves. My thoughts were racing over what the next stage had in store for us (wellness score 10-12). I felt sad to be saying goodbye to the people in the medical team who had cared for and nurtured me, and was very apprehensive about being released from the containing hospital environment, yet delighted at the thought of going home, very conflicting emotions. Despite Priscilla's outward excitement at me returning home, she must also have felt great anxiety at the thought of having responsibility for me, not an easy task. To reduce our anxieties, a nurse was booked to stay at home with us for the first night but it turned out that fortunately her services were not needed after that.

When we arrived home, we found Davina, one of our daughters-in-law, standing in the hall with a great big smile on her face, welcoming us. The dining room table was laid up for Friday night dinner, with a meal ready and prepared by her, it was a very touching and supportive thing to do, and we both felt extremely emotional, tearful and grateful.

When we sat down for dinner, Priscilla put on some of my favourite music but I couldn't tolerate it, yet in my former life, I was so passionate about it. I so wanted to be able to enjoy it and feel normal in my own home, but it was impossible. It may be hard for some readers to comprehend why and what we did at Friday night dinner. It is the commencement of the Jewish Sabbath and as I have said previously I am not a believer, but there are aspects of practice that I still follow because of their family, community and historical meaning. One of those is a small Friday night ceremony. In the home, two candles are lit and a short verse sung together with a blessing over wine and bread. We have never gone out on a Friday night other than to be with our family for dinner and it has remained a special night and one that is very bonding for family. I can still feel myself standing next to my father as a small child, holding his hand as he chanted the verse. He always mispronounced one word "Hinhulttonou" as "Hinnihuloltonou" and I would smile at this and then later, my children would also smile at their Poppa. So when I recite it, I feel his, my mother's and sister's presence, and a bonding with my immediate family. I have recited that verse on a Friday night for about fifty years, so it felt very special for Priscilla and me to stand in front of the candles, my Permacath poking out over the top of my tee shirt, my emaciated arm around Priscilla and her arm around me. A gentle flickering glow from the candles suffused the room. I started and said three words and then … I couldn't remember a single word beyond that. Feelings of devastation, sadness and profound loss engulfed me. Once again, large round drops of tears rolled down my face and a deep uncontrollable sob rose up from my throat exploding from my body and then a feeling of, "I am alive, I will survive and beat this to the extent that I am able, I will do it, I can and I will."

PART 3

Home and Outpatient Dialysis
27th March 2009 – 28th February 2010

15

MUCH-NEEDED SUPPORT

Home, and how different it was now compared to life before illness. The many almost unnoticed freedoms that we had previously enjoyed, such as sharing a meal together without severe dietary restrictions or the reinforcement of a deep love by a caring physical sexuality, were gone. The ridiculous feelings of not having enough time, due to our own self-inflicted timetables. Now we had so little time as our weeks revolved around my dialysis, sleeping and hospital appointments. I received dialysis three days per week as an outpatient at a satellite unit of the Royal Free Hospital. The NHS care was commissioned from a private company. During the first three months of this period, there was an overwhelming feeling of sleepiness. It took great effort to wake up in the morning and then even more effort to stay awake during the day. I have explained this feeling earlier, but it felt like the sleep of the dead, virtually nothing could shake it off and, furthermore, sleep did not leave me refreshed. A bath was not possible, since the dressings on my feet could not be soaked, nor could water be allowed to enter the Permacath penetration into my neck. However, after wrapping the Permacath and my feet in polythene bags, a gentle shower was feasible. A simple routine procedure before illness was now a struggle. I did try a specially made protective waterproof sock but it didn't work very well so showering was a long drawn out procedure and very exhausting. It was impossible for me to get in the shower unaided, let alone stand there and wash myself. It was such a feeling of helplessness to need so much assistance from Priscilla, and I felt so dependent.

Every morning, with great effort and substantial willpower, I forced myself to do some exercise in the hope that I would gradually be able to build it up. A physiotherapist came to the house, but, unfortunately, she came to see me at the end of the day on her way home and I never felt that she was interested. She failed to really motivate me or give anything like the help that the physiotherapist had provided in the hospital. Ultimately, motivation has to come from within. While I appreciate that is always the case, my experience has been that other people can also help enormously. Sometimes it takes very little to give you the resolve to pick yourself up and try. Priscilla was an expert at this, with her gentle but persistent encouragement. A part of the exercise regime was the use of a static bike. In order to describe the effort required it may be helpful to rewind the clock about ten years, when in the summer we regularly hiked in the Italian Alps. We frequently stayed in the small village of Gressoney-Saint-Jean located at 1385 metres, with the summit at 3275 metres, so we were high when we were climbing. On one occasion, we nearly killed ourselves by setting out unprepared on what looked like a lovely day. It was at a time when we did not own mobile phones and anyway there was no signal in the area. We reached a point from which we could not turn back because we would never have been able to return to the village before sunset. Suddenly, the weather turned bad, rain, wind and a substantial drop in temperature. We ended up walking on a narrow track which had half fallen away. It was about 20 metres long, a hundred metres above an icy lake and was now only one boot width wide. There was a sheer rock face on the one side and a vertical drop into the lake on the other and nothing to hold onto. Turned towards the rock face, the heels of my boots hanging over the edge of the path, I inched my way along the track with the fear of falling or of the earth giving way. Fortunately, I made it, turned to Priscilla, and said, "OK now you do it." Frozen to the spot, she replied, "I can't." I said as gently as I could, "You have to, you can't go back, you can't stay there, you have to do it." She took a deep breath and began her ordeal. When she arrived into my arms, she said that once she'd started, the fear left her and it seemed like a dream. The fear certainly didn't leave me as I watched her tentative moves along the path. Her dream-like state had a happy conclusion but for weeks, nightmares followed for both of us. We imagined a UK news report, middle-aged British couple found dead in Italian lake. Proper preparation was essential in future. However, that required me to carry a heavy rucksack. The first parts of our climbs usually felt as if they were almost vertical and would last for about one and a half hours. The energy expended and the effort carrying the rucksack at the high altitude were enormous. Why do I describe this? Because at times when I felt that I didn't have the strength or will to fight to recover, I recalled this episode and told myself that we survived and I can survive my present predicament. Also, the effort of getting on the exercise bike and pedalling for five minutes initially, and gradually building up to twenty minutes per day, felt vastly greater than the effort of that initial climb. I would say to myself that I managed to climb the mountain and I will do this, "I can and I will." Sir Winston Churchill once said, "Some people dream of success while others wake up and work hard at it." I had to remain realistic and recognise that if I was going to get anywhere near my goals, it was down to me and hard work would be required. During this period, it would have been so easy to have just buried my head under the covers in the morning and succumbed to the weakness and go back to sleep. With the passage of time, the exercise partly helped me to shrug off the feeling of sleepiness, but I could never eliminate it. Accompanying the sleepiness there was the constant nausea and itchiness, which I just could not shake off. Exercise however, did enhance my feeling of well-being (wellness score 20 after four months).

An upbeat district nurse came to change the dressings on my feet three times a week. She used special dressings on the gangrenous lesion on my heel, as prescribed by the vascular surgeon. Despite her care and my visits to the vascular surgeon once every three weeks, there was very little improvement in the healing of the gangrenous lesion in particular and there was talk of perhaps needing to treat the area surgically.

I always looked forward to the district nurse's visits; she was caring, empathetic and highly professional. She walked into the room with a big smile on her face asking, "How's my baby?" How lovely it was to see this ray of sunshine. I wonder how many lonely, poorly motivated (particularly elderly) patients are pushed into needing to use expensive hospital and GP services because of the cutbacks in social care in the UK. These cutbacks profoundly affect members of the team who can do so much in the home. We hear of appointments being limited to fifteen minutes, what can be achieved in such a short time? Certainly not the motivational outcome of caring, sympathetic help. If these reports are correct then as a patient, it feels appalling and disgusting. It is perhaps an example of the effect of healthcare being looked at solely as a commercial profit-making enterprise. If the NHS continues to be used as a political football, there is a real risk that the greatest such service in the world may become another crumbled empire.

Visitors were very welcome and I found that conversation, although difficult, lifted me partly out of the sleepiness. One friend in particular provided an endless supply of food, keeping strictly to my dietary requirements, so helpful for Priscilla, taking away another cause of stress for her. I understand that it is common for the partners of Intensive Care Unit survivors to have a great fear of separating from them even for short periods, yet Priscilla did need time for herself and my niece Serena would come round and "uncle sit". This was doubly nice, it was always lovely to see her, but I also knew that Priscilla felt safe enough to go out and have some necessary time for herself. It is so important for the carer to have respite, both for their own sake and for the one being cared for. From the patient's perspective, it relieves the feeling of being a burden and seeing your loved one becoming exhausted. I found it so hard to watch her becoming thinner and thinner and although she tried to hide it, looking anguished on many occasions. Small and large offers of help make such an enormous difference. A very lovely person, who for many years had helped us in the house and had seen the children grow up, contacted us and said that she would like to come back to help out, without any pay. She wanted to give Priscilla some respite and to help me in any way she could. What a wonderful thing to do and we gladly accepted her offer, but insisted on payment. We felt so grateful.

I loved our garden and for many years I had help to maintain it. It was necessary to inform the person who helped me that unfortunately due to circumstances, we could no longer afford the upkeep. He immediately responded with, "Pay me whatever you feel you can afford and I will continue to help you in the same way as before." What an act of generosity. How therapeutic it was for me to sit and look at the lovely scene as it blossomed. I think that besides the beauty of flowers, it was something to do with the revitalisation and regeneration of nature, perhaps an inner yearning for my own revitalisation.

It was uplifting to see my family and friends, but I found it very difficult to tolerate long visits. Our immediate family continued to be amazingly supportive and helpful, which felt so good. A very close friend, who is also our solicitor, gave unconditional, professional help and friendship over a very long period. Both hugely relieved a source of stress. My next-door neighbour came in regularly every Sunday morning to have a chat, it felt so good to know that he cared, and our discussions were very wide ranging and stimulating. On two occasions, our Canadian friends came over to be with us and sit with me on dialysis, giving Priscilla some respite. What an act of love, how do you say thank you? Other Canadian friends also offered to come over, but unfortunately the timing was not good for us and so they did not but it meant so much that they cared. Support during the long, often lonely dialysis sessions was particularly welcome. Priscilla hardly ever left my side during dialysis; she only did so when she knew that I was comfortable and secure with a visitor, or fast asleep. Only the medical team can treat the illness as such, but the psychological effect of so much support is incalculable. After all, who we are and the expression and experience of our emotions reside in our brains. Many factors can affect this amazing organ and deeply influence our feelings of illness and self-worth.

I was very conscious of many dialysis patients being alone day after day; perhaps they preferred it that way? But perhaps they didn't; I felt very fortunate. Another very close friend came regularly once a week to my dialysis session to play chess with me, this was greatly appreciated but created an amusing situation. I was so grateful for his company but, under normal circumstances, he is a far superior chess player and would be able to beat me off the board. However, with my head spinning, fuzzy and feeling half-asleep, there was no chance! I needed to start with him only having four pieces on the board to have any possibility of winning, but I wouldn't have missed those sessions since they meant so much to me. I had my feelings about the importance of friends reinforced while listening to the Nobel laureate psychologist, Daniel Kahneman. In August 2013, he was the guest on the BBC's Desert Island Discs. He said, "Friends are crucial for imparting wisdom to you and help you through difficult times; they can see things that you, being involved in a situation, cannot see." They certainly did and still do this for both Priscilla and me. In these awful circumstances, we could feel a reinforcement of these important relationships. It has always seemed to me that to have good friends, it is important to be a good friend. I am sure that this "pay-off" has a deep evolutionary basis. Primitive man needed friends in order to survive. For example, if a man killed an animal that was too large for him and his family, he could share it with others and they would reciprocate in his time of need. The people who made such friends would be more likely to survive. I am not in any way suggesting that friendships are developed consciously with the pay-off in mind but I do think that this is deep in our evolutionary psyche. Perhaps only cynical, manipulative and/or power-seeking people consciously think of the pay-off. In those circumstances, this is not true friendship. I was aware of my mother making the effort to phone her family and friends, and the need to reciprocate in friendships is always reinforced for me by Priscilla. The number of people who I have heard say, "He (or she) never phones me," intrigues me. The question in my mind is, "Do you ever phone them?" This concept does not detract from the fact that human beings carry out acts of altruism which do not seem to fit into this idea of pay-off. However, the feeling of giving and saving a life could easily be the pay-off, which in no way detracts from the selflessness. Having been on the receiving end, by having a live kidney donation (a kidney was given to me by a living person), I must conclude that, fortunately, there are human beings who are simply good people. There may be an evolutionary rationale for altruism but I would prefer to just consider myself immensely fortunate to have been given back my life by a special person. Priscilla and I found that good things could come from bad times if you allow them to, especially when people reach out and you accept their help and support with deep gratitude. This is certainly not a time to be proud and reject help.

During this period, and ever since, my NHS GP has been extremely helpful and available. Not that I have called on him for very much but just knowing that he cares and wants to help gives a feeling of security, which is definitely needed when you find yourself outside the institutionalised life of the hospital. On several occasions, he has phoned me with proactive advice and recommendations. Whether or not the fact that his father, who was also our GP before him, had chronic kidney failure and was on dialysis, gave him greater insight I do not know, but I am very grateful to him. I often wonder how the personal experience of the carer influences the delivery of care. Are obstetricians who have had a baby better and more compassionate than those who have not? Are dentists who have received dental treatment more caring than those who have not? Perhaps an interesting study for someone?

On many occasions, I thought about the immense support that a display of compassion gave to me. Illness can distort or remove the sense of who you are. Feeling compassion can lift your mood, help you to cope and restore your sense of self. You are a person, people care about you, you have worth. In my professional life, extending it to my patients was a primary objective. I tried never to be dismissive of their predicaments, fears, anxieties and concerns. However, I was now a patient, experiencing the effects of compassion or of its absence. Anatole Broyard, essayist and former editor of the New York Times book review, eloquently recounted his perspective as a patient. He described the psychological and spiritual challenges of facing metastatic prostate cancer and the emotion of it being a devastating event for him, yet for the typical physician it was a routine incident in his rounds. He stated, "… I just wish he would … survey my soul as well as my flesh…".

I feel desperately sorry for him. Of course, it may not be as straightforward as Broyard makes it sound. Some clinicians may be expressing compassion in a way that is not recognised. Obviously, this does not help the patient. It is also possible that patients' moods or debilitations will not enable them to recognise compassion even when it is clearly shown.

Fortunately in my many encounters, the overwhelming majority of the medical team has been caring, thorough, compassionate, kind, encouraging, professional and respectful. They have also gone out of their way to maintain my dignity, which is so important. On many occasions, I felt very humbled by individuals, ranging from receptionists to clinicians, and I still do.

However, a few could do much better. For example, while on dialysis, I consulted a dermatologist for a rapidly developing flushing and visible enlargement of blood vessels on my nose (rosacea). I felt as if I was transforming into Rudolf the Red-Nosed Reindeer. The dermatologist took my history and made no, and I mean no, comment on what had happened to me regarding the toxic shock and the loss of my kidneys. This felt painful and I considered that this individual needed to get a grip on life and understand what is important. I was not just a nose sitting on the other side of the desk, I have feelings. There was no way that I was going to value his opinion, even if it was strictly dermatological. I consulted another dermatologist.

It became very clear to me that as a patient I wanted to trust my clinicians, and to do so I needed to examine them as well as for them to examine me. Did they have good reputations, were they adequately qualified, were they in the correct speciality for my needs, did they have experience of my problems? These are some examples of my reverse examination. However, whether they demonstrated compassion was also an important consideration. They would have to do extremely well on the other factors to counter the effect of a lack of compassion and for me to feel that I could trust them if something went wrong. This applied to both physicians and surgeons.

When I was saddened by the absence of compassion, I reflected on the many situations in which it had played a primary role, prior to my illness. I will recount two examples.

At the end of a long, tiring day at work, I rushed to Euston station in the pouring rain. I dragged two large suitcases full of photographic slides behind me, in preparation for the presentation of a seven-hour course in Manchester the following day. It was before the era of digital presentations. I slumped into my seat in the rear coach of the train and tried to dry myself as best I could. Looking around, I could only see three other people in the coach, all sitting quietly reading. Suddenly, a young woman was virtually pushed into the train by a policewoman, shattering the silence. The woman was directed to a seat, into which she crumpled, screaming hysterically. To my horror and surprise, the policewoman then left the train, the door closed and the train departed. The young woman was left alone. Within about two minutes, the other three people in the coach stood up and left. Suddenly, the guard came storming through. It was in the 1980s and industrial relations on the railways were not great. He stopped by my seat and said, "It's none of my business, I'm not having anything to do with it." I asked, "What's the problem?" He replied, "That woman has been told by the police that her seven year-old son has been knocked off his bike and killed. She has to go back to identify the body."

With that, he disappeared into the next coach. I sat there for a minute or two in utter disbelief that in such a situation she was left without support. I stood up, went to her and sat talking to her while holding her hand. She slowly managed to calm down. When the train reached Rugby, she assured me that she would be okay, a friend was meeting her. I helped her off the train and watched her bedraggled, hunched, almost ghostlike figure slowly shuffling along the dark platform in the unrelenting rain. The darkness was broken periodically by pale pools of orange glow from the platform lighting. She disappeared into the darkness and then reappeared in the pools of light. With each reappearance, she seemed more defeated. I watched her from the window and, while thinking of this in my hospital bed, I found it very haunting.

On returning to my train seat, I started reading some dental journals. There are some situations in which you can sense somebody looking at you, without actually seeing them. I looked over my shoulder to find another woman looking at me. She had entered the train at Rugby. She asked, "Are you a doctor? They're medical papers you're reading."

"No, I'm a dentist."

"Well, that's pretty close to a doctor; I wonder if I could talk to you? I've just come from my psychiatrist. I tried to commit suicide last week and I don't want to be alone."

Before I knew it, she was sitting next to me pouring out her life's story. She was a very sad person and I just sat and listened. We reached Manchester and she thanked me profusely for helping her.

The person organising the course met me and his first words to me were, "You look shattered." "I certainly am," I replied. "It's a long story." I was shattered, it would have been so easy to walk away from those women in the train but I didn't, and felt satisfied that I had shown compassion. Interestingly, in the clinical environment I could be compassionate and empathetic with many consecutive patients, without feeling such an emotional strain. Perhaps the draining effect was because I was outside my comfort zone of a clinical setting or that after a tiring day, I was looking forward to relaxing on the train journey. It was not to be.

I will give one other example of where my thoughts led me. This was a much happier scenario. I was privileged to know a world famous violinist. We spent many hours talking and discussing a wide range of topics. He was a charming, sensitive, highly intelligent and insightful man. One day he came into my practice carrying his violin. My cousin Michael, who had suffered the devastating stroke that I described earlier, was also there. I explained what had happened and added that Michael loved violin music. I asked, a little cheekily perhaps, whether he could possibly play something for him. Here is where the compassion and humility of the man came into play. His response was, "I'm so delighted you asked me, I'm giving a concert tonight, and it would help me so much to practise in front of someone." So, Michael and this violinist, who would be welcomed on the stage of any concert hall in the world, went into my waiting room. I closed the door and returned to work. About an hour later, I went in to see what was happening. There was the maestro playing his violin, sitting directly opposite Michael who was on a chair with floods of tears streaming down his face. It was the uncontrolled emotion from the beauty of the music and the effect of the stroke combined. Sadly, when I talked to him about it many years later, he had no recollection of this experience. Once again, an incident during illness had led my mind to associated experiences.

A clinician's bedside manner is a way of expressing compassion. How about feedback from patients on the health professional's bedside manner and attitude to patients? This could be implemented for both in- and outpatient treatment. The same could apply to other members of the team, including reception staff. They are, after all, the first point of contact for an often anxious or truly frightened patient. Their attitudes have an enormous effect. My experiences lead me to think that some of these front line members of the team have received little or no training in interpersonal skills. Attitudes seem to range from prompt, friendly, warm efficiency (the majority), to absolute disregard of the person on the other side of the desk. Some receptionists may continue a personal conversation with a colleague without making any eye contact whatsoever with the patient or not even acknowledging their presence. They then address them as if they almost shouldn't be there. That is not supportive, it is rude and unprofessional. Even when very busy, a smile costs nothing and makes a vast difference. Perhaps CEOs or, failing that, managers in hospitals should make appointments for themselves and go to various clinics to see how the staff treat them? To see good practice, they could start with the Renal Clinic at The Royal Free Hospital since the busy team there is superb. In most cases, being nice to people leads to a reciprocal response which makes life more pleasant for both parties. Certainly, patient feedback could be useful, although someone would have to analyse it and then actually do something about it – no point collecting data in order to have it filed away and not acted upon. That kind of feedback may make a difference to the few who would and should be identified. Obviously, it is possible, for example, to have a brilliant physician/surgeon who has a poor bedside manner, but maybe education in this area would be helpful. This may make an enormous difference to the patients under their care and their feelings of support and trust. Of course, there is the difficulty that patients may be afraid to give feedback, fearing poor care as retribution. It is also possible that patients may be vindictive but positive feedback would balance a single negative report. A culture that welcomes feedback and can make patients non-fearful of giving it cannot be created overnight but, in my view, is highly desirable and supportive to patients.

It is important that the medical team recognise that some people have a fear of the medical environment and it would be beneficial if they could be compassionate and acknowledge that to the patient. What is normal to the professionals can be very fearful to both patients and visitors. Some people need support, not just for the illness, but also for their aversion to the intimidating, strange environment. A friend brought this home to me some years ago. He was a very successful dentist who, in his forties, decided to give up dentistry and study architecture. One day, he came to my practice as a patient. When he walked through the door, he said that the smells of dental materials hit him and gave rise to fear. Smells that I was oblivious to and of which in his previous life he too was unaware. Throughout my illness, I cannot recall anyone making comment about the possible impact of my new surroundings. Providers of healthcare in all of its ramifications should remember that environments and situations which seem normal to them might be of enormous significance to a patient.

I prefer clinicians to be straight with me about the current situation and the potential for the future. I want them to be candid. That feels supportive. I want to be told what invasive interventions, ranging from a blood test to major surgery, will entail. If something goes wrong, I want to know what happened and the implications of the incident. I need clinicians to look me in the eye when they are talking to me, not aggressively, but not avoiding me by looking down at their desk, or writing or looking over my shoulder with a distant glazed look, or gazing at a computer screen as if it were the patient and not me. There is a difference between using the computer screen to explain and using it as an escape from personal involvement. The clinician's demeanour should be encouraging, and empathetic, not stern, anxious or aggressive. They should not be dismissive of my concerns, nor give the impression of being rushed. I appreciate that they cannot become emotionally involved in my illness, nor are they gods who can make everything better, but it takes a special skill to be emotionally detached and yet show compassion. This does not make interactions daunting, but it does mean that healthcare professionals, from the receptionist to the clinician, need to have a soul, they need to care, they need to have insight into the human condition.

Support is essential for the ill patient and can come from many sources. None are too small and none too big. Without it, I doubt that I would have survived.

16

NOT A GOOD EXPERIENCE

I have described the details of dialysis earlier but I think some of the specifics of this particular period are worth describing. The dialysis unit was located about a thirty-minute drive from our house, and Priscilla drove me there. During my journey I could barely keep my eyes open, usually nodding off to sleep; once again, it must have been horrific and so sad for Priscilla to watch. I felt very fortunate because many patients relied on hospital transport. My understanding was that it could arrive many hours before the dialysis appointment and so add to the length of the already lengthy process. While appreciating that the journey, the waiting room experience and contact with nurses could and probably does provide a source of much needed social interaction for many patients, I was grateful that I did not have to rely on transport provided by the social services.

Frequently, when I was sufficiently awake in the car on the way to dialysis, I found myself watching the large numbers of people who were often rushing along the busy streets, carrying on with their normal lives. As I said previously, I hate the feeling of envy but it did raise its ugly head again and I would frequently think, "I wonder how many of you have healthy, normal functioning kidneys and don't give a thought as to how fortunate you are?" Of course, it was ludicrous to conceive of such a thought ever entering their heads, why should it? It was also obvious that many of them could have enormous problems in their lives but I focused on the kidneys since, for me, the effect of their loss was so profound. Yes, I was envious of these people seemingly going about their normal daily routines, and I didn't like myself for it.

The experience at this corporate dialysis centre was not a good one. I was required to be in the waiting room by 1 pm, which realistically meant leaving home at midday. There was a company mission statement in the waiting area. Top of the list under overall objectives was, "to maximise shareholder return" and at the bottom of the list "to develop a positive culture with particular focus on openness, respect, integration, participation and recognition". As a patient, that is not what you want to see, namely the money for the shareholders coming first. Of course, I recognise the need to have budgetary control but, in my view, there is a big difference between healthcare provision from a company with a duty to create profits for shareholders, and a charitable trust, an individual or the State, where profits are reinvested for the benefit of patients. It certainly felt as though the financial well-being of the shareholders came before the psychological and perhaps medical well-being of the patients.

I had regained body mass and my weight was now eighty kilos. I required four and a half hours of dialysis, on Monday, Wednesday and Friday, whereas other patients with lower body weight required considerably less time attached to the machine. Although the limitation of an intake of a litre of fluid per day was difficult, but manageable, Sundays could sometimes become more problematic since a Sunday was two days after the Friday dialysis session, whereas during the week dialysis was on Monday, Wednesday and Friday. On a Sunday therefore there could be more fluid retained, which led to a bloated feeling and occasionally some breathlessness. Connecting me to the dialysis unit took about twenty minutes to half an hour and the nurses always seemed to leave me to one of the last before calling for me. I frequently had to wait an hour before being called in, then half an hour while being disconnected at the end of the session, making the whole experience six and a half hours. I can only assume that the reason patients requiring shorter dialysis were taken in first was something to do with transport or perhaps availability of machines, but it seemed like very poor management. In fact, there wasn't a manager, there appeared to be a senior nurse but I'm not sure if that was truly her role. Some of the nurses were very caring but generally the ethos did not seem to be to provide a caring environment. They were overworked, with little time, certainly no time to explain what was happening and, unfortunately, too many of them seemed to enjoy exerting their control over patients. Patients in the waiting area would often talk about their anxieties about upsetting the nurses and the possible consequences.

There was continual racial and verbal sexual abuse from one male patient towards a particular female nurse, and the patients around would lie there squirming but with no ability to complain or draw it to anyone's attention. This nurse was extremely caring and she continued to offer gentle compassionate care to this individual, a remarkable expression of professionalism, which I admired.

I could empathise with her predicament since I remembered receiving abuse from a patient. She was a very beautiful, blonde twenty-nine year old who had snorted cocaine for many years. This resulted in the loss of bone from the inside of her nose and dental neglect. The neglect caused extensive deterioration of her teeth and an inability to chew properly. She was beautiful until she smiled when she revealed teeth that could be attributed to a wicked character in a fairy tale or horror movie. All of her teeth had been severely affected except for her lower front ones. These ideally required treatment, but this was not essential. Following examination, several consultations and discussions, she decided to proceed with treatment but excluded her lower front teeth. I wrote a detailed letter to her explaining the treatment, the fact that the lower front teeth would not be involved and the estimated fee, all of which she agreed to. Treatment was started and proceeded well. We reached a stage in which she had interim restorations. It was not possible to leave her with just the interim restorations and so it was essential that she completed treatment. One day, she requested a consultation and said, "I've changed my mind, I'd like the lower front teeth treated as well." This was a perfectly reasonable request and I said, "That's fine, this is a good time for you to have told me. We can modify the plan of treatment, but I trust you realise that there will be additional work for both myself and my technician and this will incur an additional fee?" (Such disclosure is quite rightly a requirement of the General Dental Council.) She responded, almost spitting out the words, "I didn't expect anything else from you, you're just a dirty Jew." I was astounded and initially lost for words, but then responded with, "Did I hear you correctly?" She said, "Yes, you're just a dirty filthy Jew, I wouldn't expect anything else." I said, "I'm amazed, you've come requesting my help, you need me to be on your side, yet you are abusive to me. However, I will not lower my professional standards because of this, I will complete your treatment, but you will have to go elsewhere to have the lower front teeth treated." The remainder of treatment proceeded well but I had to withstand a barrage of verbal attacks. I was not so incredulous, just horrified and amazed that somebody should have sought me out, placed her trust in me, needed my help, knew very little about me as a person and yet was willing to be so abusive. It is hard to know exactly what her motives were, obviously anti-Semitic, but perhaps she was mentally ill. I had no idea how frequently she was under the influence of cocaine but did notice that on many occasions she would come into the practice in one mood, go into the toilet and come out in another, presumably having snorted the drug. I completed the treatment for her and she was delighted with the outcome. However, she did not pay her final bill. About six months later, I received a phone call from a surgeon in France to say that this patient had been involved in a serious car accident and in order to "put her face back together" he would be very grateful for my help. He did say, however, that she had told him it was very unlikely that I would do so. I was determined that her abuse would not undermine my professional integrity and so I agreed to give whatever help I could. About one year later came the sting in the tail. I was working in my surgery when my receptionist came in to tell me there was an urgent phone call from the police. I went into my office and took the call. I cannot remember the name of the Detective Inspector who was on the line. He asked me my name and some other details and asked if the patient owed me money. I said that she did. He then said, "We would like you to come down to the police station for questioning." I asked why and he said, "She was found murdered in her bed and you are on the list of suspects." (Or something similar. I can't remember the exact wording.) Shocked, horrified, dumbfounded, I let this sink in and then said, "Could you not question me over the phone?" He said that he would ask some initial questions and, fortunately, my answers satisfied him and he said he would not be pursuing this. I must say that I found the whole episode incredible, almost as if she had planned to get me from beyond the grave. I could empathise with and admire the dialysis nurse.

I do not know whether my general debilitation or the quality of the dialysis was the cause but I frequently experienced episodes of very low blood pressure (hypotension), particularly when getting off the dialysis couch. On many occasions during a dialysis session, the plastic tube connecting my jugular vein to the machine would frighteningly block with a blood clot, triggering an alarm. The dialysis would be discontinued until the clot was cleared by a nurse. Unfortunately, the response of nurses to the alarm was frequently slow, probably due to staff shortages; the shareholders must come first? Maybe I'm being unkind but that's how it felt. Frequently, by the time the line was eventually cleared there wasn't enough time left for me to be fully dialysed so I would get home feeling rotten. On several occasions, I was referred to the hospital for the tube to be cleaned out with a metal wire. This was disconcerting, since there was a lapse in dialysis and concern that the tube may need to be replaced. In addition, the question arose in my mind, "What would happen if the clot was inadvertently displaced into the circulatory system?" After all, my mother had died from a blood clot which travelled through her blood stream (an embolus) and cut off the blood supply to one side of her brain.

On one occasion, there was a substantial blood spill from a patient who had finished his dialysis. He walked between the rows of dialysis couches with blood pouring from the access site (fistula) in his arm. I watched a junior nurse try to soak up the blood with paper towels and then smear the blood over the floor trying to wipe it clean. When she had finished, I was so horrified that I called the "senior nurse" over and explained to her what I had observed and that it appeared to be an inadequate response to blood spillage and cross infection control. She agreed and took the mop, placed some liquid in a bucket and proceeded to smear the blood even further around the floor. In dentistry, we are particularly concerned about even minor blood spills and ensure that they are managed appropriately. Following smearing the blood around, she then asked a junior nurse to change the mop head for a dry one. This nurse was wearing gloves and proceeded to hold the bloodied mop head with her hands and unscrew it, she then with the same gloves, proceeded to connect and disconnect tubes to dialysis machines. I could not believe what I was seeing. Unless they had checked the notes, how would anyone have known whether that patient with the blood spill carried, among other blood-borne infections, hepatitis B or C, which can be transmitted through minute drops of blood? Or how would they know if the patient was a carrier of the HIV virus. Even if the notes showed no infection, one could have been acquired subsequent to the last blood test. At the end of that dialysis session, Priscilla and I placed polythene bags over our feet to walk through this area. You may think this is over the top, I don't.

In addition to my previously described symptoms, I found myself becoming extremely cold during the dialysis sessions, regardless of whether or not the temperature of the blood was increased in the machine. For about nine months, it was necessary to wear gloves at many sessions to try to keep warm. Another cause of discomfort developed, restless legs syndrome. This is a very unpleasant feeling of needing to move, bend and stretch the legs to relieve the restless feeling in them. It goes on and on and on with no respite. In one study, 50.22% of dialysis patients experienced this and the condition was associated with insomnia and excessive daytime sleepiness, both of which I experienced.

I developed bad halitosis, which I couldn't control. This wasn't just unpleasant but seemed ironic since, as a dentist, I frequently helped and advised patients who had this condition. The worst aspect, however, was that one of my small granddaughters has a very sensitive sense of smell and I could feel and see her shying away from me the second she experienced the briefest whiff of my breath. It made me so sad because I really needed the hugs of my family, the little ones in particular; they transmit such a feeling of life, vibrancy and love. To her credit, she tried desperately to overcome her distaste and, even though she was only three, seemed to be very sensitive to my feelings and did her best to snuggle up to me, often holding her breath.

Dialysis resulted in my skin adopting a slightly yellowy sun-tanned appearance which, to me, looked very unnatural. It was very painful when, at a later stage, a patient accused me of neglecting her treatment in order to go and lie on a beach. How wrong some people can be in their perceptions and conclusions.

As winter turned to spring, I was moved to a dialysis couch beneath large windows. This may sound pleasant, but the windows faced to the west so that when the afternoon sun was out the patients in this area boiled. We were already having fluid removed by the dialysis and it didn't take much to make me hypotensive. There weren't any blinds to shade the sun and it was not surprising that the frequency of my hypotensive episodes following dialysis increased. There was a consultant nephrologist present only once a fortnight and so it seemed that there was little medical control over the unit, other than that provided by the nurses. With the passage of time, although my feeling on my wellness score improved slightly, maybe a wellness score of 18, I really did not feel well, nor particularly cared for. It became even more difficult to motivate myself to keep going and fighting and I think that this was primarily due to the demotivating effect of this dialysis clinic. I was there for three days per week, taking up most of each day, with hardly a smile from a nurse. Of course, when staff are busy it becomes difficult for them to give time but a smile costs nothing, nor does the suppression of a "huff "or a "sigh".

During this period, I was referred to several clinicians for a variety of opinions, tests and checks, the details of which are not particularly relevant. Nearly all, particularly in the private sector, took a history and gave their opinions from behind large desks, frequently with Priscilla and I sitting lower than they did. My impression has always been that whatever the scenario, whether medical, business or something else, the aim is to put the person on the higher side of this big desk in a position of power. Is this what is required in modern medicine? Many years ago, I went for an interview to apply for a place on an M.Sc. programme. The Dean of the Institute, who rather reminded me of Alfred Hitchcock in his size, visage and manner of speech, carried out the interview. I was ushered into the room and sat down opposite him, viewing him across a large mahogany desk, almost sitting on the floor with him towering above on a high leather-backed chair. On the desk was a water jug with a glass turned upside down covering the narrow spout of the jug. About ten minutes into the interview, he said, "I am very thirsty," and he then just sat there silently. I was confused, what was going on? Obviously, this was some kind of test, what was I supposed to do? With difficulty, I tried to reach the jug from my diminutive position. Impossible. I stood up, took the glass from the top of the jug, turned it the right way up and slid it and the jug over the desk to position it in front of him and then returned to sit just above the floor – it was very obvious who held the power here. He said, "You did the right thing. If you had left the glass on the jug and pushed it to me that would have been impertinent, if you'd have poured the water that would have been grovelling, you showed just the right amount of respect. You can have a place." I thought this is ludicrous, is he really making a judgement based on how I responded to a glass and a jug of water? If so, did I really want to be a part of this programme? Fortunately, that afternoon, a letter arrived resulting from an interview that I had had the previous week; it awarded me a Harkness Fellowship for two years of study in the United States. It was with great delight that I turned down the London offer. That incident has always left its mark on me and reinforced my views about "the power play and the desk". In my view, it is inappropriate in modern medicine; perhaps in the days of the omnipotent consultant, but not today. For that reason, in my practice, I never took a history or gave an opinion across a desk and always did so in a room separate from the dental chair to make the environment less intimidating for the patient. It has been very satisfying to observe that at the Royal Free Hospital and at my GP's surgery, consultations are not across a desk, but with the patient sitting at the end of the desk next to the clinician. I suspect that this arrangement is more to do with space restrictions than any thought of the psychological impact on the patient, but there's an example of the law of unintended consequences having a positive outcome. Perhaps the best environment would be for the clinician and patient, with or without a relative or friend, to sit at the same level in comfortable chairs. A wireless voice recognition programme could overcome the problem of note writing. These "little" things are not so little when you are ill and feeling vulnerable, they can have an enormous effect on the psychological well-being of the patient and their carers. Of course, I appreciate that some patients may prefer an "all singing, all dancing, authoritarian consultant", yet I cannot imagine a counsellor or psychotherapist providing care across a desk. So many thoughts, so many impressions, yet they all added to my involvement and a feeling of being a participant rather than a helpless victim.

During the entire experience of this illness, one of the few activities that consistently improved my feeling of well-being and reduced symptoms has been exercise. While I was on dialysis, I woke in the morning feeling nauseous and wretched, just wanting to put my head under the covers and go back to sleep. It took tremendous effort to force myself to get up and even more effort to get onto the exercise bike, but I did it virtually every day, "I can and I will". Slowly, I increased the time to fifty minutes and felt substantially better for it. I kept remembering something that a ski instructor had told me. He said, "When you are up a mountain in the freezing cold and are injured or exhausted, there is a desire to curl up into a ball and lay there. This means certain death and it takes great mental strength to pick yourself up and fight through the cold." I could see the similarities to my situation and the words helped me to get out from the cocoon under the covers and onto the bike.

Life at this time revolved mainly around dialysis, doctors' appointments, sleeping, disorientation, uni-dimensional vision, trying to control nausea, seeing well-disguised anguish on Priscilla's face, watching the garden and seeing friends and family. There was an inability to listen to music, read, watch television or play my piano. I must stress again that, as far as I am concerned, I was not in a depressed state but my energy, senses and drive had diminished. On one occasion, I forced myself to sit down at the piano and try and play. The first page was possible but, by the second one, I felt very confused. The notes seemed incomprehensible, making me feel very sad, until I suddenly realised I had the page upside down, not surprising it was incomprehensible! I gave up.

Libido had disappeared, and this was particularly distressing. It was not there and the loss drained energy and emotions. To consider that this will not affect someone because the feelings are not there may be a big mistake.

Perhaps it is like the loss of any other human activity, which was so natural and part of being but, once lost, the memory and desire for its return are not eliminated. The thought that I may be like this for the rest of my life haunted me. Fortunately, it slowly returned, but it took a long time for it to become re-established. I understand that it is common for both dialysis patients and following critical illness but, sadly, no help was offered, other than being told those facts. Perhaps there is nothing that can be done.

17

AN EMOTIONAL BOOST

In 2008, I had been elected to be the President of The American Dental Society of Europe, which was established over one hundred and fifty years ago and is the oldest dental society in Europe. Members all have an American dental degree and practise in Europe, most have a postgraduate degree. It was a very great honour to have followed in the footsteps of many distinguished presidents. The annual meeting in June 2009 was due to take place in Lugano, Switzerland, five months after I was first ill. Prior to my illness, I had put in a great amount of effort, and called in many favours from professional colleagues to arrange a high quality scientific meeting. My youngest son Jon had studied flute with a teacher who was also a successful opera singer. She had remained in close contact with the family and generously agreed to fly over to Switzerland with her accompanist to perform on the evening of the banquet. I was not going to miss this meeting unless I really had to. The physicians gave me clearance to travel and the travel insurance company agreed to cover me. It is imperative to obtain a letter from the doctor to state that you are fit to travel, otherwise the travel company may decline to pay in the event of a claim. I searched for a dialysis unit and found one that looked good. Treatment could be provided under the European Health Insurance Scheme. The dialysis unit in London corresponded with them and everything was arranged. There were then the logistic problems of how we would travel to Lugano with our luggage. It required a flight followed by a train journey and I just didn't know how we would cope with this. Once again, our Canadian friends stepped up to the plate. Without us asking them, they said that they were coming over, would spend a week helping us to prepare for the journey and would then accompany us to Switzerland to help. Can you imagine what this generosity did for both of us? It certainly was going to be a challenge, filled with trepidation and uncertainty, but also a feeling of being loved and moving back into the world of the living. My wellness score improved, probably to about 25. The day came, and with it excitement and fear (especially for Priscilla). I still had a Permacath hanging out of my neck and the only thing between my jugular vein and the outside world was a plastic tube with a plastic cap sealing it, a bit precarious to say the least. Nevertheless, I was determined to go and we were going, that meant an enormous amount to me.

The journey was uneventful and fun, I even succumbed to a glass of champagne out of my litre daily fluid allowance, as the four of us chugged over the Swiss mountains in a train. I looked out of the window at the beautiful countryside and mountains, bursting with the life of late spring, flowers, newly-born animals in farms, people going about their work and everyday lives with what seemed to be a smile on their faces. I expected everyone to erupt with one glorious yodel. Corny, I know, but it felt as though life was bursting out and Priscilla and I were part of it. I looked across the table and saw her chatting, laughing and seemingly carefree. So long as nothing untoward happens, this was the right decision. Get out there, enjoy life as much as you can, take some risks but, what the hell, as I know only too well, you never know what tomorrow may bring; enjoy today if you can, while you can.

For many years, one of the objectives of Priscilla, our Canadian friends and me has been to drink a glass of champagne together in as many different places as possible, to celebrate happy occasions and carry with us my motto that "this life is not a rehearsal". We certainly have done so, even celebrating one wedding anniversary with the four of us in a horse and trap going over the Gap of Dunlow in Ireland. We drank champagne, the driver drank champagne and we even gave the horse a glass! We certainly were celebrating another happy occasion now; I was alive and we were all together going off on an adventure, although none of us could have predicted this celebration, of course we had a glass on the train. We arrived at a lovely hotel and I immediately contacted the dialysis centre. There was a nagging anxiety that perhaps the arrangements would not work out, mainly emanating from the poor management at the UK centre – could I be sure that they had set it up correctly? A very friendly and efficient-sounding receptionist answered the phone; they were expecting me the next day. Exhausted but exhilarated after the journey, it felt as though I had been released from prison – not that I have experienced that! An early night, breakfast and a taxi to the dialysis centre. It was in a pristine building and the centre contained only six dialysis stations, compared to the thirty or more in London. Onto the dialysis couch within ten minutes, compared to the hour wait at home. There was one nurse to two patients. I don't know what the ratio was at home, but would suspect one nurse to six patients, or thereabouts. Furthermore, amazingly, there was a nephrologist present the entire time, walking around the unit and constantly checking on the patients – compared to once a fortnight at home, and then you only saw him or her if you had an appointment. Whether the nephrologist's presence was necessary or not, I don't know, but in what felt like a very precarious situation, it certainly gave a feeling of security. I was in Switzerland for a week and didn't experience a single hypotensive episode. This dialysis centre was offering me care under State provision and the European Health Card, not under a private contract. What a contrast to the quality of the dialysis care that I was receiving at home.

The dental meeting went extremely well and, on the last evening, there was a banquet and the entertainment was very well received, overall making me feel very satisfied. It is the president's role to make an after-dinner speech and to include a joke or funny story. I had what many others and I have considered an extremely funny story, which I was able to deliver well, and then conclude my speech. Then something magical happened, everyone rose to their feet as one and gave me a standing ovation. It was totally unexpected. I have given many major lectures around the world, which have been well received, but never a standing ovation. The feelings of unreality, happiness, gratitude, achievement, being alive and sharing this moment with Priscilla swept over me like a tidal wave and I struggled to hold back tears, but didn't succeed, nor did I care even if these were professional colleagues. The decision to take the risk was worth it, a life without risk can be safe, but then you sacrifice the possibilities.

18

BACK TO THE SAME ROUTINE

We returned home and I was back at the dialysis centre. The trip boosted my feeling of wellness, but I was exhausted (wellness score about 28) but it soon dropped back to maybe 15-20. We carried on pretty much as before and day by day my strength and awareness improved. July 2009 was six months after the initial kidney failure and there had been no improvement in urinary output. The consultant who saw me from time to time at the dialysis centre convinced me that it was time to have a biopsy and he admitted me to the Royal Free Hospital for this. Wheeled on a bed to a small room, on to a couch face-down, some painless local anaesthetic in my back, a feeling of pressure followed by a loud click and a small thump which I presume was the spring-loaded biopsy needle being propelled into my kidney. Before sitting up, it was necessary to lie very still on my back for the next four hours to ensure that any bleeding had stopped. The result came back a few days later and showed that there was 88% chronic injury with no hope of recovery. I can honestly say that this did not come as a surprise; it was obvious to me that after six months with no improvement it was highly likely that permanent damage had occurred. When, as a clinician or as a friend or relative, I was party to patients having to receive bad news, I had often wondered how I would react in similar circumstances. Interestingly, I found myself perfectly calm and accepting, the word that I would use to describe my feelings was, as before, sanguine, which the Oxford English dictionary defines as optimistic or positive, especially in an apparently bad or difficult situation. I felt that this is the way it is. Now it's necessary to develop strategies to deal with it and face each new challenge with a sense of interest, curiosity, excitement, determination and humour when possible. Once again, I found my lack of religious belief was supportive since I just accepted that these things could happen. In my view, they are not preordained nor a punishment for sin, I am but an animal.

That July, we decided to make a trip to Cornwall. Having travelled to many places around the world, the Roseland Peninsula is still one of our favourites. The Royal Cornish Hospital NHS trust in Truro offered holiday dialysis and so we set off. The staff in the hospital were very caring and helpful and immediately put us at ease, recognising that we were relatively new to the concept of being dialysis travellers. The ward was very crowded but that didn't seem to matter, the care was so friendly that it made the crowding insignificant. One difficulty was that they could only offer what is termed "twilight dialysis", meaning that it started at 7.30 pm and finished at 11.30 pm, and then I had to come off the machine and get back to the hotel. Priscilla had to negotiate tiny, winding, unlit roads late at night, often in torrential rain. That was no fun for either of us and was very stressful and tiring. Overall, although we loved being in Cornwall and felt exhilarated by being able to take control of the situation in which we found ourselves, I think that the stress outweighed the benefit of that trip.

We returned home, back to the same regime. In August, I decided that I was getting fitter and it would be nice to try a jog. Being in my jogging gear felt so good, flashbacks of pre-illness, would I ever get there again? Within five minutes, there was a strange feeling in my neck. I put my hand up to it, to my horror I found myself holding the entire Permacath, and felt the warm moistness of blood, which was now streaming down my shirt. Realising what had happened and assuming that there was now a hole in the side of my jugular vein where the Permacath had previously been positioned, it became obvious that the bleeding needed to be stopped and something done rapidly to gain access for dialysis. I sat on a wall and applied firm pressure to the bleeding site and breathed slowly and deeply to remain calm. After about five minutes, the bleeding stopped and I walked home tentatively. Priscilla rapidly whisked me to University College Hospital where the consultant who had previously placed a Permacath for me, painlessly and without too much difficulty inserted a new one. Everything seemed OK and dialysis resumed. But all was about to change.

19

SETBACK

About five days later, I suddenly felt unwell, my temperature shot up to 39.5 degrees Celsius and uncontrollable shaking started all over my body. It was obvious that I had an infection: the precariousness of dialysis and a piece of plastic tubing inserted into a major vein – the Permacath. Rapidly to the Royal Free Hospital, through Accident and Emergency and admitted to the renal ward. Once I put on a hospital gown, whether it is for an admission or for outpatient procedures, I immediately feel like a patient and vulnerable. It feels as though my dignity has been removed, all patients dressed in the same faceless uniforms; I am less a person, more a patient-prisoner, not a nice feeling, I wish that there was some other way. This time, however, because I felt so awful it was good to be converted to the patient and be cared for. Blood tests revealed a staphylococcal infection in my blood, another septicaemia. The Permacath was removed, a needle (cannula) placed into a vein in my hand and through it I started on a four-hourly intravenous penicillin antibiotic regime (Augmentin). There were two "unfortunates" besides being seriously ill again. The first unfortunate, dialysis could not be resumed, there was not a tube in my neck to connect me to the machine. A consultant decided that it was too dangerous to insert a new one. The second, every time I had the intravenous shot, I had severe pain in my hand, which immediately swelled. I reported this and suggested that the cannula that had been inserted for administration of the penicillin was not in the vein, but the nurses repeatedly assured me that all was well; I couldn't see how it possibly was. Why were they so indifferent to me raising the problem? Ignorance? Lack of caring? Too busy to pay attention? Sadism? I doubt the last, and sincerely hope not but these thoughts certainly went through my head and they were scrambled by the unceasing feelings of septicaemic and non-dialysis wretchedness. Finally, when the consultant made a ward round, I explained the situation, the cannula was removed and a new one inserted, what a relief. Improvement slowly occurred. However, the adjacent wards had an outbreak of a bug which causes forceful vomiting and watery diarrhoea (norovirus). This meant that my ward was virtually in lock down, with severely restricted visiting. This did not enhance the hospitalisation experience. The nursing was generally excellent and caring (except for the cannula episode) and my bed was by a big window with a lovely view of Hampstead Heath but I felt wretched. It is difficult to describe the feelings: burning hot, sweaty, nauseous, sleepy, but sleep did not relieve the sleepiness, confused, distant, going through a long dark tunnel, falling, alone, pain from the antibiotic being in my hand not in a vein – why won't they listen to me? Sounds coming in and out of my consciousness, am I here or am I somewhere else, but where is somewhere else? (wellness score 8). As I slowly improved, I felt very concerned for the man in the bed next to me. We had great conversations but he went off to theatre for a transplant and returned to the same bed, next to me. My concern was that he was now on immunosuppressants which would lower his resistance to infection and I was next to him with a severe infection. I felt very responsible. I know it was not my responsibility, but how could I not feel that? We frequently struck up conversations and I learned much about the post-transplant period by observing and talking to him, information that was to help me later in my journey.

The septicaemia slowly responded to the antibiotic (now that it was getting into my blood stream and not collecting in a swollen hand!) and my temperature returned to normal. After five days, it was considered safe enough to have a new Permacath inserted, by a registrar this time.

I fully appreciate the need for training. When I think of my clinical skills now compared to those that I had during my training (a true apprenticeship together with academia), I shudder. The very first local anaesthetic injection that I gave was in the local anaesthetic extraction room at the London Hospital. We all queued up and one patient followed by another sat in the chair waiting to be injected, it was like a production line, how barbaric. The student in front of me had to give an injection named an inferior dental block which entails using a long needle and injecting horizontally behind the last lower molar tooth, heading more or less in the direction of the ear, but a bit lower. With an incredibly shaky hand, he approached. I imagined that it must have seemed to the patient as if the student was holding a giant spear. The needle was inserted, nearly to its full depth, the plunger pushed and to my horror, I watched local anaesthetic solution squirt out of the patient's face just below the ear. The needle is supposed to be inserted until it is near the bone of the lower jaw, not out through the face. My turn followed and I approached, also with a shaking hand, but was delighted to "hit the bull's eye", but that moment is imprinted on my memory.

When I was a child, I had to have a series of penicillin injections in my rear end. The doctor would tell me to look away at the wall while I lay on the medical couch. However, he didn't realise that there was an Anglepoise light positioned to help illuminate my delicate behind and it threw up a shadow of an enormous needle on the wall. I would lie there petrified, certain that the needle would pass right through me and pin me to the couch. Fortunately, it never did but I vowed that if ever I had to give an injection to anyone I would do my best to put them at ease and not hurt them, a skill that I have taught myself and passed on to many students. So when I was informed that a registrar would insert the new Permacath into my jugular vein, I thought of my early days in training and my personal injection experience. Not unreasonably, I felt some apprehension.

A very small dose of sedation was administered, followed by a local anaesthetic. The registrar then tried to insert the Permacath into my neck and under my skin to penetrate the vein. Tried, tried again, tried again, and tried again – I could go on and on, each time I could feel discomfort rather than pain accompanied by a lot of pushing and pulling and rising panic. Poetic justice perhaps for all of my training? Had I met my nemesis? At least if I ran into difficulties I always had the compassion to call for help immediately I sensed it. At last, she gave up and said, "I'll have to get my boss." A consultant came, and in what seemed to be about two minutes, the

Permacath was in. I don't know how hands-on training can be improved, perhaps a supervisor watching and listening to multiple trainees via closed circuit TV and able to intervene rapidly?

As I was lying in my bed coming round from the sedation, my mind started wandering over my experiences of poetic justice and I focused on one that brought a smile to my face, it actually made me chuckle. When I was a student, we had one particularly obnoxious lecturer. He was so full of himself, never stopped talking and seemed to take great pleasure in ridiculing people. In one session, he was demonstrating to a group of us how to extract a canine tooth (eye-tooth) from the upper jaw. The shape of the root of this tooth is tapered and he explained, "If you position the forceps correctly and squeeze, the root shape will direct the force and the tooth will pop out of the socket without the need to push, pull, twist, or apply any of the other manoeuvres that patients find so detestable." The patient was a very sad meths drinker who lived on the streets in Whitechapel and whose mouth was like a cesspit. The tooth in question was rotten from decay, covered in debris, calculus and general detritus that you can find in a mouth of such a person. The gums were swollen, red, and bled almost on looking at them. So after giving a local anaesthetic, this lecturer applied the forceps. He never stopping talking and looking very swanky, squeezed the handles in the manner that he had explained. The tooth shot out, straight into his still open mouth, because it seemed he hadn't even come up for air to close it between sentences. It landed on the back of his tongue, reflex reaction, swallowed, down the hatch as you might say, blood, calculus, "schmutz" and all. It couldn't have happened to a nicer person! That's poetic justice for you, and even though it was unfortunate for him, it made me feel good to think about it now. My fellow students and I dared not make eye contact because, knowing the dynamics of the group, we would have dissolved into fits of hysterical laughter. How about him? He gulped, went a pale shade of grey and then much to my amazement continued talking, as if that was how we should dispose of an extracted tooth. Now that's showmanship. I had to give him a grade A for his performance! Another amusing incident that came back to me during one dark and lonely period in the middle of the night related to an episode that occurred when we were living in the USA. We had been invited to a party at the house of one of my cousins in St Louis. She was married to a Professor of psychology, the guests were from his department and we thought that they were decidedly weird. The weirdest one was a man who walked around wearing a cloak and very proudly presented his walking stick, saying that it was made from the stretched, dried, twisted penis of a bull. How weird is that? These sticks are known as pizzle sticks, derived from the old English word for a penis. Many years later, after Priscilla had decided to study for a degree in psychology, I saw my cousin and recounted the story, saying that it made me a bit concerned about Priscilla's choice. She said, "The guests at the party were weird, but as it happens, the one with the walking stick was a dentist!" How could I fail to smile when I thought about that? I could recount many humorous situations but will give just one more example, since thinking about this one again lifted me during another long and lonely night. For many years, I have invited foreign speakers to address my study groups and at one time three American speakers had come over in quick succession. I entertained each of them at a restaurant by Tower Bridge which had lovely views of the bridge. When sitting by the window with the third one, he looked out and asked, "Isn't the bridge lit up at night?" I looked out and saw that the lights were not on, which was unusual. I called the head-waiter over, who by this time knew me, and asked if the lights would be coming on. He picked up a phone by the table, dialled a number and said, "I have Dr Wise with me and he would like the bridge illuminated please." Within about ten seconds, the lights burst into life, the bridge was illuminated and my American guest nearly fell on the floor in amazement. I have to say I nearly joined him.

In many ways this strategy of raising my mood by forcing my mind to search for the humorous rather than dwell on the sad and difficult is reflected by the words in *My Favourite Things*, composed by Rogers and Hammerstein and sung by Julie Andrews in *The Sound of Music*. The words describe how thinking of favourite things can lift mood. We watched this film repeatedly with my youngest son Jon when he was small, the connection reminded me of those good times, and the words frequently went through my head.

Dialysis was resumed as an in-patient at the Royal Free Hospital and the nurses were really kind, caring and efficient. I slowly improved (wellness score about 15) and, fortunately, the sister in the unit informed me that a place for twilight dialysis was becoming available at The Hospital of St John and St Elizabeth; she thought that it might be good for me. It's strange that, even though I felt that the dialysis centre I was attending was not offering me particularly good care, there was a sort of security in the known and a fear of giving it up for the unknown. I understand this emotional tussle much better since listening to the psychologist Daniel Kahneman on the radio programme in 2013, which I have referred to previously, Desert Island Discs. He described the essence of his loss-aversion theory, for which he and his colleague Amos Tversky won the Nobel Prize. Essentially, he found that individuals are willing to take the risk of a loss if the perceived gain is twice the perceived potential loss. A bird in the hand is worth two in the bush. Put in another way, losses are twice as powerful psychologically in comparison with potential but untested gains. This can freeze people so that they remain stuck and not realise their full potential because they are so fearful of the potential loss. It can happen in so many different situations and I am convinced this applied to me at that time. Fortunately, with Priscilla's encouragement, I decided to make the change.

20

WHAT A DIFFERENCE

Dialysis at The Hospital of St John and St Elizabeth started in August 2009. It was initially difficult to adapt to the new timings, arriving at 5.30 in the afternoon and spending the evening on dialysis, three days a week, until about 10.30 pm. It was frequently difficult to sleep on returning home, and all in all an exhausting experience. However, there were two enormous bonuses, the level of care and that I could return to work part time. My understanding is that although it is a private hospital (also providing dialysis for the NHS), the objective is not to generate profit for shareholders but to maintain the hospice facility, "All our profits fund our on-site Hospice – St John's – which treats over 2,000 terminally ill patients and their families every year." Immediately, the different ethos was palpable, there was a general feeling of calmness and, dare I say, fun emanating from the staff and patients. The manager/senior nurse was superb and she clearly ran the department really well. The team was very attentive and caring; they certainly were a team and the feeling that I had was of watching good dancers dancing together. The nurses seemed to go about their work effortlessly, never tripped on each other's toes, were synergistic and in harmony, developing a rhythm particular to them, achieving their desired goal. They always seemed to have time to sit with me and explain what was happening and, contrary to the previous centre, the alarm on my dialysis machine rarely sounded. Dialysis proceeded smoothly, generally reaching its targets. One nurse was dedicated to supervising my care and therefore he developed a good knowledge of my condition. He could make decisions quickly when required, imparting a feeling of quiet confidence in me. He was knowledgeable, gentle, extremely caring and professional. It seemed that my wellness score rapidly improved (wellness score 35) and I put that down to care, attention to detail, a feeling of calm, a general lightness of mood of the team and more efficient dialysis. A few hypotensive episodes occurred but nothing like before. The difference in quality of care between a nurse dedicated to my care in this centre compared to the rotations in the previous one brought home to me the waste of time and risks to quality of care that exist in the NHS. Patients frequently see different clinicians for the same condition. The rotation of consultants and junior staff and the movement of patients from consultants to junior staff mean that clinicians are frequently not familiar with the patient's history. Either they have to waste time discovering information or cut corners by being ill informed. That's inefficient and costly in terms of all resources: time, energy and money.

There were two teenage patients in the ward, one of whom had been on the TV programme the X Factor. He insisted on wearing headphones and singing a very loud accompaniment to the music. This had dual and conflicting effects on me. On the one hand, it felt very intrusive, but on the other, there was great empathy for one so young being in that situation. I was aware of difficult conflicting feelings on several occasions during my illness. What was best for me and what was better for people around me, they weren't always the same and sometimes the feelings made me feel guilty. Priscilla and I started to watch the entire series of The West Wing wearing headphones, to block out as much of the singing as possible, and leave him blissfully unaware of the effect he was having. We pretty well became addicted to that series and would almost look forward to the dialysis so that we could watch it. This gave a focus to our time; it captivated us and took us out of ourselves. It also gave us a tremendous feeling of togetherness, so much better than being alone. At least I was now able to watch some television to pass the time.

One of the big moments of a dialysis session is the food trolley, it is brought around about half way through the session and patients are allowed one small cup of tea (to keep within fluid intake requirements) and a sandwich. How good the tea tasted and, instead of downing it rapidly, as I might have before illness, I relished every sip and extended the drinking time – how perspectives can change!

It is necessary to connect a large blood vessel to the dialysis machine and the best way to do this is by the creation of a fistula. To do so, an artery and vein in the arm are joined to produce a swollen vein which grows larger and stronger. This makes repeated needle insertions for haemodialysis treatments easier and more efficient. There was a discussion with a surgeon about the risks of creating a fistula in my arm to obtain safer and better access for dialysis than could be obtained with the Permacath. It would also reduce the risk of a septicaemia, since with the Permacath, bacteria could gain direct access to the jugular vein as had previously happened.

My left arm was not a suitable candidate because of damage resulting from the necessary arterial lines that were inserted in intensive care. My right arm was a possibility, but the surgeon could not assure me that there was no risk of nerve damage which could affect my fingers. If that occurred, it could completely remove any possibility of working as a dental surgeon. After giving it some thought, even though I had suffered a septicaemia, I made the decision to continue with the Permacath, at least for now, to see what transpired.

As I improved a little, on our way home Priscilla and I stopped off at the beautiful Kenwood in Hampstead. I measured my progress by how far I could walk. To start with, I more or less shuffled about a hundred metres, had to rest and then return to the car. Very slowly, my distance improved and I could make it to the café, about half a mile. Big disappointment though, because I was only allowed a half a cup of tea. However, at least I could sit and watch the people and feel life around me. Then over a period of about two months, I managed a circular route of about one and a half miles, a real sense of achievement.

In September 2009, I returned to work, it was good to be back, albeit very part time. Although it was very tiring due to the general fatigue of kidney failure, the effects of dialysis, which is exhausting, and late nights, since the dialysis finished so late, it certainly gave me a lift. Increased exercise helped to counteract some of the symptoms and gave me energy to work, my wellness score rose to about 40. It seemed that the decision to keep the practice going was a good one.

As my general condition slowly improved, I was asked if I would like to go on the National Kidney Transplant list. Usually, both professionally and in my personal life, I carefully investigate situations before making major decisions yet in this instance there was absolutely no hesitation in saying, "Yes, please." If I could come off dialysis and resume a more normal life, the benefits would be incalculable. Realism was once again important since the chances of receiving a cadaveric transplant (from a dead donor) in the foreseeable future were not great. Quite rightly, there is a very careful system for allocating kidneys for transplantation. At sixty-three, I wasn't sure where I stood. Furthermore, there needs to be a reasonable blood compatibility, and my blood group of B+ is only present in 8% of the UK population. An organ could, however, be received from a donor with blood group type O which represents 44% of the population. Not only does there need to be a blood group match but also "a good match for the HLA genes (Human Leucocyte Antigen)" which are within the genetic material of virtually all the cells making up the body. It is difficult to find two people who are perfectly alike but it is possible to achieve a good enough match for a successful transplant. The larger the group of patients and donors, the more chance there is of a good or perfect match between donor and recipient. That is why kidneys are shared throughout the UK. It has been shown in many studies that good matching between donor and recipient leads to longer kidney survival, and hence is in the best interests of everyone. In a situation where there is a shortage of donor organs, it makes sense to maximise the benefit in prolonging kidney survival. The average waiting time for a kidney transplant is three to four years but is likely to be longer with the rarer blood groups and/or rarer tissue types. Once again, the feeling of being sanguine was present but my mind did wander over the realistic possibilities of receiving an organ. Whether or not I had been "so knocked for six" by the toxic shock that I was too ill to undergo the necessary surgery, whether with my blood group an organ would become available, whether with the passage of time my age would be even more against me. It was necessary to focus very hard on trying to eliminate negative thoughts and remain sanguine. I was able to do this with the support of my family but I would think that many people may require psychological help to deal with these issues and, unfortunately, as I recall, this was not offered.

I do not know the figures for 2009 (when I was put onto the list), but at the 1 April 2013 there were 9,242 patients on the kidney transplant list, with a further 3,672 patients joining it between March 2013 – March 2014. Of these, 3,090 received a kidney transplant, 583 were removed from the transplant list and, sadly, 279 died while waiting for a transplant. A further 8,962 people remained waiting for a kidney transplant at 1 April 2014.

Life assumed a routine pattern: work, dialysis, sleep, rest, some socialising but going out to eat was very difficult due to the fluid and dietary restrictions. I did manage to attend some football matches at Spurs and that gave me a bit of a feeling of normality, although the lack of three-dimensional distant vision was a handicap. On a few occasions, my nine-year-old grandson came with me and it gave me such a thrill to hold his little hand in mine as we walked to the stadium. At an earlier stage, with an enormous feeling of loss, I thought I would never experience that again. How we yearn for the little things that we realise are so important to us and are now lost. Perhaps too frequently we take them for granted and they are unnoticed. Repeatedly, the invigorating feelings that arose from small things, a hand in mine, a smile, a genuine enquiry about how both Priscilla and I were feeling, an offer of help, a visit both at home and at the dialysis centre, did so much to help both of us cope on a day-to-day basis. There is no denying that life was a struggle but I was determined to remain positive, enjoy what I could and do whatever was necessary to maximise my extremely compromised health. The most pain that I was feeling was in seeing Priscilla having to cope with me in my weakened state and having her life so altered by the events. It is so hard to see a loved one compromised by your predicament. On the other hand, it was obvious that severe illness is a little bit like an octopus with extending tentacles. At the centre is the body with the primary problem but the impact extends outwards creating a large organism of illness of varying forms, affecting and pulling in many people. My wellness score fluctuated between 30 and 45.

It became clear to my family in particular that my best option for a transplant was a living donor. If that were possible, it would reduce the waiting time, improve the prognosis and give more options since there are now methods available to use less biologically compatible organs. It is also possible to arrange four-way transplants in which donor A wishes to donate to recipient B and donor C wishes to donate to recipient D but the incompatibilities are too large. It may, however, be possible for donor A to donate to recipient D and donor C to donate to recipient B. The logistics of coordinating all of this must be enormous and even more so with the arrangement of six-way transplants.

There is an additional benefit to a transplant over and above the direct enhancement of my life. It is the cost to the NHS. In 2008, it was reported that the annual cost to the NHS for haemodialysis of one patient for three sessions per week in a satellite unit (which is where I received dialysis) was, on average, £32,669. That figure excludes the treatment and management of all of the medical complications that can arise as a consequence of dialysis. According to the NHS Blood and Transplant Service in 2009, "the average cost to the NHS of a kidney transplant (excluding fees to the NHS blood and transplant service) is £17,000 per patient per transplant. The subsequent immunosuppression costs approximately £5000 per year. Kidney transplantation leads to a cost benefit in the second and third years of £25,800 per annum. The cost benefit of kidney transplantation compared to dialysis over a period of ten years (the median transplant survival time) is £241,000 or £24,100 per year for each year that the patient has a functioning transplanted kidney. At the end of March 2009, the UK Transplant Registry had records of over 23,000 people in the United Kingdom with a functioning kidney transplant. In that year, these patients save the NHS over £512 million in the dialysis costs that they would have needed if they did not have a functioning kidney transplant." These costs do not include the cost to the patient in terms of lost income for time related to dialysis. I am not a health economist but to me, if the patient is sufficiently well to undergo surgery and a suitable kidney is available, the financial benefits of transplantation are a no-brainer and the psychological benefits are incalculable. Another no-brainer is that whenever possible, acute kidney injury should be prevented so that the subsequent treatment is not required. In order to bring this about, a substantial educational programme for the medical profession, politicians, managers, patients and their carers is required. The financial and health implications of this are enormous.

21

THE WORD GETS OUT

Due to failures of transplants, some people have more than one transplant in their lives and some have both a kidney and pancreas transplanted simultaneously. According to NHS figures from 2012/13, in adults, the survival rates of a first kidney-only transplant from a dead (cadaveric) donor are 92% at one year and two years, 86% at five years and 59% at ten years. The figures for adults receiving their first living donor kidney transplant are an average of 97% graft (kidney) survival after one year, 95% survival after two years, 91% after five years and 78% after ten years. The figures for cadaveric donors, according to Kidney Research UK, are slightly different, 85-90% at one year, 70% at five years and 50% at fifteen years. The corresponding figures for live donors are 90-95% at one year, 80% at five years and 60% at fifteen years. Of course, it needs to be remembered that the longer the survival data, the longer ago the transplant was performed and it is likely that procedures have improved with time and therefore perhaps survival rates as well.

There was no way that I was going to ask anybody to become a donor. However, Priscilla and my sons immediately offered but their matches were not particularly good. It might have been possible, but the advice was to wait to see if anyone with a better match might come forwards. There are many emotions being on the receiving end of this process. On the one hand, the thought of somebody electively undergoing this kind of surgery for you is almost abhorrent, on the other hand, there is a great elation that somebody else would be willing to do this for you. My emotions swung, often violently, between the two. The potential for a major enhancement of my life seemed to be great but the possible sacrifice for someone else was also great and I realised it wasn't for me to make the decision. Of course, I could make the decision about whether or not I wanted to undergo surgery and receive a kidney but I could not make the decision for somebody else, and that recognition gave me peace. There are very strict rules about live donation. Fortunately, in the UK, it is not possible to purchase a kidney; I dread to think of the pressures that might be applied on someone to sell an organ. In the UK, if the donor knows the recipient they must not be coerced and they have to undergo psychological testing to ensure that is the case and that they are psychologically suitable for donation. For an altruistic donation, the donor will never know the recipient and vice versa, although they can exchange unnamed letters.

There are, of course, risks to the donor which are very clearly explained to them. For the interested reader, the specifics and the answers to common questions can be found in Appendix VIII.

Without my knowledge, the word went out, "Would anybody consider donating a kidney?" I can't blame my family for spreading the word and am extremely grateful to them for doing so. I could never have done it myself. Some offers came in, which when I heard about them made me incredibly emotional, grateful, touched and moved by this selfless human generosity. The exposure to such altruism was tremendously uplifting, particularly since it came at a time when I considered a significant part of society consisted of individuals and companies who were only out for themselves. There were offers from friends, none of whom were suitable due to diabetes, hypertension, blood group incompatibility, and one had even suffered a cardiac arrest and been resuscitated! An ex-nurse of mine offered, as did Jon's opera singer/flute teacher. One of the members of my dental study groups considered donating, and a member of our synagogue came forward to make an altruistic donation, he did not know me personally. One of the rules for altruistic donation is that, unless you know and have a personal involvement with the potential recipient, it is not possible to specify to whom you wish to donate a kidney, therefore that offer could not be followed through. Then, unexpectedly, Lorraine, the daughter of Priscilla's now deceased cousin Lynne, stepped forward. Lorraine was forty-eight at the time, had never been in hospital other than for a tonsillectomy as a child and to be with her mother during the terminal stages of her life when she was suffering from complications of diabetes. We had known each other for a very long time and she had always had a special place in our lives, in fact at the age of seven she was a bridesmaid at our wedding. Lorraine had no idea which blood group she was but, remarkably, it turned out to be the same group as mine. She has written a section of her recollections explaining her thoughts and feelings (Appendix III).

From my point of view, it came as quite a shock, since this was for real as opposed to talking about the possibilities. Psychologically, once again it became extremely difficult to

191

accept that someone could be so generous and be willing to do this for Priscilla, the family and me. While I desperately wanted a kidney, in no way did I want to transmit any feelings of pressure or guilt to Lorraine should she decide to withdraw at any stage. There was also the difficulty of making a decision as to whether or not to accept the kidney from a small female should the tests show that it was suitable. This may sound extremely ungrateful but it certainly was not that. The transplant surgeon had advised me that being a six foot one inch male, ideally the donor would be a young, six foot two inch bricklayer or rugby player who would provide a large kidney. What a disturbing thought that in some countries such an individual could be forced to do this for financial gain. The decision whether to accept this gift or not was a very unpleasant dilemma. On the one hand, there was this person being so generous and giving but, on the other hand, there was what seemed to be the very selfish consideration of should I accept it or wait and see what transpires, after all it does involve surgery. I decided that if Lorraine was willing to go through the testing procedure and if the results were positive, then I should gratefully accept her offer. I was feeling so unwell that the prospect of having life renewed was overwhelming and anyway, we can't always have what we want in life and I was not a twenty year-old with a long life expectancy.

The clinical and psychological assessments of the donor are rigorous and, obviously, the possibility of diabetes becoming a complication had to be investigated as thoroughly as possible. As the results of each test came back positive, I became more and more anxious since it would be reasonable for Lorraine to change her mind and not proceed. With each test result Priscilla and I explained to her that if she now decided to withdraw we would fully understand and not in any way hold it against her – how could we? We certainly did not want her to feel any form of pressure from us. With each test result, she seemed to become more and more resolute and determined to see this thing through, and I became more attuned to the fact that she really did want to do it. The testing took about three months and the further she moved along this pathway, the more I felt a greater significance attached to the possible result. In my mind, there was a feeling of there being more to lose as the final tests came closer. In reality, all of the tests were important and any one of them could have precluded the transplant but that was not how it felt. The results kept coming back positive and there was tremendous support from Lorraine's father Malcolm all the way through this, and still to this day. He has been constant in his love, concern, care and true humanism towards Priscilla and me and, of course, Lorraine. He was and is an important part "of our team".

It must be difficult for the reader to put themselves in my place, the swinging emotions complicated by a feeling of un-wellness, were hard to deal with. Priscilla was a constant source of stability, calmness, rationality and counsel (she was, after all, a psychodynamic counsellor but it was perhaps complicated for her to apply her professional skills to her husband). She too had swinging emotions. She felt and feels a tremendous sense of protectiveness and obvious overwhelming gratitude to Lorraine, something that we frequently discuss. The final test was a psychological assessment of Lorraine and me separately and then jointly. There had to be absolute certainty that she was doing this of her own volition with no coercion. On reading her account, it becomes very clear that this was the case. We passed the last hurdle and then another enormous hurdle for me, how do you say thank you to somebody who is willing to do so much for you, take risks, leap into the unknown, know that they will suffer some pain and subject himself or herself to a major surgical procedure without having any pre-existing disease or trauma? I found that there were no words I could use to express my true feelings towards her, and that is what I said and keep saying. I have said and say words along the lines of, "Lorraine, there is nothing that I can say or do that would truly convey the deep feeling of gratitude that I have towards you. I hope that by seeing me and by extension Priscilla and the family living our lives again you will understand what you have done. There are few people who would be so kind, generous and truly selfless."

The transplant surgery was booked for 3rd March, 2010 and my mind started wandering over the benefits of a successful outcome. One thought that preoccupied me was a desire to ski with my grandchildren, if that goal were attainable, what an achievement, not just for me, but also for everyone who would have taken me through this journey to that place.

Priscilla, Lorraine and I attended a talk by a transplant patient and a donor at the Royal Free Hospital which was very positive from the recipient viewpoint but the donor told it as it was and I was a little bit anxious that the realities might put Lorraine off. On the contrary, she became more determined and reassured us that there was no doubt in her mind about proceeding. I'm sure my relief was palpable.

Wanting to find out more about the experience, I was put in touch with a recipient who approximately three years previously had received a transplant from his brother. He was so honest, upbeat and positive about the whole experience that he projected these feelings and views onto Priscilla and me. He looked well, said he felt well, did have some side effects from the anti-rejection medication but was able to cope with them. We spent an hour with him and it removed any doubts that we may have had about moving forwards. I'm incredibly grateful for what he did. Fortunately, I had met him before an experience in the dialysis centre. There was a regular visitor to one of the dialysis patients and she had received a transplant approximately eighteen months previously. I asked her whether she would be prepared to talk to me about her experience and she readily agreed. So there I was on the dialysis couch, hooked up to the machine through a tube in my neck, impossible to go anywhere. Conversation: "Thank you very much for coming over to speak to me, can you tell me what the transplant experience was like for you?" Immediate response, "It was the worst experience of my life." Just what I wanted to hear! She then went on for an hour telling me how awful it had been, and there was no escape for me, I couldn't hop out of bed and run down the ward lugging a dirty great dialysis machine behind me. She had me as a captive, but not captivated, audience. I tried to get her to stop but once she started, she was like an express train. I had encountered many patients like this in my professional life. They tend to escalate everything into real or potential disasters, not only matters related to treatment but also to life in general. The Americans have an excellent term for it, "they awfulize". Having received such positive feedback from the patient I had met previously and the patient who spoke at the Royal Free Hospital, I decided to bury her comments in the deepest recesses of my memory, perhaps a warning about whom you should ask. This does not mean that patients should not be honest about their experience and not disclose negative experiences, but there are ways and ways of doing so, particularly if you realise that the listener may hang on to every word you say. No more questioning of patients, I had enough information and was eager to proceed. The transplant team was very supportive during the build-up, as were the dialysis team with whom I obviously had regular contact. They had seen it all before, didn't make light of it, but were helpful, practical and reassuring. Let's do it.

22

A HEARTBEAT AWAY FROM DISASTER

Since there had been some damage to the left major chamber of my heart (left ventricular damage), as shown by an early echocardiogram, I requested a referral to a cardiologist for a pre-operative assessment. A little information about my heart is pertinent. My maternal grandfather had angina, as did several of my uncles. There was also a history of diabetes in the family. It seemed sensible, on reaching my mid-forties, to have an exercise electrocardiogram (ECG) every few years to check my heart. At no time did this show up any abnormalities. As is commonly known, high levels of blood fats (lipids – cholesterol and triglycerides) can be related to heart disease. For many years, my lipid levels were normal and then suddenly, at the age of forty-three, they jumped to a high level. Statins were prescribed. I very quickly developed muscle weakness and discomfort, which felt very flu-like. My GP and the specialist who had prescribed the statins both assured me that the symptoms were not due to the medication. At that time there was a denial that statins could cause such side effects. We then went on a hiking holiday in the Italian Alps. Whereas I had done this for many years without any difficulties, that year was not at all pleasant.

The feeling of muscle weakness and a constant ache, together with flu-like symptoms, were pervasive. On return to the UK, I stopped the statin and within about ten days, all symptoms disappeared. It was felt that there was no need for further investigation regarding the symptoms and another statin was prescribed. This time it took about six months before symptoms developed but when they did they were identical to the previous ones. Perhaps this was an example of how important it is to listen to the patient and not just go by what the books say, since my reporting was disbelieved. Subsequently, it became known that these drugs could cause these side effects and I think one statin had been withdrawn from the market because of adverse kidney effects. To cut a long story short, I went through most of the statins and each time the side effects were similar. While I am not one to give up easily on things, these were so debilitating that my decision was to stop taking them, the quality of life just wasn't worth it. Fortunately, with exercise and a low fat diet, although slightly raised, the lipid levels never returned to their very high levels.

But back to my story. I now saw a cardiologist and a new stress echocardiogram once again showed some left ventricular damage. I don't know whether the cardiologist was just trying to reassure me or genuinely believed what he told me, he said, "There was some mild ventricular damage, it didn't really need anything doing but since you are having surgery, it would be sensible to do an angiogram." I suspect he knew that it was not an insignificant problem. A mild intravenous sedation took the edge off the procedure. A tube was passed through an artery in my leg up to those supplying my heart muscle with blood, and a dye injected. Access was through my upper leg because of the damage to the arteries in my left arm. It was a painless experience other than at the very end when considerable pressure was applied to stop any bleeding. How the tube was manoeuvred to the correct artery so quickly was truly remarkable. On looking at the screen, the cardiologist very gently said that he was very, very surprised by what he saw, namely that the major artery supplying blood to my heart (the left anterior descending coronary artery) was 90% blocked and there was near total blockage of a diagonal branch. He considered that the latter was prognostically insignificant but the former certainly was significant. He went away for about ten very long minutes (long despite the sedation) to discuss the findings with a colleague and then returned. There were two options, namely bypass surgery or trying to place a stent (a small metal tube which is positioned inside the artery to hold it open). A major problem with the first approach was that the planned transplant surgery would be delayed for a considerable time, and there was no knowing what might transpire in Lorraine's life or mind, perhaps she would withdraw from her offer. Even if she did continue to be positive, I knew that she wanted to get it over and done with as soon as possible. The problem with the stent was that the cardiologist did not know if he could insert it successfully. After further discussion, I opted for a ballooning in both arteries (a balloon would be inserted via the tube in my leg and inflated). This would hopefully stretch the artery and widen it, followed, if possible, by placement of a stent. A thought flashed through my mind, what if the balloon causes the artery to burst? Not a good thought to have. Obviously, this didn't happen since I am here to recount the tale.

Then the next decision, if a stent was viable should it be a bare metal stent or one that has a slow release drug on its surface (drug-eluting stent)? The cardiologist explained that there is some evidence that the latter may reduce the risk of blood clot (thrombus) formation within the stent. However, whereas following the insertion of a bare metal stent, aspirin is required for life (to reduce the risk of blood clotting), a drug-eluting stent requires a combination of aspirin and another drug to do so (clopidogrel). The clopidogrel must be continued for at least six months before it can be stopped temporarily. This would make the risk of post-transplant surgical bleeding too high, unless the surgery was delayed. Furthermore, the drug on the stent is an immunosuppressant, and these are prescribed following the kidney transplant to prevent rejection. Therefore, my blood would have high levels of a similar immunosuppressant following the transplant, perhaps reducing the risk of the bare metal stent. The diameter of the stent required would probably also mean that the difference between the two types of stents regarding prognosis would not be very different. An interesting situation to be in, since I was making decisions under the influence of intravenous sedation. Of course, I was given the option of stopping the procedure, thinking about it and then having it performed at second stage. However, I felt that my mind was clear enough to make the decision there and then and I opted for the bare metal stent. I have often reflected on this episode. I am delighted with the outcome and feel that the cardiologist was in a difficult position regarding obtaining consent. He obviously only had my welfare at heart (once again an interesting automatic use of a word, heart) and I am eternally grateful to him. However, I do wonder what the legal ruling would be regarding obtaining consent in such a fashion. The position regarding consent changed quite dramatically in the UK in 2004, following a court case in which Miss Chester sued Mr Afshar, a neurosurgeon. Its effect was to make it more important than ever to ensure that patients are fully informed, understand the information they are given and have sufficient time, where possible, to reflect on their decision. It is imperative that patients are warned about all of the important risks that may influence their decision and, when time permits, they are encouraged to consider their options over time before deciding whether to undergo treatment.

'The paternalistic model of doctor/patient relations has gradually been replaced over the years with a much more patient-centred approach to consent. Nowadays, doctors are expected to work in partnership with patients to agree on treatment options, with the patient's needs and wants as the primary consideration.' This is the approach adopted by the General Medical Council in its 2008 guidance. I suppose the issue that could arise in my situation relates to "they are given and have sufficient time, where possible" and whether or not I could make a proper decision under the influence of sedation, even though it was very mild. One person could argue that I could return on another day, and another could argue that it would be best and safer to carry out the procedure there and then. The only reason that I raise this is that consent is a very big topic in dentistry and one that I frequently discussed with students. It was therefore intriguing for me to consider my own involvement as a patient. How many clinicians practise defensively, to the detriment of the patient, because of the possibility of litigation? I often wondered how much the litigation culture has distorted our society in general. This culture, lawyers and the legal system have, unfortunately, placed clinicians in an invidious position. It cannot be healthy when professions are reluctant to accept that accidents will inevitably happen. I am not referring to malpractice, this is not the same as an accident. Atil Gawande, an American surgeon bravely addresses the problems of surgical accidents in his intriguing book, *Complications*. Henry Marsh is one of Britain's foremost neurosurgeons. In his book, *Do No Harm*, he gives heart-rending accounts of the agony that he has experienced in relation to neurosurgical accidents. Frequently, all that a damaged patient may want is an explanation and an apology but the fear of litigation leads to defensiveness on the part of the clinician. The result in medicine and dentistry is that clinicians may be penalised, and open discussion about the cause of the accident is inhibited. This may lead to unnecessary repetition, causing harm to future patients. This does not feel right to me.

Whereas a stent could be placed successfully in the left descending artery, it was not possible in the diagonal and, to date, I do not seem to have suffered any detrimental effects from that. It seems remarkable to me that until my illness there had not been any heart symptoms, and exercise electrocardiograms did not show any abnormalities. In the early days following the toxic shock, I did have some breathlessness at night but there was fluid in one lung. It has been suggested that the toxic shock may have caused some inflammation within blood vessels and that the dialysis may have accelerated the precipitation of fatty deposits and scar tissue in the walls of arteries (atheroma), narrowing the vessels. Maybe there were some already present which were not giving rise to symptoms. Regardless, the need for statins was now more acute, yet I had previously experienced adverse reactions to them. It seems to me that without the cardiac intervention there would have been a very good chance of my not surviving the transplant surgery. If the atheroma had been present prior to my illness and not due to the toxic shock and dialysis, then I could have been one of those people who drop dead when jogging or playing tennis. Without intervention, on the operating table, jogging or playing tennis I was a heartbeat away from sudden death. Perhaps the illness was a good thing! The inner drive to get on with the transplant was enormous, let's do it. However, the gangrenous lesion on my heel had not responded to treatment provided by the vascular surgeon. Quite rightly, the transplant surgeon was not willing to proceed in the presence of such an obvious infection risk. Since I didn't seem to be getting anywhere with the current treatment, at my request a referral to a plastic surgeon was arranged. He cleaned the lesion, removed dead skin and prescribed Terra-Cortril cream to be applied twice per day. Within a week, the wound made great progress and had virtually healed. Thereafter, E45 ointment and a light dressing for protection were used for a couple of more weeks and there it was, healed. Never be afraid to seek a second opinion if you are uncomfortable with the first one. Now I was ready for the transplant. The transplant surgeon was compassionate, clear about risks, benefits and choices. He looked me in the eye, but not aggressively. He had an excellent reputation; he was the right person for me. He said, "Forget everything about your practice and things like that, we want to get you better." That was a tremendously important thing for him to say. I felt that he was without doubt with me, for me and wanted to help me, and so I just wanted to get on with the job.

PART 4

The Transplant and Subsequent Recovery

March 2010 – November 2014

23

A PART OF SOMEONE ELSE
INSIDE ME

Monday 1st March 2010, Priscilla had packed my bag and we were ready to go to the Royal Free Hospital. I felt tired as usual, but a real sense of excitement percolated my being. Here was an opportunity to regain life, although the thought of having an organ from someone else's body placed into mine was strange. Would I feel it? Would it be pulsating? Would it feel like a part of me or like an alien? I was determined to observe every stage concerning both what happened in the hospital and how my family and I reacted. Once again turning it into a project, from which I could learn, made it feel almost separate from myself. It was probably very hard for Priscilla to appreciate my lack of concern. Of course, I did have some anxieties, but truly not many. I had looked into the possibilities of having the transplant privately but my insurance company would only pay for a live donor transplant if the donor were a blood relative or a member of the insurance scheme which was not the case. More importantly, however, was the consistent advice that it was better to be under the care of a team who had experience in the management of kidney transplants, rather than be isolated in a private room. In the latter scenario, there would be nurses and junior doctors caring for patients with many different post-surgical conditions and with little if any transplant experience. The advice was correct; the care that I have been receiving on the NHS is outstanding. Sadly, however, over the past five years, I have been aware of cracks appearing because of the ill-conceived Health and Social Care Act of 2012.

I was admitted to a four-bed male ward in the afternoon but it was not necessary to change into "the gown" and so I did not feel totally like a patient. I was allowed out for supper following the formalities of admission, questions, blood tests and blood pressure readings. The family came along to have a meal with us and overall everyone was pretty relaxed, it did not raise my anxiety levels to be with them. I returned to the hospital around 9 pm, changed into "the gown" and instantly became a patient. It was necessary to take zopiclone to help me sleep and it was very effective. Dialysis occupied me for most of the next day, in preparation for surgery. Everyone was so encouraging and kind that it was a pleasant day and, of course, as always, Priscilla was by my side throughout. Lorraine, my donor, was admitted that day and in the evening we went out for a meal with her and Malcolm, her father. I could certainly sense her anxiety, perfectly reasonable and to be expected, but it did make me feel even more guilty about what she was subjecting herself to. I think we both were thinking, let's get on with this as soon as possible.

Wednesday 3rd March 2010, I woke early with the usual hospital routines but no breakfast, no fluids. That wasn't particularly difficult since the fluid restriction for dialysis was a good training. Lorraine went to theatre at around 9 am.

A roughly S-shaped line was drawn in my right groin area, the surgical site, and the wound has healed now to a straight line approximately twenty centimetres long. It's interesting that some friends and family think the kidney has been placed into the site of my now defunct kidneys (which were not removed); actually, it is in the right groin area connected to arteries and veins at the top of my leg.

At about 10 am, I was sent for and told that everything had gone well with Lorraine; they were ready and waiting for me. Onto a trolley and wheeled down the corridor, watching the overhead lights pass by, with a feeling of being in some kind of movie, was this for real? It was for sure, with Priscilla holding my hand, right up to the theatre doors. The kiss, the sweetness of which I can still remember, after all this could have been our last, "See you later," and I was off on the next stage of my journey. Into an anteroom and met by a very congenial anaesthetist who chatted while he placed a cannula painlessly into my hand and then told me I may feel a sensation moving up my arm. There was not the classic movie line of "count backwards from ten", we just chatted and one second I was chatting and the next, oblivion, with no sense of moving from consciousness to unconsciousness. There was absolutely no awareness of the surgery and when I awoke in the recovery room, my first thought was, "Wow, I'm alive," and my second thought was, "I don't feel any nausea." To me, this seemed amazing. A general anaesthetic is often associated with nausea or vomiting, yet there was none and for the first time in fourteen months, no nausea. My thoughts then turned to Lorraine. "How is she? Is she in pain? Is she alive?" Fortunately, I vocalised these thoughts and a nurse reassured me that Lorraine was fine. An enormous feeling of gratitude engulfed me and I felt that I had licence to enjoy the lovely feeling of drifting in and out of a warm cosy sleep. Each time that I awoke, there was no pain or discomfort. I have no memory of how long I was in recovery, but how wonderful it was to see Priscilla and David's faces as they peered over me expectantly in the recovery room. It must have been a great relief for them to see me smiling (apparently) and talking to them. The stress on relatives should not be underestimated, especially after such a long journey. I was wheeled back into the ward and told that the kidney had started working as soon as it was connected to the blood supply, great news to receive. An immediate emphasis was placed on me drinking vast quantities of water, jugs of it were put in front of me and I was encouraged to drink. Am I going mad? Just a few hours ago, and for fourteen months, I had been limited to one litre of fluid per day and now it felt that I might drown, but that was a relief.

There was a patient-controlled pain control pump (PCA, patient-controlled analgesia) inserted through a cannula in a vein. This allowed me to administer morphine in very controlled doses as needed. I am not one of those stoic people who refuse pain relief until it is absolutely necessary, I can't see the point unless it makes you feel worse than the pain you might experience. I was always intrigued in dentistry by the patients who refused pain relief medication but who would not dream of having a procedure carried out without local anaesthetic; both are drugs designed to help with pain control. As such, I pumped away, knowing that over dosage was not possible, and I felt great. I think the family was a bit concerned by my love of the drugs and I can see how easy it could be to become addicted. However, in the circumstances, it seemed perfectly reasonable to keep myself comfortable and that I did. No pain, and I mean absolutely no pain or discomfort. Apparently, I was pretty high. On one occasion, the visitors to the man next to me were asking him how he was and I responded that I was "doing really well thank you," and joined in their conversation even though the curtains between us were closed!

Immunosuppressant medication (anti-rejection) was started a few days before surgery. The nurses carefully counted and dispensed pills at twelve-hourly intervals. Since my donors DNA will remain in the transplanted kidney, the medication is required for as long as it survives, unless some new development occurs. I hope that, in the not too distant future, it will be possible to create a replacement kidney in the laboratory in order to remove the need for donors. Perhaps this will be achieved by using stem cell and 3-D printing technology. Immunosuppressant medication would no longer be required.

Blood was taken directly from the tube in my neck (central line) at frequent intervals, both day and night. A doctor unscrewed the plastic cap which sealed the top of the tube, took a sample and screwed it back in place; there wasn't any pain or discomfort. There were surgical drains in my groin, a tube into my bladder (urinary catheter) and the central line, so I imagine I looked a bit of a mess. Due to the tubes, I found it necessary to learn to sleep on my back so as to not disrupt them, a little difficult for one who always slept on his side, but manageable. How we patients need to learn to adapt! Once the drains were removed, there was the dilemma of whether or not I could sleep on my right side. I was afraid of putting pressure on the kidney and damaging it and so I slept, and now sleep, either on my left side or on my back. The day after surgery, there were voices of encouragement from nurses and the specialist registrar to get out of bed and go for a walk. This felt really good, walking, initially nervously, with the help of a nurse and then with Priscilla. Tentatively holding my mobile drip and wheeling it along the floor with one hand, a bag attached to the catheter held in the other hand. It was wonderful to see Lorraine and speak to her. I looked at her. She was lying in her bed, somewhat pale, having undergone major surgery for me and my family, given up a part of her body for me and my family, risking complications and indeed, in a worst-case scenario, her life, for me and my family. Despite the drugs, waves of emotion rose up inside me, they threatened to engulf me, what an amazing, selfless act of generosity. We had always been close but now life had changed our relationship in such a deep and profound way. I think that you have to be a recipient to really understand it. There are truly good people in this world.

24

THE OLYMPIC PEE

One morning, I was sitting in bed reading when I experienced a sudden, searing, penile pain. A nursing assistant had tripped on my urinary catheter, giving it a sharp yank. Not what you want to experience, I can assure you, and the pain was not obscured by my medication. Other than that, the nursing care was superb. There was no inclination to strike up conversation with other patients and, from that aspect, being in a four-bed ward was a little difficult. On the other hand, having nurses around and them being able to watch from the nurses' station was comforting.

I have no recollection of how long I was on the PCA but it was fairly soon replaced by tramadol tablets, which also completely controlled any post-operative pain or discomfort. Tramadol is a very effective analgesic for me and does not give me any unpleasant side effects. There was no holding back on my part from taking whatever was offered.

As I slowly improved and became more aware of surroundings, the feeling of vulnerability crept over me. Immunosuppressants lower the resistance to infection and there was no knowing what my susceptibility would be. The reduction would last for as long as the kidney was viable and I was taking the medication. It felt very precarious. I was aware that, in the early stages, the immunosuppression would be higher than at a later stage, and being in a hospital environment made the risk seem even greater. There was a very sweet, elderly man in the bed next to me, not a kidney patient, but this was the only bed available for him. Unfortunately, he had eleven visitors at a time. The nurses did nothing to control this and it did seem to me that the risk of infection must increase with the number of visitors. I could fully understand why the nurses didn't intervene since, on one occasion, there was a fistfight in the ward between two of these visitors. Talk about feeling vulnerable! There was also concern about using the ward toilet, having witnessed the consequences of norovirus in an adjacent ward during my previous admission. Priscilla was scrupulous in cleaning the toilet before I used it, maybe over the top, but it made us feel safer. On that point, it is very strange experience using the toilet with a urinary catheter hanging out of you, it takes a while to arrange "the bits". It did seem strange that there was great emphasis on everyone, including visitors, using hand gel, yet visitors could have walked across Hampstead Heath, through dog excrement, which is in no short supply there, up to the ward, sat down by the bed (not allowed, but it happened), touched their shoes and then me or my surroundings. I am not sure how this problem is overcome, maybe it isn't a real problem, but when you feel vulnerable, it goes through your mind. Anyway, my concerns were unnecessary since I did not develop any form of infection.

It was with great disbelief that I drank and ate whatever I wanted, other than grapefruit juice, grapefruits or foods that could give rise to infection, such as pate, raw eggs, raw fish, shellfish, blue cheese, some soft cheeses such as Camembert or Brie, and unpasteurised cheese. What a transformation, and how suddenly it occurred. It's quite a shock to the system and a little disorientating.

The days did not present a problem, visitors were in and out and Priscilla was with me, as always. It was particularly uplifting to see Lorraine up and walking. While I was conscious that she had experienced difficulties in the early periods, she seemed to be making a rapid improvement. My sons and daughters-in law were constantly popping in and, once again, it was so good to be with smiling, positive visitors. Obviously, I was weak but on a high from the medication. The absence of pain, swelling, discomfort and nausea was amazing. Prior to the surgery, my mind had briefly played over the post-operative possibilities and the thoughts were incorrect. My conversation with the positive transplant patient before surgery had greatly relieved the anxiety and helped me to put it away somewhere in the recesses of my mind. The nights, on the other hand, were a different matter. The relentless snoring and groaning of other patients, the loneliness and the often uncontrollable workings of the mind combined to make me a little scared of this time. Fortunately, zopiclone finally gave me a good night's sleep and helped overcome those feelings. I certainly wasn't going to put up any fight against that drug. However, it took about an hour to start working, leaving my mind playing mental gymnastics while I waited to feel sleepy. The 6 am nurse's visit for blood pressure and other observations was something to look forward to; it was good to have human contact. Observations took place regularly during the night as well but the early morning one meant the start of a new day.

The ward rounds by consultants were interesting. I was always happy to recount my tale to students trailing behind them. The nephrology consultants were at all times friendly, interested and very caring, although sometimes quite rushed. However, there were some consultants from other departments, obviously on a teaching ward round, who seemed to treat the patient without compassion, more as an object than a person. I sometimes felt like giving a little wave and saying "Hello, I'm here, I can see you, can you see me?" I would speculate upon the impact that the consultant's approach to me may have on the students and the way that they in turn will relate to their patients. I kept a mental scorebook, scoring their bedside manner out of ten, it kept me interested in and observant of behaviour.

On about the fourth day after surgery, something profound happened. The kidney started to produce masses of urine and the bag, which was attached to the catheter, needed to be changed regularly.

Despite this, on the fifth day, the decision was made to remove the catheter. Never having experienced catheter removal before, but with the painful experience of the orderly tripping on it, I can't say that I was looking forward to it. Needless fear, the nurse came along and within two seconds painlessly removed it. Then the worst part of this whole episode started, which had been fairly pleasant from admission until now. What was it that changed? I'm not sure if it's Lorraine's kidney or my kidney now or both of ours (we often joke about that) but it went berserk. I had to get up to pee every fifteen minutes, twenty-four hours a day. Perhaps this was also related to my bladder function which had been virtually zero for fourteen months, maybe it wasn't responding normally. I presume it didn't know what had hit it. I also knew that my prostate was enlarged, which had not been of any concern, but this must have added insult to injury. I cannot really describe how debilitating this relentless peeing was, but it was absolutely exhausting and terrifying. There was reassurance from the medics that it would settle down but nobody knew how long it would take. I felt that if this was to continue for the rest of my life then I would need to have the kidney removed; pessimistic, but that's how it felt. Ultrasounds were taken to ensure that the bladder was emptying properly otherwise there was the risk of urine flowing backwards into the kidney which would not be good. Fortunately, this was not happening. I was discharged from the hospital on day six and could have won a gold medal for any Olympic peeing competition. Up until the marathon peeing, I would put my wellness score at about 45 but that dropped perhaps to 25 because of the frequency.

Many years previously, when Priscilla and I were at the theatre, I went for a pee during the interval. There were two men standing side-by-side at a urinal. They were obviously acquainted and chatted with strong cockney accents. Next to them stood a distinguished-looking man dressed in a grey pinstriped suit and waistcoat. He had neatly parted thick grey hair and wore a deep purple tie with a distinctive emblem emblazoned upon it. All three seemed to finish at the same time and the cockney pair went to the sink to wash their hands. The distinguished looking gentleman headed for the door. Suddenly, one of the cockneys turned round to him and said, "Oi mate, don't you wash your bleedin' hands when you're finished?" The man in the pinstripes looked down his very aristocratic nose at this lesser being and said with a strong Etonian accent, "Actually, old boy, we, (emphasis on "we" followed by a pause) are taught not to pee on our hands." With that, he turned on his heel and walked out. I have often recounted this highly amusing episode in lectures, to emphasise the importance of trying to prevent something from happening, rather than having to deal with the consequences. Right now, with this uncontrollable need, I was certainly peeing on my hands, and I wondered how the posh gent would have reacted! At least, once again, a story from the past could make me smile in a difficult situation.

25

THINGS THAT ARE SAID

It was great to be home, but so debilitating because of the peeing frequency. On several occasions, I suffered from severe hypotension which was not pleasant. Stand up and I needed to immediately lie down, being just on the edge of losing consciousness. This eventually necessitated a rapid return to the hospital to be re-hydrated with an intravenous infusion of saline. On arrival at the hospital renal department in my hypotensive state, they were extremely helpful, no hanging around, they just got on and did it. A question arose in my mind, was I discharged too soon in order to satisfy a managerial requirement to vacate a bed? I'll never know.

I can't remember the exact timing, but it was so motivational to have the Permacath removed from my neck. Why? Because it meant the medical team had confidence in the function of the kidney and I wouldn't be requiring dialysis. What a boost, what a moment to celebrate, even if it did seem to take forever for the junior surgeon to remove the tube which, fortunately, was a painless procedure. He used local anaesthetic but it seemed as though he was sawing away at my skin for a very long time; never mind, we all have to learn and to my relief, the outcome was good.

Spring had arrived; the garden and the life that was emanating from it were amazingly therapeutic. It's interesting that when I look back on this immediate post-operative period, of all of the stages of my journey, this is the most obscure in my memory. I know that I had to return to the hospital three times a week for consultations, blood and urine tests, blood pressure measurements, ultrasounds, some radiographs and nuclear medicine scans, all very tiring. Transplant patients are required to keep a daily diary of weight, temperature, fluid intake and output and to bring it to the clinic for every visit. It was amusing to see us all sitting in the waiting area clutching our precious little records, badges of the club, each of us wondering whether they held good or bad news. I learned not to be influenced by the other patients' assessment of what were good and bad levels for various tests, we each had our own stories. It seemed that there could be so much variation in results; it had to be particular to each of us. On listening to the fears and anxieties of other patients, it became clear that some of them might have benefited from counselling with a therapist who understood the post-transplant period but, to my knowledge, this was not offered. Priscilla and I had been told to expect ups and downs, especially during the first three months post-operatively, and not to become anxious, any problems would be taken care of. We tried very hard to adopt that attitude but, of course, we had uncertainties and anxieties, after all this was a new experience. It becomes very disconcerting if a clinician indicates concern and doesn't explain why he or she is concerned. On all occasions, we found the renal consultants empathetic, seemingly unrushed and caring, similarly the nurses and other staff. We have found the team in the renal unit at the Royal Free Hospital to be exemplary in the quality of care and personal attention that they deliver; there is nearly always a happy and relaxed atmosphere in the department. However, as with any team, there are always some "blips". On one occasion, my creatinine level had risen (creatinine being one measure of kidney function, high not being good). For some reason on this occasion, the specialist registrar rather than the consultant saw me. An ultrasound was taken, I think to assess whether there was any narrowing (stenosis) of the artery connected to the kidney, and then we saw the registrar to find the outcome. I can only say that I have never seen a look of such seriousness, concern and uncertainty on a clinician's face. I can't actually remember what she said but Priscilla and I walked out of the room and we both felt that if I had thirty minutes left to live, I was lucky. This is not an exaggeration, it was an awful experience. I requested to see the consultant who very kindly stayed late at the end of her clinic and, in fact, there was nothing untoward occurring. This episode reaffirmed my view that clinical encounters are not just about data, interpretations and knowledge, they are very much about human communication. Individuals who come into contact with patients at all levels, in all spheres of medicine, dentistry and other disciplines need to be properly trained in communication skills and recognise the impact of their body language and the words that are used with regards to their possible effect on the patient. I experienced many unthinking comments made by people. I won't go into details of all of these but a few examples may give a reasonable idea.

On one occasion, a nurse said to me, "It's a shame you weren't in intensive care here, we would have saved your kidneys." I hoped that this was said because of a feeling of being proud to be part of a very special team but, of course, it put a doubt in my mind as to whether or not this was true. I dismissed it because I felt that I had been in superb hands but even if it were true there was nothing I could do about it, why raise the doubt? On another occasion, when I attended for a biopsy of the new kidney, I had to give a urine sample, and the comment was, "My goodness, that's so clear it's almost like water." What did that mean, did it mean that the kidney wasn't functioning? Was it a good thing? Was it a bad thing? Did it mean that there was something wrong with the kidney? It is very precious after all. Before I could ask, the sample and the nurse disappeared. I put the clarity down to me probably drinking a lot of water as instructed, but it was an unnecessary comment. Medicine is about people, and patients are people. They have anxieties and are seeking reassurance. They pick up cues from everyone whom they contact, family, friends, visitors, other patients, receptionists, cleaners and the medical team.

Regarding the precious kidney. This is another factor the recipient has to come to terms with. It is somewhat strange psychological feeling to have somebody else's pulsating living organ embedded inside me, receiving 25% of the blood from every heartbeat. Not that I am actually aware of its physical presence. My concerns before the surgery were unfounded. It does feel as if it is a part of me.

I hesitate to think of the number of needles that have been stuck into my veins to obtain blood samples (venepunctures). At my request, they have been in my hand rather than in my arm. The reasoning behind this is that should the kidney fail and it is necessary to create a fistula for dialysis, a damaged vein in my arm could be problematic. Since the vessels in my left arm were damaged from the procedures that were required in the Intensive Care Unit, they would not be available to provide good access so I didn't want to risk the other one. It's interesting to reflect on the abilities of various phlebotomists (people who take the blood) essentially doing the same task. Most are superb, friendly, caring and efficient but there's the occasional one who goes in one side of the vein, comes out the other side, goes back in comes back out and so forth. Again, it makes me reflect on how the ability of the individual influences the outcome of any invasive procedure and this has ramifications at all levels, ranging from the outcome for the patient to the outcome of research data. The outcomes of clinical trials may be influenced by the attitude of the staff. There may be a psychological impact on patients of caring, compared with non-caring attitudes of providers. This may affect clinical results. I can't think of any dental studies which take into account clinicians' attitudes and abilities, although multi-centre studies would help overcome these variables.

Back to my examples of comments. After numerous painless venepunctures in my hand, I requested that a new phlebotomist use my hand as the site. She said immediately, "Oh, that will be very painful but I'll do it if you want," really setting up the expectation of pain – "Yes, please I said," and was intrigued to watch and find out what the result of the "sharp scratch", a term that they use, would be. It was painless and she had set up an unnecessary expectation, it didn't bother me, but I could imagine that some patients would have anxiety because of such a comment. "Could be painful" is very different to "will be painful". Of interest, perhaps, is that I do find that watching the phlebotomy is preferable to looking away. I'm still not quite sure what a "sharp scratch" is but on the other hand, I can't work out what alternative terminology could be – "a sharp prick" or similar would not be politically correct! On venepunctures, why do so many phlebotomists say, "I'm going to bleed you"? Does that really give confidence to nervous patients? "Bleeding patients" or "blood-letting" was used in the treatment of patients for almost two thousand years, up until the nineteenth century. Why use such an antiquated term?

These examples reminded me of a story told to me by my niece who required fairly major surgery. She recalls being wheeled into theatre by a porter. As he pushed her, he was singing a song by the rock group Queen, "Another one bites the dust"!

Regarding things people say, I found it, and still do find it, remarkable how many people tell me stories about friends or relatives who have had kidney transplants that have failed. One visitor told me, "Her nephew had three transplants and they all failed and he was on dialysis and how terrible that was." What was her purpose? To let me know how lucky I am? To let me know it could fail? To offload some of her feelings of sadness on someone who she felt would be receptive? Just to make conversation? Some other reason? Of course, such statements have an impact, and the effect depends on the mood and the transplant experience of the recipient. It is necessary to be aware that if you are going to socialise, some people will make unthinking comments.

26

REGAINING WHAT I HAD LOST

After about a year, much to my relief, I noticed that the feeling of surrealism slowly decreased, three-dimensional distant vision returned. I could also drink water from a glass without a bad taste and I had a desire to listen to music, play the piano and read, although for the first six months I could only do this for short periods. Hypotensive episodes continued but became less frequent, and occurred mainly when standing rapidly from a low seat or getting up after lying down. However, these episodes were very controllable by sitting down and lowering my head. There was once again a loss of libido and a sexual dysfunction which I understand is very common following a kidney transplant. I raised this with the consultant, and with a modification in drug regime normal function slowly returned and, if anything, I would say it was enhanced by a deeper appreciation of the precious gift of renewed life. I did not find any difficulty in discussing this problem with the consultant but I could imagine people who would find it embarrassing. Although there is a section regarding sexual dysfunction following transplantation in the brochure given to patients to take home with them after surgery, I did wonder whether it would be preferable, in addition, for the clinician to raise the possibility, rather than wait for patients to raise it (interesting use of words). Hopefully, this would help those patients who find it too embarrassing to do so, do not remember what they read, or did not read it. I must admit that few of the contents of the brochure actually sank in and were retained in my memory.

Between March 2010 and January 2014, my wellness score steadily increased from about 35 pre-transplant to 80, which is where I would put it now. Of course, there have been many ups and downs during the post-transplant recovery stage and some of the downs were pretty down, mainly associated with drug side effects. I don't know how much of the recovery was impeded by the original devastating effect of the toxic shock but I'll gladly settle for my present score of 80.

The three times per week hospital visits continued for about four weeks and the "peeing for Britain" for about two. Initially, cortisol tablets partly reduced the latter and then, as the kidney and bladder settled down, it did so by itself. During those two weeks, there was absolutely no way I could get to the hospital without resorting to using a bottle in the car. I hoped that I wouldn't be arrested for indecent exposure, always covering myself with a blanket to minimise that possibility. I was aware that the offence is "genital exposure in a public place with the intent to shock those who do not want to see them". So my thoughts were ridiculous, but I suppose it gives an indication of how my thinking was scrambled because of exhaustion. Such an arrest would indeed be "the icing on the cake" after having gone through so much. I'd arrive at the hospital and make a mad dash through the entrance to the nearest toilet, since standing up from the sitting position in the car brought on a dramatic urinary urgency. I dreaded the thought of needing to wait for the lift to arrive, with the possibility of subsequently being stuck in it with masses of people and an uncontrollable urge to pee. While waiting for my appointment, the nurses became very conscious of me frequently running to the toilet and enquired after my well-being. They tried to help me but I couldn't see that there was much they could do other than give me a giant bottle or perhaps a piece of string to staunch the flow, not a good idea! Those two weeks were exhausting, completely broken sleep every fifteen minutes, back and forth to the hospital and no possibility of catching up with sleep during the day, because of the urinary frequency. This was combined with a need to keep the kidney functioning with large fluid intakes. I was advised that for my body mass, a minimum of three litres per day was required which kept driving the output. What a relief when this kidney and my bladder, which seemed to have minds of their own, suddenly decided to start behaving and life became more normal. Now on our way back from the hospital, Priscilla and I stopped off again for a walk in Kenwood and then went to the café situated in the grounds. Previously, when I was on dialysis, my walk here had been agonisingly slow and I could only have a half a cup of tea. Now, I could eat and drink whatever I wanted, other than the small limitations previously described. I could walk much faster than on my previous trips and with much less effort. I was soon able to walk two circuits of the path, about three miles. To be given back something that had previously been taken for granted, but lost, was an amazing revelation. How much of our lives are spent not truly appreciating the things that we have, only really recognising them when we lose them? What a gift to be able to regain them, relish and savour what they offer us. I am not talking just about food, but life itself. It made me think of some quotes from Arthur Schopenhauer, "When, at the end of their lives, most men look back they will find that they have lived throughout ad interim. They will be surprised to see that the very thing they allowed to slip by, unnoticed, unappreciated and unenjoyed was just their life. And so a man, having been duped by hope, dances into the arms of death."

"To enjoy the present, and to make this the purpose of one's life, is the greatest wisdom; since it is the present alone that is real, everything else being only the play of thought."

How grateful I was to have the opportunity to reassess my life and see it through slightly different glasses, but more of that later.

27

MEDICATION

After about six weeks, the clinic visits were reduced to twice a week for about two months, then weekly for three months, when I was often seen by very knowledgeable specialist nurses. Then the frequency slowly reduced to once every three months. In October 2013, this was reduced further to once every four months. Every visit was associated with blood tests to check on the drug levels and kidney function and a urine test for protein. In the early period after the transplant, perhaps for the first year, it was essential that Priscilla accompany me to these appointments to remind me of any difficulties. I also took notes with me about symptoms, since I found it impossible to keep them in my head. I think that I presented some challenging problems for my consultant regarding my drug regime and I am full of admiration for the calm, pragmatic, empathetic and analytical way in which he modified it until it was as good as possible. At all times, he instilled great confidence in me; a doctor who understands the human side of being a patient. At this time of uncertainty, it was immensely reassuring to have such professional support.

When recounting how I feel to clinicians, I have noticed that from the inception of my conscious appreciation of illness until the time of writing this book, I have found that frequently it is so difficult to convey these feelings. Interestingly, that's from somebody who is used to taking clinical histories. It's not like having pain in an area that can be described and pinpointed; it is often a feeling of total body sensation which can fluctuate throughout a day and from day-to-day. Sometimes the feelings may be specific to a particular location but at other times they are more generalised, with feelings of malaise, debilitation, weakness, fatigue, pain, tingling, light-headedness, disorientation and other descriptive terms. On many occasions, I would report that I was feeling much better but then, when I looked back on it, realised how weak and debilitated I was feeling at that time. It was just an improvement on what had come before, "a better stage of feeling unwell", but not truly better. Would this be how I would stay? Was it the best I could be? There was no way of knowing. I had to remember: one step at a time up the mountain, focus on that and not beyond.

I presume, therefore, that sometimes clinicians may make assumptions based on inaccurate reporting by the patient. In these situations, it requires a very experienced and insightful clinician to ascertain the true nature of a patient's condition.

The drugs that I was taking initially to suppress my immunity (immunosuppressants) and reduce the risk of rejecting the kidney were a steroid (prednisolone) and two other drugs (tacrolimus and mycophenalate mofetil). I think that I was weaned off the prednisolone after about six weeks but cannot remember the exact timing. Tacrolimus and mycophenalate mofetil are for the life of the kidney, unless something better comes along, and I hope that that is a very long one. The only way that I can consistently remember to take the drugs at the correct time is to be reminded by alarms set on my i-Phone. The need for this is partly because I'm certain I have lost some short-term memory recall as a result of the illness. Recently, I was giving a lecture in a large venue when a strange tinkling sound came over the loudspeaker system. It went on and on and, finally, a technician was called, only to discover it was the alarm going off on my phone which I had placed on the podium near the microphone. Did I feel stupid? Yes, but at least I did take my pills! Shortly after the lecture episode, one day I had a long wait in the waiting area for a renal outpatient's appointment. During the delay, I was trying to read some dental articles which were quite complicated and required concentration. The man opposite had his phone out and I could hear a loud radio programme. It was very distracting and I found myself giving the patient sitting next to the man with the phone some sideways disapproving looks. He responded with a glare. A few minutes later a repeat and once again a glare. Then the normally friendly nurses walked by and again a glare. I now panicked, felt inside my jacket and removed my phone and as I did so, the broadcast became louder. I had checked an e-mail and, as I put the phone back in my pocket, must have pressed the radio app. Did I feel stupid? Yes.

Currently, I am regularly taking a variety of medications, the immunosuppressants and various tablets for my heart, prostate, cholesterol, stomach and acidity of my blood; eleven tablets/capsules at night, fourteen tablets/capsules in the morning and three capsules at midday. That means much preparation of medication and once every two weeks Priscilla and I sit down and cut up the packets of drugs, keeping the pills or capsules within their wrappers but sorting them into daily pillboxes so that they are ready for the next two weeks. Some of the pills are particularly difficult to remove from their packs, omeprazole being one of these (although the packaging has recently improved). I shudder to think how partially-sighted, elderly patients may struggle with these. I hope that they have special training and are not just left to their own devices, or that the pharmacist organises the medication in containers. I find that on some packets the expiry date is impossible to read. I am amazed that the manufacturers are allowed to be so unthinking.

Since immunosuppression increases the risk of developing skin cancer, very careful protection from ultraviolet light in sunlight is needed. This means using a good factor fifty sunblock as a minimum and keeping out of the sun, particularly at midday. Even on a cloudy day, especially in the summer, ultraviolet radiation levels may be high. To be safer, I have purchased sun protection clothing to wear when I am in a sunny place. For added protection when driving, it was also easy to have ultraviolet protective films placed on the inside of the windows, windscreen and sun roof of my car. An American study reported that skin cancer was more common on the left arm and that driver-side automobile ultraviolet light exposure is a likely contributing factor. The authors recommended that people who are prone to skin cancer should take appropriate sun protection when driving. With a southerly facing house, we will do the same on the windows at home. There is a yearly check with a consultant dermatologist and patients are urged to report any changes to existing moles, in particular, but skin surfaces in general. There is also an increased risk of a cancer which affects the cells responsible for immunity (lymphoma) but there is nothing that the patient can do to protect themselves against that.

Besides increasing the risk of acquiring an infection, immunosuppression may prolong it. Because of this, an infection may be harder to eradicate than prior to the transplant (a common cold, for example, can linger for ages) and serious infection may be even more dangerous than before. All that the patient can do is to try and avoid infection. Hand hygiene is very important. The US Centers for Disease Control and Prevention state, "Keeping hands clean through improved hand hygiene is one of the most important steps we can take to avoid getting sick and spreading germs to others. Many diseases and conditions are spread by not washing hands with soap and clean, running water. If clean, running water is not accessible, as is common in many parts of the world, use soap and available water. If soap and water are unavailable, use an alcohol-based hand sanitizer that contains at least 60% alcohol to clean hands." In an interview with the health website Web MD in 2013, Dr Philip Tierno, director of clinical microbiology and immunology at the New York University Medical Center stated, "Eighty per cent of all infectious diseases are transmitted by contact both direct and indirect – direct such as kissing, indirect such as shaking someone's hand. The best solution: don't avoid the social norm of shaking hands, but practice good hand hygiene by washing your hands regularly with soap and water. If you eat or drink something without washing your hands, or if you touch your own nose, mouth, or eyes after shaking someone's hand, you can introduce whatever germ was on their hand, and now your hand, into the portals of your body."

Certainly, for the first six months following the transplant, I avoided handshaking and cheek kissing, except with my immediate family. With the passage of time, I have become more relaxed about this, avoiding people with obvious upper respiratory tract infections and never shaking somebody's hand if I see that they had a cold or "have been picking their nose or something similar". (It's amazing to observe how many people seem to pick their noses while driving alone; do they think that no one can see through the windows?) I do use alcohol gel if for some reason it's not possible to wash my hands, and do so particularly after touching support rails, seats, etc. when travelling on public transport. On many occasions, I was aware of medical students who were about to examine me without first washing their hands. I reminded them of the requirement and wondered whether they had forgotten or not been instructed. They probably could recite in detail the intricacies of treatment but were missing a basic skill. Patients and relatives should not be afraid to speak up, whether it is to a student, a nurse, a doctor (junior or a consultant), any other provider of care or a member of the management team. Every organisation, however large or small, requires feedback and an honest self-appraisal from the feedback but that in itself is not sufficient. It then requires the courage to act when action is required, rather than being indifferent or, in worst-case scenario, covering up shortcomings regardless of their cause.

On one occasion, when sitting on an underground train, it was interesting to observe a woman with a streaming cold. She blew her nose into a tissue much of the time but sometimes wiped her nose with her hand. She then placed her hands on the seat armrests and then, when she stood up to get off the train, she wiped her hands across her nose. She held onto a vertical pole, then onto a horizontal one and followed by pushing the door open release button. Other passengers then followed her "handprints" and left. I wondered how many of them would develop colds. Obviously, it would be easy to become paranoid but, on the other hand, common sense and risk assessment come into play.

So, for example, while I avoided crowds for the first six months, once this time had passed and I felt well enough to attend a Spurs football match, I did so. There was a massive crowd, with risk, but on the other hand, it was a return to normality. Remembering that my life had completely changed as a result of an infection, I am not prepared to take unnecessary risks in my now more vulnerable state and will always weigh up the pros and cons of risk. I will not be influenced by others (and they do exist) who think I am mad or who simply don't understand. I have tried to avoid pets, either touching them or being touched or licked by them. Since I don't have any, that does not create a big emotional problem for me. However, I do find that generally pet owners are oblivious to my concerns and make absolutely no effort to control their animals. Obviously, if the pet was very important in my life then the balance of risk assessment would alter. I avoid close contact with people who are unwell and while it is important to have a flu vaccine, it is essential to decline any live vaccines. Attending the GPs' surgery is a concern, sitting in the waiting room with all those coughing, spluttering children in particular is not something that is easy to avoid. Working as a dentist presents a particular risk of infection transmission and I deferred returning to work for six months, partly until I was at a stage when I was less prone to infection but also because I was not well enough to return before that.

There is a risk of infection from some foods, particularly during the first three post-operative months. There are some basic precautions. I have spoken about hand washing but in addition it is important to: keep raw meat and fish covered at the bottom of the fridge away from cooked foods; avoid buffets and food from uncovered counters; not use food after its use by dates; make sure that cooked food, especially chicken, sausages, eggs and burgers are completely cooked; wash and peel fresh fruit, vegetables and salad before eating or cooking them; not leave food lying around and to keep hot food hot and cold food cold. Some foods in particular carry risks such as: unpasteurised milk and yoghurts; food made with raw or undercooked eggs; raw fish and shellfish; cheese made from unpasteurised milk; raw or undercooked meat such as pâté or rare cooked steak. Sugar intake should be kept to a minimum, since some immunosuppressants can cause an increase in blood sugar or worsen existing diabetic control. In addition, grapefruit and starfruit should be avoided since they can interfere with some of the drugs, as can some herbal medicines. Considering the restrictions on dialysis, these precautions are minimal and by taking them I am happy to say that I have had very few infections since March 2010, perhaps a couple of colds which lingered a bit but nothing serious, long may it last.

If the blood level of tacrolimus is too high, there is a risk of damage to the kidney but if it is too low, there is a risk of kidney rejection. Unfortunately, for me the therapeutic window, namely the range between the two and the level which keeps me reasonably free from side effects, is very small and can be readily unbalanced. The side effects were worse initially, they have slowly decreased but not all have been totally eliminated. They have always been and are worse when I am tired but frequently exercise relieves them. A substantial tremor developed in my hands which, for pretty obvious reasons, would make my return to providing surgery impossible, and for one who has always had fine control, it was a real loss. Fortunately, as the tacrolimus levels were decreased, the tremor slowly decreased until, by six months, it was gone. A horrible tingling sensation developed primarily in the extremities of my limbs. There was nothing pleasant about this and, while exercise helped relieve it, it never eliminated it. It, too, has decreased with the passage of time but will re-occur when I am tired or run down and is particularly likely to happen on retiring to bed at night, making it difficult to fall asleep.

Probably because of the mycophenalate mofetil, I developed severe stomach pain and altered bowel movement, producing vast quantities of excrement with sudden uncontrollable urges to defecate. This is no laughing matter and, while it lasted, really curtailed my ability to leave home; it was very demeaning and upsetting. This side effect did not suddenly stop but slowly decreased, firstly reaching a manageable level and then disappearing after about a year. However, several years later it did reappear. I developed severe diarrhoea, which persisted for three weeks. I felt as though I had Mount Vesuvius bubbling away inside me. My volcano would suddenly, uncontrollably, and without mercy, erupt ten or more times a day, expelling large quantities of liquid, foul-smelling human larva. It was completely debilitating and caused me to lose five kilos. It was essential to keep myself well hydrated during this period to avoid kidney damage. A change of drugs for three weeks resolved the problem.

The stomach pains precipitated a camera examination of my colon (colonoscopy) and two camera examinations of my stomach and beyond (gastroscopies). The colonoscopy revealed nothing; the first gastroscopy revealed a polyp on the upper intestine wall, the second one aimed to remove it but only partially did so. It required a third one to completely remove it. The intravenous sedation for these procedures was actually a very pleasant relief from the drugs' side effects. The procedures themselves were painless and of no great inconvenience, other than the need to take a strong laxative to prepare for the colonoscopy.

It did not take long for me to become further aware of side effects of the drugs and the damaging effects of my illness. Muscle pain was a side effect that was really debilitating. It is best described as an aching, painful-to-touch muscle state accompanied, once again, by restless legs. It felt similar to the symptoms that I had from statins but about twenty times worse. It was always worse when going to bed at night and, at its height, made me fearful of bedtime. In order to test the hypothesis that the tacrolimus was exacerbating the statin side effects, various combinations of drug doses were tested until I made the decision that it was impossible to continue with the statin. I stopped taking it and this reduced the symptoms substantially and they reduced even further with the passage of time as the tacrolimus dose levels were decreased. The severe symptoms lasted for about a year. One day, my GP phoned me to say that he had checked my records carefully and found that there was still one statin that I had not been prescribed, namely pravastatin. "Did I want to try it?"

After about three months at the lowest dose of 10 mg per day, severe symptoms started to occur again. The advice from my GP, hospital consultant and cardiologist was that nothing else could be offered to me with regards to statins. I then thought that perhaps it would be worthwhile trying half of the minimum dose and see what the outcome was. With the consultant's agreement, I tried this and it had the effect, perhaps with the help of one Benecol yoghurt per day, a low fat diet, skimmed milk and a cup of oat bran with my breakfast cereal, of bringing my lipids down to very acceptable levels without any substantial side effects (October 2013 total cholesterol 3.9). If I am tired, muscle symptoms do re-occur, but they are tolerable and well controlled by exercise. There was one occasion when the muscle symptoms actually made me feel good. At an appointment with my consultant, I reiterated the nature of the muscle symptoms and he said, "Well, when you get to my age, you have muscle aches a lot of the time." I asked, "How old are you?" I can't remember his exact answer but it was about sixty-two. I said, "Well, I'm sixty-six!" Besides being amusing, it signified how far I had come, from virtually a corpse lying in a bed in the Intensive Care Unit to a vital human being who, to an experienced clinician, didn't look his age. Of course, he may have been using some very clever form of psychology but I doubt it. It truly gave me a boost.

Another side effect that started to build slowly was itching on my face which started when I put my head on the pillow to sleep. It still occurs. It doesn't feel like an allergic reaction but, interestingly, many of my allergies, such as to dust and pollen, have disappeared, probably due to the effect of the immunosuppressants, a positive side effect. The itching feels more like some form of nerve damage (neuropathic damage) causing pricking and itching, as if it is deep within the skin.

It is impossible to resist the urge to scratch and that does help relieve the symptom but not eliminate it. This itching certainly makes it difficult to fall asleep.

During the period in which the medication levels were being adjusted, I seemed to be able to assess fairly accurately if the tacrolimus level was too high, since the symptoms, particularly the muscle ones and itching, increased substantially. When that occurred, a blood test was requested and most times a reduction of the tacrolimus level followed. It is now pretty stable at 2.0 mgs in the morning and twelve hours later, 2.0 mgs at night. I must admit that I frequently look at the small capsules of this drug and wonder at the strength of its effect. It reduces the rejection of another human being's organ, which is connected inside me to my blood supply, and it also produces side-effects all over my body. The capsules just don't seem big enough to do that but, of course, they are.

I can therefore never escape the fact that I am a patient, a prisoner to pills. They need to be requested, collected from the pharmacy or received by courier, stored, sorted, counted, removed from packaging and taken at the correct time. There must be no possibility of running out of them so an adequate supply is mandatory. The side effects are a constant reminder that they have been taken. Yet with all of that, the regime is not so onerous. It becomes a part of life and life without them could very rapidly become no life or a life of dialysis.

I developed other symptoms, but it is not possible to say whether they were a result of the toxic shock, the medication or a combination of both. For a long time, Priscilla has suffered from Raynaud's phenomenon. This is a spasm of the arteries to the extremities, especially the fingers. It is typically brought on by cold or vibration, and leads to pallor, pain and numbness. I now joined her. It is a little strange in that about a centimetre at the tips of my fingers is not affected but the entire area from there to just beyond the knuckle is. It is best to try to prevent it from starting in the first place, by keeping warm, because it is difficult to alleviate once it has occurred. I now knew what Priscilla had been experiencing. While previously I could observe it and listen to her, now I had a different perspective, which reinforced my view of the difficulties of truly conveying to others how you feel when ill. Whether or not it is related to the Raynaud's, I do not know, but my whole body response to cold has changed. If I become cold, my entire body can start shaking uncontrollably, something that had never previously occurred. Remedy: don't get cold in the first place, but it is difficult if, for example, we find ourselves in a building that is poorly heated and I have arrived unprepared. Since the intensive care experience, I have substantial splitting of the tips of four fingernails. Iron supplements have not improved this and I wonder if it is related to damage caused by the near gangrene that I experienced in my hands. It is a minor handicap but is quite annoying when the nail catches in clothing.

Skiing and mountain walking have been one of our great loves, so altitude and vertical drops were not a concern. It was, therefore, very disconcerting to go to a concert at the Royal Albert Hall, have front row seats high up and suffer from appalling vertigo. I felt as though I was trapped in my seat, with a great fear of moving, like a rabbit caught in the headlamps of a car. In the interval, I slowly eased myself along the row with this terrible feeling of being pulled over the edge,

I didn't return for the second half. Apparently, tacrolimus can precipitate vertigo, what a change from my former self. The vertigo has persisted, but fortunately at a reduced level. Mountain hiking along narrow paths with drops is, I fear, no longer for me. While some of these side effects have been very unpleasant, it is important to keep them in perspective compared to dialysis. For me, there simply is no comparison; the benefits of the transplant are enormous. I must emphasise, however, that my dialysis experience may be atypical, since I was so ill when I started and the first dialysis centre did not provide a particularly caring environment. When I moved to a more caring environment, the experience was vastly improved. I would not want every reader who needs dialysis to be put off by my experience; it is mine not theirs.

While on the subject of the drugs, I understand that some transplant failures are related to patients not maintaining their drug regime. This may be for many reasons but I would suspect that a significant one could be a dislike of side effects coupled with a lack of appreciation of the importance of taking the medication as prescribed. If any transplant patients are reading this and fall into that group, I urge you to discuss your feelings with your clinicians. They have vast experience and will know how to manage your difficulties even if the results are not immediate; perhaps you owe that much to the human being who has given you such an incredible gift, namely their kidney.

28

THE NEXT STAGE

The stent placed in my ureter (the tube connecting the kidney to the bladder) at the time of the transplant was removed at six weeks. The function of the stent was to hold the ureter open and maintain proper drainage of urine until the surgical connection between the transplanted ureter and the bladder healed. Removal requires a tube to be inserted, with some topical anaesthetic, via the penis up through the urethra into the bladder and then into the ureter. The stent is then grabbed and pulled back out. I was informed that it would be a painless experience, but it didn't sound great. Maybe it would be painless for the clinician but I wasn't so sure about me. Nor did I have the energy for it to be performed without intravenous sedation to take me out of it. Fortunately, the doctor responded to my request. Intravenous sedation was administered and the stent removal was trouble free. I have to admit that I like the feeling of intravenous sedation. I used it frequently for my patients, to reduce anxiety and make very long dental appointments comfortable and very acceptable to them. Many would say pleasurable. I had often wondered how they felt as the sedation was stopped and, throughout my many sedations, I could experience it for myself. There was a lovely warm, cosy, dreamlike feeling, almost like being insulated from the outside world, very little recall of the procedure carried out and definitely a feeling of disorientation and lack of reality. Let me take you back five years to one of my patients and how she responded to sedation.

In front of me there is a bright light connected to a moveable arm and an additional even brighter light shining from a lamp positioned just above my magnifying glasses. Sitting comfortably on my chair with my dental nurse close by my side I am focused on the mouth of a patient who has lost her front teeth and a substantial amount of the supporting bone. The nurse is gently holding the cheeks and lips away with one hand while removing water with a sucker held in the other hand. The anaesthetist is nearby administering intravenous sedation and the patient is lying calmly and relaxed, as she has been for the past four hours. Classical music is playing quietly in the background and I can just hear it above the whining sound of the dental drill which is rotating at three hundred thousand revolutions per minute. Water is spraying from the drill like the fine but powerful mist of a fountain caught in the wind, it is required to keep the teeth cool while they are being cut. Peering through the mist, it is necessary to cut the teeth with great accuracy. Errors of even an eighth of a millimetre are not acceptable. When viewing the inside of the teeth in a mirror, everything is back to front and the water spray can obscure the mirror view unless the nurse continuously keeps it clean with an air jet. This is difficult work, requiring absolute concentration. If the patient moves her head to swallow, it's essential to immediately remove the drill from the tooth otherwise a massive error in cutting can occur or the lips, cheeks or tongue can be cut. I've been doing this for four hours. I cement temporary crowns so that she can leave the surgery with a good appearance but, as is common, the temporary cement seems to go everywhere. It takes a further fifteen minutes to clean it up. Tired, but satisfied, I get up and leave the patient with the anaesthetist for him to lift the sedation and help her out of the dental chair. I drink a glass of water, walk into my office, sit down at my electric keyboard, put the headphones on and start playing a Chopin Mazurka to relax. As usual, I play very, very badly but it takes me out of myself. I can feel the presence of somebody hovering behind me and look round to find the patient standing there with a quizzical look on her face. She is an excellent pianist. Reading the music, she says, "My goodness, you're good, very good." I continue playing and, once again, she says, "You're so good." I look up at her and say, "I'm really not." She says, "You really are, you're just being modest." Puzzled, I ask, "Anyway, how can you hear me, I've got headphones on?" She says, "I definitely can." I take the headphones off and to my surprise find that, completely by chance, there is a CD playing in my waiting room with the superb concert pianist Murray Perria playing exactly the same Chopin mazurka at exactly the same place in the music. It's unbelievable. The patient is obviously disorientated from the sedation and confused about the source of the sound, thinking it was coming from my keyboard, not the CD player. I explain this to her. She refuses to accept this and, as frequently happens following sedation, she completely forgot my explanation. Many months later when it was my birthday, she came in and said, "I've brought you a birthday present." I said, "That is really lovely of you, can I ask what it is?"

She said, "Yes, I'm very friendly with the second conductor at the Royal Opera House in Covent Garden and he is a superb pianist, I've told him about you and what an amazing pianist you are and have booked you a couple of piano lessons."

To put it mildly, I was gobsmacked. How could I go along to someone like this with my pitiful playing. I explained that it was just not possible for me to accept her very kind present and, finally, I think she got it. It's all very amusing, but certainly shows how disorientating sedation can be. I don't think any of my disorientations from sedation ever matched that of this patient.

At three months, a biopsy of the kidney was performed. Local anaesthetic, ultrasound, the thump of the biopsy needle being propelled painlessly into my new kidney, followed by the need to lie still on my back for four hours. Fortunately, there were no signs of rejection, a great relief for me and the family and, in particular, Lorraine. I imagine that it would be an enormous disappointment for a donor to discover that there was early rejection of their kidney, although I understand that much can be done to arrest the process. There was a short period of concern about the possibility of urinary retention from an enlarged prostate, since urinary frequency had developed at night. A consultation was arranged with a "conservative" urologist. Following a thorough examination, he concluded that cancer was excluded and nothing needed to be done other than perhaps trying some medication to shrink the prostate. This rapidly resulted in a loss of libido and I wasn't going to tolerate that unless it was absolutely necessary, so I came off the medication and, since then, I have not had a retention nor frequency problem. It seemed to settle by itself. I am very pleased that I did not see a knife-happy surgeon.

Six months after the transplant surgery, a routine stress echocardiogram revealed that all seemed stable with my heart, a relief for both Priscilla and me. In order to make me feel a little bit more secure, I subscribed to Medi Alert which, for a very small annual fee, provided a necklace carrying a disc with a freephone telephone number which can be phoned from anywhere in the world. In the event of a hospital admission, my medical details and drug regime could be accessed rapidly.

Everything has slowly improved and most of the time I now feel good (wellness score 80). However, I often feel as though I have a menstrual cycle. For about a week a month, I do feel very below par, sometimes needing to rest a lot and, on some days during that week, I feel particularly rough (wellness score about 40). Interestingly, I have noticed that during this period my lower eyelids frequently swell and become quite red. Nothing that my GP nor optician have given me have helped resolve this but it resolves spontaneously within a week, with or without treatment. Generally, my need to have a mid-morning and mid-afternoon sleep, due to an overwhelming drowsiness, has gone, although the need does recur to a lesser degree during "the week". Even now, over four years after the transplant, it is very rare for me to wake up feeling good, there is a general feeling of, being a bit under the weather, lethargy, not having enough sleep, even if I have slept for eight hours. I wonder if that's related to the fact that I take minimal fluids from about 9 pm. Perhaps I'm dehydrated, maybe it's just my age, but I don't think so. It takes a while to get going. Pushing myself to do exercise first thing helps alleviate the morning feeling and makes my body feel more vital and my mind more alert but I do need to force myself to get out of bed to do it, I recite "I can and I will do it."

There was severe discomfort in my quadriceps in particular when climbing stairs, coupled with a feeling of muscle weakness, presumably due to a lack of muscle mass and strength following the initial period of illness. It's incredible how much muscle mass is lost in such a relatively short time in intensive care and the difficulty of regaining it. The NHS was lacking in this side of its care and so, through my private medical insurance, I sought the advice of a consultant in sports medicine and he referred me to a physiotherapist. The physiotherapist made such a difference to my life. I know that I presented an enormous challenge to her, since I suspect that she had no prior experience of the side effects of the medication and the muscular implications. She treated me with a great sense of humour, a tremendous motivational attitude and exercises targeted at the problem areas which, with perseverance, helped me so much. I can climb stairs now with absolutely no muscle pain or discomfort, walk eight miles without a problem and do the other activities already described. I am greatly indebted to her.

However, I think that this episode demonstrates something, namely, that it is sometimes necessary to be proactive and generate the care that you think you require. This doesn't mean that an aggressive attitude needs to be adopted but it does mean being active rather than passive. I have described this approach concerning the statin pravistatin, when I was told that nothing more could be done.

There were many other experiences, one that readily comes to mind relates to a Permacath. On one occasion while on dialysis, a new Permacath had been inserted into my jugular vein and I returned home. Later that day, on removing my sweater, I saw blood streaming down my shirt and chest. Priscilla immediately drove me to Accident and Emergency where the renal surgical registrar was called. He took one quick look at it and said the Permacath would need to be removed and a new one inserted. I wondered if it was going to become more and more complicated. Several had been inserted and removed, some none too pleasantly, possibly there was scarring which would hinder the placement. I couldn't see any bruising in my neck or chest nor any swelling and on inspection it looked much more like the bleeding was coming from the skin perforation site rather than deeper from the jugular. I said that unless he was absolutely certain of jugular bleeding, or if he had reason to believe that I would die from the loss of blood, I would like to give it some more time lying still with pressure applied to the skin site. He agreed and, thirty minutes later, the bleeding had stopped. The removal of the Permacath would have produced a very different outcome. Of course, patients shouldn't override medical advice but they should never be afraid to raise their concerns and feelings. These should always be considered, listened to with empathy and respect, and acted upon when appropriate.

29

GETTING ON WITH LIFE

I have described the medical side of the transplant, but what about getting on with life?

Rarely does a day go by when I don't think of Lorraine and what she has given to me and my family. I frequently think of her health, and hope that she is fit and well and is still feeling good about her amazing gift. How can you not feel a sense of responsibility for your donor's well-being and vice versa? On that point I was horrified, no, sickened and disgusted would be better words, to describe how I felt about the content of a report in the Guardian newspaper in 2009. A medical doctor had been a live kidney donor for his wife; unfortunately, subsequently, the marriage ended in divorce, and here's the unbelievable bit – he was suing her in the Supreme Court in Mineola, New York for return of the kidney or $1.5 million as part of the settlement! Fortunately, it seems that the case was a non-starter but the mind boggles even to think of it!

Besides my short-term memory loss, I am also aware of some long-term loss. For example, the week prior to the initial illness, we had spent the weekend in a country house hotel and, apparently, had a great time. Interestingly, I have absolutely no recollection of that weekend; it has been obliterated from my memory. So much so, that four years later, we returned to the hotel and I was intrigued to find out how much would come back to me. Walking around, trying hard to remember, nothing surfaced from my memory except for the clock high on the wall in the indoor tennis courts. When I say nothing came back, I really do mean nothing, bar the clock. I tried so hard to pick up clues, cast my mind back, searched my memory banks but nothing happened. It feels weird, since our initial time there pre-dates the illness, why should the memory be erased?

I am certain that I sustained some minor brain damage during the intensive care period. One effect is that I sometimes blurt out something inappropriate that I would previously have withheld, usually so as not to hurt someone else's feelings. It's out before I can do anything about it; my filter seems to be impaired. After forty-five years of jogging on pavements, Priscilla recently required a hip replacement. She needed to consult a haematologist and, subsequently, I had difficulty paying his bill. Finally, a few days before her admission, I spoke to him and he explained how I could pay. One day when I was with Priscilla in the hospital, he unexpectedly appeared in the room. I looked up, said, "Hello," and then totally out of character said, "You've only come for the money." I didn't know where to put myself. It's the sort of thing that I may have said to a friend who knew my sense of humour but never to a medical consultant whom I hardly knew. Episodes such as this may be funny but they are upsetting.

For all of the reasons previously described, exercise was once again imperative for me, and still is. It would be so easy to keep promising myself that I will do it tomorrow

251

but the reality is that I have to do it today, unless of course I feel so unwell that this precludes the possibility. After the transplant, it did take a tremendous amount of will-power to pick myself up and get on with it. Starting slowly with more and more walking, light weights and stretching, progressing to the exercise bike and building it up to fifty minutes of constant speed pedalling per day or thirty minutes with one minute bursts of very fast pedalling every five minutes. I usually exercise five days a week. Once I was over the most susceptible period for infection, I started swimming and then, a big-test, tennis. A very dear friend of mine encouraged me to try it with him; he was so patient, motivating and kind. To start with, I felt very insecure since other than my left big toe, the remaining nine had been reduced to stumps. Very rapidly, however, and to my delight, I pretty well forgot about them (or should I say lack of them) and moved in a similar way to before my illness, although in eighteen months I have had a couple of falls on the court. I did try jogging but for some reason, and I'm not quite sure why, maybe the lack of toes, I found this very difficult. I am however, perfectly okay on a treadmill which I use if we go to a gym.

For about a year after the transplant, I could not tolerate the feeling of water on my skin. This didn't mean that I walked around stinking of BO, showering was manageable but a bath certainly was not. I don't know whether the intolerance was an effect of the medication or the toxic shock, or both, but it has now completely gone. There have been a few episodes of nausea, nothing like the pre-transplant period and very readily controlled by domperidone.

It was very therapeutic to be socialising with friends and family. From September 2010, it was so good to be back in my seat at Spurs with my son David by my side, but I did notice something strange. The surges of adrenalin had gone and my emotions felt flat. Whether this was and is the effect of heart/blood pressure pills (beta-blockers), toxic shock, the transplant or a combination of all of them, I do not know but it felt as if a part of me was lost. It doesn't mean that emotion has gone but its expression is different. If I see or hear something that is so human: a touch; an act of kindness; a term of true endearment, whether it be real or fictional in theatre, opera, film or television, it can bring tears to my eyes and sometimes overwhelming deep sobs, coupled with waves of emotion. Reading something tender or deeply loving can have a similar effect. I clearly remember walking along White Hart Lane with my eldest grandson on our way to a Spurs match. He was nine years old and so excited. The tears started, no possibility of control. I realised that there was now an incongruence in my emotions. The uncontrollable tears, yet frequently an absence of the surges of adrenalin that I had experienced previously. Acknowledging the damping effect that medication seems to have on me, I do sometimes ponder the question of whether modern medicine may have suppressed creativity for some people. Perhaps, some of those with psychosis controlled by medication may have been our greatest creative talents?

In August 2011, five months after my transplant, we decided to go to the part of Cornwall that we love and gives us so much peace but also challenges us physically. I managed the difficult coastal paths well and felt good for it. Another measurable stage of progress and a challenge met and overcome. One day, we stopped during a very strenuous walk and I sat on a rock looking out across a blue, blue sea listening to the end of Mahler's second Symphony, the so-called Mahler's Resurrection, on my iPod. The next day, I wrote the following letter to my family and people close to me who had helped me so much:

24 August 2011

Hi Everyone

We are just getting towards the end of an absolutely magnificent week in Cornwall. We have had a great time and I am feeling the best that I have felt since being taken ill in January 2009.

I just wanted to describe an experience that I had yesterday.

We went on a spectacular coastal path walk. Really hard work but incredibly beautiful. I had my protective sun wear on, the hood of which partly restricts lateral vision so that I felt quite cocooned in it. I had my headphones on and was listening to Mahler's 2nd symphony, the Resurrection. I know that this may sound sentimental but I had one of the most profound musical experiences of my life. I love the music and I found that the beauty of the surrounding nature enhanced the music, and the beauty and passion of the music enhanced the beauty of nature; I heard and saw things in a way that I had never experienced previously.

As the music reached the finale, the resurrection, I was sitting on a rock on the edge of a high cliff looking out across deep blue crystal clear water, with the sun dancing and glistening off the tops of the shallow waves. My slightly restricted vision from the hood focused my view on this beauty and the gentle warm wind was causing the material of the hood to float, almost in time to the music. I was suddenly overwhelmed by the beauty of the music and nature and realised that in many respects, what had happened to me was a resurrection – not in a god sense – but in the sense of being virtually a goner in intensive care and being able to sit on this rock, alone with Priscilla and be able to understand, appreciate and revel in the beauty and miracle of life, music, nature, evolution and love. I wondered at the spirit of human beings that gave me the will to fight, the doctors the thirst for the knowledge that saved my life, Mahler the power to write such glorious music, Lorraine the courage and desire to donate a kidney to me, my family and friends the ability and wish to give such incredible support and love, and Priscilla, to be the love of my life and share the bad times in such an incredibly loving and supportive way.

As this realisation dawned on me and engulfed me in sheer happiness, I suddenly found myself sobbing my eyes out – not out of sadness but out of the joy of living and all the good things that this was giving to me. Some may say that this was a god moment, but let me stress that this is definitely not what it was for me. What an incredible gift you have all given to me – for without your love, support and selflessness I would never have been sitting on that rock.

Thank you from the bottom of my heart.

All my love
Me

In September 2011, I returned to work, initially one day per week and then built this to three days per week. It was good to be back, I suppose it made me feel potent, leading a team, making decisions, taking responsibility and, perhaps most importantly, I was helping other people as opposed to being helped. I did, however, find it tiring; dentistry is by no means an easy profession. Dentists are working with patients who do not want to be there, who often have great anxiety and fear, and the dentist is performing very intricate procedures in a dark wet orifice, often fighting a gigantic tongue and sometimes facing unrealistic patient expectations. At the same time, it is important to lead a team and ensure that all is running well from many viewpoints, such as patient service, team cohesion, financial competence and keeping abreast of the vast scientific literature. There are very stringent regulations to comply with and, with the litigious society in which we live, there is always the possibility of a disgruntled patient suing you. UK dentists are sued two or three times more often than UK medics, and much more often than dentists in most other parts of the world, including the USA. Despite all of that, I loved my work and have always felt invigorated, satisfied and challenged by it but it required a very positive desire to return to it after being so drained by illness.

I began to see aspects of life that I thought I had seen before, but did so now with far greater clarity. The robin red breast that sat on the rail in our garden, the flowers blooming, shades of light that seemed to burst through the leaves of the trees, buildings, their shapes, sizes, architectural features, the little smiles on Priscilla's face, that I thought I knew so well but which were now further revealed to me, the sounds of children playing, my grandchildren's little idiosyncrasies, music, people sitting in cafés chatting, not rushing, just enjoying human exchanges, mothers holding babies, so much life. Then there were the people rushing around like lunatics, running for trains, rudely bumping into others, not spending time with their families. Hearses with their pale-faced, puffy-eyed mourners, a reminder of what so nearly was, and inevitably will be. Listening to the news, it seemed that I was living in an "out for yourself" society, make a quick "buck", rip someone off, from the individual to the giant corporates, don't care about the disadvantaged. They are all trying to get something for nothing, only strivers shall succeed. However, none of the latter observations applies to my experience of the NHS, despite what the headlines say. There, people are generally giving, caring, dedicated and not particularly well paid. Of course, as in any organisation whether it be politicians, bankers, the police, there will be uncaring and, in some cases, criminal individuals but I have a feeling that the greater the motivation for other people's well-being rather than individual advancement, party political advantage or money, the less the likelihood of the endemic occurrence of deceit and self-serving behaviour. I may, of course, be very naïve, and I am very aware of the serious shortcomings of some highly publicised hospitals, but my experience of the NHS is such that it distresses me to hear so much bashing of the NHS. Of course, bad practice must be exposed, rooted out and rectified but what about celebration of good practice, dedication, excellent quality of care, why do we hear so rarely of these? Does it suit our political leaders and media to denigrate the NHS to justify a political agenda and ideology? In such a vast public health system it is not possible to pay large salaries. The payback for people working within it comes from seeing the good that they do and from being valued and feeling that they are valued. As a society, we should encourage that.

As I have said previously, one of my dreams and aspirations was to ski with my grandchildren and so, in February 2012, we decided to take the plunge and go. I purchased a snowboarding body armour (not that I snowboard) and had an insert made to take a sheet of the rubberised armour material which covered the transplanted kidney. Obviously, a blow to that area would not be desirable. How the Croatian international footballer Ivan Klasnic returned to professional football and to the national team following a kidney transplant is hard to imagine. Perhaps the kidney was inserted in a more protected site than the groin. The same may apply to Jonah Lomu, the former New Zealand All Blacks rugby player, who made a comeback following a kidney transplant in 2004. I appreciated that there was a risk but on balance the potential benefit of skiing with my grandchildren would outweigh that, and I was absolutely right. Fortunately, the vertigo was not a problem unless the skis took me to the edge of a vertical drop! What a feeling of freedom being out on the piste albeit dressed in my ski suit, factor fifty sun protection, UV protection clothes beneath the ski suit and a UV protection balaclava and mask – pretty hot and a need for constant re-hydration. However, playing with the children, having fun seeing them having fun, this was life, and I was living it again. What a sense of achievement and gratitude to all who had helped me.

Having enjoyed that so much, Priscilla and I decided to ski together in March 2013. Again, we had a great time, revelling in the ability to be there together. On the last day, the weather was beautiful but there was a strong wind and we decided to walk up the mountain to a little restaurant. We had lunch and a bottle of wine sitting by an open fire, enjoying every minute, no, every second, of those magical things called life, relationships and love. At the end of the meal, the restaurateur gave us a rather large bottle of homemade blackcurrant grappa to try. Neither of us usually likes grappa but this was delicious and we sat outside in the shadow of the Matterhorn protected from the sun. We had an intense feeling of being free, and drank the whole bottle! Fortunately, we didn't feel intoxicated, just happy. We hired a taxi back to the hotel and then another one to the airport, where I sat clutching my bag of drugs in the departure lounge.

It is important to explain the potential problems in relation to medication when travelling. I understand that it would not take very long for kidney damage to occur, possibly rejection, if the medication is stopped for even a short period. Therefore, it's not sensible to take the chance of losing the medication, for example, on a plane journey, by putting it in the hold baggage or by not having sufficient supplies to cover a reasonable delay. Therefore, we travel with each of us carrying supplies in hand baggage and another set in the suitcases. On this occasion, for some reason without thinking, I had packed all of the medication in my hand baggage; after all, we were returning home. We sat down in our seats, the plane took off and after an hour Priscilla asked me where my medication was, I said, "It's in the overhead locker of course," and looked for it. To my horror, it wasn't there. I obviously was intoxicated and had left this precious bundle in the departure lounge. Fortunately, there was sufficient at home to see me through before I could obtain some more from the hospital but I learned a lesson, do not take chances with the transport of medication. A friend of ours is a psychoanalyst and when I told her this story she suggested in a very psychoanalytical way that perhaps I felt so trapped by the medication that it was a subconscious response to leave it behind, a way to escape from it. While I respect the psychoanalytical perspective, I really did not feel that this was the case and was very amused by it, I simply think that I was a little bit intoxicated and learned an important lesson!

In June 2013, I plucked up the courage to make a transatlantic trip to New York and Washington DC. The significance of this should not be underestimated. It meant being a long distance from all the known support mechanisms and care, and not having the availability of a familiar hospital. I needed to carry a large quantity of drugs in case of a significant delay. Since we would be in a different time zone, there were the implications for the regular taking of medication, needing to keep on UK time for this. There was also the risk of dehydration, caused by being in an aeroplane for a long time. We were fortunate enough to have accumulated a two-for-one voucher with British Airways and enough BA miles to take both of us to New York in Club Class, and back from Washington First Class so that helped to make this a truly memorable, enjoyable and entirely trouble-free trip. It certainly beat travelling in Economy and almost felt like a reward for perseverance against all the odds. It was an exciting adventure, I think Priscilla had more anxiety than I did, but then maybe she had more of a responsibility, namely me. We can ask a lot from our carers without even realising we are asking it. The trip was certainly enhanced by drinking a glass of champagne once again with our Canadian friends who came to New York to celebrate with us. A major milestone in the road of recovery, another challenge faced, met head on and overcome.

For many years I had a recurring dream which has been termed the Harvard dream because so many Harvard graduates have it. It is always about taking an important exam, not being prepared for it or never having studied for it. For me, it was always an A level exam and I would frequently wake in a cold sweat and then feel a great relief with the realisation that I never had to take an exam again. Since my mother died the day before my A level exams, it is not surprising to me that this dream was so powerful but it suddenly stopped and was replaced with another theme. A burglar would enter our bedroom and as he was about to attack me I lashed out with my feet, the only problem was that I was usually kicking Priscilla who would wake up in a panic. I think that, although at a conscious level I have come to terms with the inevitability of my own death, this dream is an unconscious expression of death (the burglar) coming for me and I am fighting it off, as I have done since 2009. A variation of this is a recurring dream of my father's funeral, except that I think my father represents me. It's interesting that the day before he died, my father said to me, "I looked in the mirror, I saw my father and I was scared." These dreams were very troubling until I realised the interpretation that felt right for me and, at least, I was able to put "the night-time grim reaper out of my subconscious mind" although recently he occasionally returned to torment me.

The lease on my practice premises expired in December 2011. I decided that at the age of sixty-five, and considering all that I had experienced, it was not a good time to renew it. While I could still be active and enjoy life, it would be sensible to transfer the practice to a colleague but continue to teach; I still have so much that I want to pass on to others. I have absolutely no regrets about doing this, which is interesting. I loved my work and could never imagine giving it up but I realised that nearly all of the goals that I had set myself in this area of my career had been achieved and therefore my priorities could change without regret. Finishing clinical dentistry has also enabled me to recommence my national and international lecturing activities without having to fit preparation time in while working "at the coal face". Lecturing is performing, and performing started way back in my life when, as a dental student, I was in that rock group. I love lecturing, from conceptualising the topic, developing a coherent story line that will be educational, assembling the various slides and video material, rehearsing and delivering. It feels as if I have reached a major milestone since I am well enough to stand before an audience, be it small or large, and deliver with confidence; this is very important to me. It gives me a sense of potency and self-worth once again.

As a patient, I am delighted that the NHS is placing an emphasis on AKI. In 2011, the London Acute Kidney Injury Network was initiated. It is a collaboration of healthcare professionals and organisations based in and around the capital. The goal is to provide equitable, high-quality AKI prevention and care in London. In 2014, a programme to raise awareness of AKI was initiated by NHS England. It is a privilege to be a patient representative to both of these groups, working with remarkably dedicated and professional people who have a wide range of expertise. Perhaps one of the most deeply satisfying aspects is that all members have one objective, namely better care of patients and none of them seek personal gain. These people are extremely busy and have massive workloads, yet all give their time for no benefit other than to provide improved kidney care by helping to provide better systems to prevent and treat AKI. How refreshing and what a contrast to our energy companies and some of our banks, for example, which seem to have no morality remit nor a social conscience. My experience has stimulated me and opened new doors through which I can go. This has enhanced my life and allows me to help others in a different way from that in which I did before.

On my retirement from the practice, Priscilla insisted that I buy myself a retirement present, two of the best seats at the Royal Opera House in London for the complete Wagner Ring Cycle. Many people would think that was a punishment rather a pleasure, but not for me, and why requires some explanation. In the 1970s, we had returned from my two-year programme at Indiana University and for many years we were very unsettled in the UK. Should we stay here or go back to America? In 1976, an unsolicited invitation came from the University of Alberta in Canada for me to head the department of Restorative Dentistry, a remarkable opportunity to make a start in North America. So, we arranged to make a trip there to assess the possibilities. The week before departing, after much preparation and encouragement from a friend, I went by myself to my first live Wagner Opera, Das Rheingold. It is the first opera of the Ring Cycle and was conducted by the then Mr Colin Davis, later to be Sir Colin Davis. It was a very controversial production but it simply blew me away. I had never had such a profound musical experience. The power and beauty of the music (even if you have to wait a long time to reach those moments, but how sublime when you do), the set and the message; if a leader is not true to his word and is devious, collapse will follow. Then followed massive moral dilemmas for me, could I love and explore this masterpiece with the feelings that I had about the composer and his views. I decided that you do not need to like the artist to appreciate and be moved by their work, although I could understand why many people would have nothing to do with it. We then went to Canada, still mesmerised and with the music pounding through my head. The university and the people were lovely, but I said I would have to know more about its cultural life before we could think of living there. We were taken to the Edmonton Symphony Orchestra where we attended a concert of some Mozart symphonies, the Wagner was pounding through my head and I could not shake it off. The Edmonton performance was, to be kind, mediocre, yet there was a standing ovation – I looked at Priscilla and said, "If they think that this deserves a standing ovation, I can't live here after London," and she agreed. There were other reasons for not accepting the position, such as my father living in London, but the music was an important one. From that period Wagner's music has been a love of mine so to have the opportunity to experience and melt into the complete Ring Cycle was truly a gift. Over sixteen hours of it in four operas produced within a week. It was amazing, and I had to keep pinching myself to appreciate that I was there, alive, well enough to experience it and share it with Priscilla. However, there were several interesting observations which reinforce something that I have said previously. There were episodes that moved me to uncontainable sobbing, such as in Act 3 Scene 2 of Die Walkküre, when Wotan, the head of the gods, has to punish his favourite daughter Brünnhilde by putting her into a prolonged sleep, removing her special powers and creating a ring of fire around her. The administration of the punishment is more painful to him than to her, many parents can relate to that. The combination of the music, the emotion between the characters, the human experience and the visual power of the fire all combined to precipitate my response which was, however, totally and sadly, devoid of any surges of adrenalin. At no time did those surges occur in the sixteen hours, yet prior to my illness they would accompany great music, and opera in particular. Of course, it could have been that the production was devoid of "the something" that creates the effect but once again, I had the feeling that I had lost a really important part of my life. Perhaps it was a consequence of my traumas over the past years and also the beta-blocker medication but it was an enormous loss, one that leaves a gaping, sad hole inside me but it has to be accepted, there is no alternative. How strange that I find myself sobbing when there is human interaction but, other than the Mahler episode in Cornwall, not when the music should overwhelm me.

So here I am in November 2014, five years and ten months after my life changed so suddenly and dramatically. It has been a long journey to my present state, filled with multiple challenges and ups and downs, physical, emotional and financial, all of which have resulted from serious illness. I believe that among many factors, the adoption of a positive and accepting attitude helped immensely in my survival and recovery. My ability to see humour, even during dark times, sustained me. Singing to myself as I walk along a street or about the house has returned and signifies to me a joy of life and being alive, with a weight lifted from my shoulders. My current wellness score is about 80 per cent of the pre-illness level. That is not to say that it is constant at 80. It varies throughout the day, being lower first thing in the morning and again in the evening and it seems to fluctuate with an unexplained cycle, as I described previously. There is rarely a day when I feel normal or when I don't have to force myself to keep going and overcome symptoms. That is not to say that life is bad, it is tremendous, but if I were to sit around doing nothing, I think the symptoms may be overwhelming.

Since the toxic shock affected my kidneys, my heart, my lungs and my toes, it is hard to imagine that it didn't also affect my brain. Fortunately, I have not lost any motor or cognitive ability. However, my emotions seem to have been affected by all that has happened. On occasions, I feel as if I have had a stroke, in which the higher controls of emotion have been removed. I have described the partial loss of filters that control what I say. It doesn't take very much to bring tears to my eyes. If I perceive a feeling of abandonment or lack of love or rejection, however slight, from those close to me, then a feeling of sadness can overwhelm me, perhaps disproportionate to the event that triggered it. I said earlier that a high percentage of people who have been intubated in intensive care suffer from depression and that I was fortunate not to be in that group. With the passage of time, when the feeling of sadness engulfs me, I can see how easy it could be for me to slip into the wrong side and become part of that group. Fortunately, it usually doesn't take very much to lift my mood but my emotional vulnerability is a heavy price to have paid. I have adapted to the loss of toes, and play a vigorous game of singles tennis, can ski and easily walk eight miles for several consecutive days. My heart seems to be holding up well, long may it last. But, there are still significant side effects from the immunosuppressants, such as tingling and muscle discomfort, particularly when I am tired or run down, but they are greatly reduced from those experienced earlier on. There is a slight loss of my short-term memory but this is not a great handicap. One strange effect of this is that a day can be full, stimulating, energising, and enjoyable, yet on the following day, although I can remember the previous day's activities, they feel unreal as if they occurred in a dream. That day seems to have collapsed into just a few hours at the most. But life is good, so very good, with a heightened awareness of what is important to me. After being so close to death, I now have a deeper appreciation of life and what it can offer.

PART 5

Reflections

30

WHAT HAS THE EFFECT OF THE JOURNEY BEEN?

The past five years feel like a dream, not a terrible one, an interesting one, sometimes a little frightening. It is a dream filled with hope, challenges, superb medical care, an abundance of love and human kindness. In a matter of a few days, I was taken from being an active, fit human being to the very edge of the line dividing me from life and being a stiff, cold corpse. Then, over a period of five years, with considerable struggle, I once again became a vital, pretty fit, active, thinking person who loves his new lease of life, can take pleasure in his family and can participate in and take delight from life and what it has to offer. I see many things with clearer vision and have been given back not just my life but also the ability to live my life; these are two very different things.

Has this experience resulted in an epiphany, completely changing my view of life and the way that I live? Well, I have not had a sudden (nor slow) rekindling of faith. I had no need for an external supernatural power to help me through the most momentous, negative experience of my life. It was my inner strength, gained from all life's experiences combined with the external support of family, friends and the medical profession that saw me through. We have to take personal responsibility for our reactions. We can spend our lives bemoaning our lot, being angry, sinking into self-pity, blaming others and the injustices of life. Of course these feelings are natural and should not be repressed but what really matters is how we, our internal selves, respond and react to the world around us, the people we contact and to the vast array of circumstances in which we find ourselves. I do recognise and respect the need for many humans to have a god figure which they believe will protect them from harm or will explain why they suffer. Unfortunately, this need may be projected into a "belief" in, for example, alternative medicine and its practitioners, dietary gurus with their fads, lotions and potions and many more ramifications of a power that may protect. This belief is reinforced by slick advertising and pseudo-science.

In his book *Thus Spake Zarathustra*, Nietzsche introduces the question, "What if you were to live the identical life again and again throughout eternity – how would that change you?" (I often think about this question, which originated from an earlier work of Nietzsche, The Gay Science, originally published in 1891). It precipitates very powerful thought. I ask myself, "Would I curse this outcome and if so what am I going to do about it?" I stress the I.

Many years ago, I was very influenced by a parable which has remained with me and become even more significant as a result of my illness. "If a jug is filled with rocks, there will be space between the rocks for pebbles. Between these, there will be space for sand followed by some water. If on the other hand, the jug is first filled with the water, there will be no room for the rocks. If the jug represents the finite limits of time, whether this be for a day a week a month a year or longer, the important aspects of our lives, namely the rocks, should be placed into it before anything else. If the jug is filled with the water, sand or pebbles, namely the trivia, unimportant or wasteful activities, there will be no space for the rocks." I often visualise this jug and probably try even harder than before to ensure that the rocks take up most of the space. What are the most important aspects of my life? Am I wasting the precious time that is left to me, not knowing how long or short it may be? In many respects, the parable has a similar meaning to the quote from Nietzsche but the image has been a great help to me.

Of course my experience has precipitated many changes, some small and some large, nearly all for the better. It has changed the way that I live; I have, for example, retired from clinical practice. It has certainly reinforced my view of what is important in my life but this has been a reinforcement of existing values not a sudden realisation of new ones. The happiness, well-being and fulfilment of my family is a prime core value and I frequently reflect upon how fortunate I am to have a loving, caring and close family unit consisting of people with the moral and ethical values that are so important to me. My relationships with my immediate family and close friends are stronger, more meaningful and fulfilling, as if a spotlight is shining on the areas of life that really matter, these should be cultivated and enjoyed. I had a great fear that the bond with my youngest grandson, who was born during the hospital experience, would not be as strong as the bonds that have developed with the other grandchildren. I had spent time with them, loving them, playing with them, teaching them and changing their nappies, virtually from their births. An unfounded fear as, because of my illness, I had far more time to spend with him than I had with the others, resulting in a bond that is as strong, loving and fruitful.

I think that it would be impossible to be as near to death as I was, with the subsequent long road to recovery, and not be affected by a realisation of my own mortality. I do not fear death, although it would be stupid to say that I have no fear of a painful or disorientated demise. Of course, when the time arrives I would hope to slip into a quiet and peaceful nothingness, surrounded by my family, with the ability to tell them how much I love them. Perhaps I could listen to the love duet from the end of the first act of Verdi's Otello while holding Priscilla's hand and gazing into her eyes. "Gia nella notte – Now as the darkness deepens … Let death come now, that in the ecstasy of this embrace I meet my hour of hours." What a contrast to passing from this life in intensive care, with the bright lights, the sounds of machinery, the nurses and, of course, lying totally unresponsively in a bed, with tubes passing into my blood vessels and coming out from all of my orifices. My experience has, however, left me with one principal fear of my own death. It is the effect that it will have on Priscilla, if she outlives me, and on the rest of the family. Having felt some of the pain of their anguish, which resulted from the early stages of my illness in particular, I have no desire to put them through that kind of pain again. However, realistically, I recognise that we have no choice in when, through natural causes, illness, violence or accidents, we or our loved ones die and in what order. But maybe that is not so in all situations. In the face of terminal illness, it seems eminently desirable to have frank and clear conversations with physicians and family about the likely prognosis and what I may want for my remaining time.

Perhaps the ever-increasing spiral of medical intervention would not be my or my family's choice. The time to make that decision is not when you are in intensive care. It is pertinent to add here that only once, and that was when I was in a coma, did I lose the will to live. At no other time, even in my darkest moments did I think, feel or contemplate that ending it all would be what I wanted. This therefore complicates my support for assisted dying. In what circumstances would I want this for myself? A difficult question to answer and one that requires considerable thought. Some of the situations that are clear cut for me are: terminal illness as determined by more than one expert clinician, coupled with uncontrollable pain that is overwhelming my ability to live a worthwhile life (as determined by me); untreatable illness, terminal or otherwise, that I determine is making my life unbearable; locked in syndrome, in which my body would be paralysed but consciousness remains; diagnosis of brain death, by more than one clinical expert and a desire for the life support to be switched off by my nearest and dearest. If such a situation were reached, I would want to be given a drug to finish it, not be left to starve to death.

When faced with the inevitable, I do feel that the part of grief which is related to the regret of "things undone and unsaid" will be reduced if we live caring, moral and fulfilling lives with good relationships, telling our loved ones that we love them and not leaving it until tomorrow, since tomorrow may never come.

Prior to my illness, professional time was divided between teaching and my dental practice. My clinical time was spent in primarily treating patients with complex problems which frequently had resulted from the failure of extensive restorative dental treatment or accidents. Work was challenging and fulfilling, and Priscilla and I had the opportunity to travel to many countries where I gave lectures and courses, enabling us to meet very interesting people. I had been destined for an academic life, and after a two-year period of study in the USA I started on this career ladder. However, there was a deep nagging concern. While the various aspects of dentistry had been taught to me in a compartmentalised fashion, I could only find one person, in Holland, who was putting them all together and treating patients holistically. I simply did not know whether what I had been taught actually worked in the real world. This really bothered me and I could not see any way of testing it within the university or hospital systems. A book written by Hermann Hesse in 1931, The Glass Bead Game, had a profound effect on me. It described the life of a young boy who did remarkably well at school, progressed to the rarefied atmosphere of an elite university located high on a mountain. He studied every discipline of human activity and ultimately received the highest accolade, becoming the grand master of the glass bead game. For this, he had to devise an enormous puzzle integrating all aspects of human knowledge. The problem was that having worked so hard to achieve this position, he realised that he was nothing more than an administrator cut off from the people. The book helped me see clearly that I was not happy with my career path, my ladder was leaning against the wrong wall. On closing the book, I said to Priscilla, I'm leaving the university career path. It is then that I decided to start my own practice, practising what I had been taught, trying not to compromise and keeping records to see whether it had the predicted outcome. I am happy to say that it did, but this was one of the first examples for me of how literature and the arts could truly influence my life. I spent ten years intermittently writing a rather large dental textbook, which was well received both nationally and internationally and, so overall, with much hard work and dedication my professional life was very fulfilling. The illness precipitated my retirement from clinical practice and, much to my surprise, I do not miss it. Since dentistry was such a major part of my life, I often wondered what it would be like to relinquish it but I have come to the conclusion that having fulfilled nearly all the aims and objectives that I set myself in my clinical career, I am satisfied. Interestingly, I am aware that friends have been stimulated to make the decision to retire, presumably partly related to their increased awareness of their own mortality.

There is a lingering regret, however, of not having studied medicine. While I love dentistry, I have often had a suspicion that, for me, medicine would have been even more fulfilling. This feeling has been reinforced by my exposure to the medical profession as a patient. I didn't apply for medical school because I thought that I was not good enough. With hindsight that is ridiculous and one of my few major regrets in life.

Relinquishing the practice has given me more time to spend with Priscilla, and that is a tremendous bonus. After all, one of the reasons for deciding to share our lives together was so that we could be together. Now we are more together than ever before, timewise, mentally, physically and spiritually. Without work, there is also more time to spend with the grandchildren and our immediate family and friends who we value so highly.

I get up a little later in the morning, spend about an hour and a half most days exercising and showering after a light breakfast. I now have the time to write this book. Interestingly, there is not as much time as I thought there would be to pursue the many activities that I planned for; it is therefore still necessary to ensure that days are filled doing the things that I really want to do, rather than with things that I don't. That does not mean being selfish but ensuring time is spent wisely and not frittered away.

Certainly, I live much more in the moment. My desire is not to sleepwalk through what I have left. Interestingly, I thought that I lived in the moment before my illness but I now realise how frequently I didn't. The number of times I would be playing tennis, for example, and my mind would wander to a lecture that I was preparing, I really don't do that anymore.

I smile when I hear people getting angry, frustrated and intolerant about things that really don't matter. I feel like saying, "Get a life, can't you see what you're doing," but I don't. I try to avoid things that make me unhappy and that is sometimes very difficult to do because the last thing I would want is to become selfish and hurt others but, by having a greater awareness of this objective, mostly it is possible to achieve it. I find that I am more able to take pleasure in life's uncertainties, realising that however hard we may plan the path for our future, life may get in the way. This is beautifully expressed in a poem by Robbie Burns: "The best-laid schemes o' mice an' men, Gang aft agley" (Scottish for often go wrong). An unplanned event can be treated either as a disaster or as a way to see things through different eyes and gain from the new situation. Even my illness provided me with new opportunities to enrich my life.

Of course, it is not possible to have everything just the way you would like it to be but if I am happy with my life, with all its imperfections, then that is good enough. With minor adjustments from time to time, I find that this is the case.

I made discoveries about being a patient as opposed to being a clinician. Not being afraid or embarrassed to tell clinicians how you are feeling and make sure that they really listen to what you are saying are both very important. Recognise that there's a subtle difference between superficial hearing and listening. Being real with them. You are not in a competition to prove yourself to be anything other than who you are and what you are feeling. You are trying to overcome your illness or, if that is not possible, nor what you want, to live with it as best as possible. If you feel that you are not being listened to, something is not right, a mistake has been made, you are not being treated with respect and dignity, speak up or have a relative, friend or other advocate do so for you. Remember that if a junior doctor is treating you, they may have only just started training in that field and their knowledge will be limited. It may be necessary to ask them to obtain an opinion or help from someone more senior. Never be afraid to ask and don't accept being fobbed off. Try to take each step one at a time. It's helpful to have a long-term view but with serious illness, I suspect that most people can only focus on the here and now. Try to have positive thoughts but, of course, not everyone can, nor is it possible to do so all of the time, the circumstances may not be conducive to that. Try to be realistic about your situation and develop strategies and thought processes to help you and not destroy you and your loved ones. In the waiting rooms, try not to listen to other patients' interpretations of your illness, each of us have our own condition. Others, unless they are passing positive messages, may be giving worrying information that is not relevant to you and is based on their own fears, concerns, experiences and illness.

Do not be too proud to ask for help if you need it, nor too proud to accept it if offered and needed. Recognise that your carer, if you have one (a spouse, partner, son, daughter or other carer), needs a break, is human too and can only do so much. Don't beat yourself up over what might have been, it's the reality of today that matters and how you respond to it.

My awareness of the increased risk of infection due to the immunosuppression is ever present and I do take precautions that were not necessary before. That is not to say that I now suffer from an obsessive-compulsive disorder like Howard Hughes: he wouldn't touch anything without a tissue intervening, but I always carry hand gel with me and use it when travelling on public transport, for example. I am careful about contact with people who have coughs and colds and my contact with animals. Public toilets are also problematic and a quick clean of the seat with alcohol gel seems to make sense and gives a psychological boost if nothing else.

I am very aware that, fortunately, the bacteria that infected me were sensitive to antibiotics. There was a strong possibility that either of my septicaemic infections would not have been sensitive to any antibiotic and I would have succumbed. For many years, I have been conscious of the fact that the pool of bacteria that are resistant to the current antibiotics is increasing. The overuse of antibiotics by the medical, veterinary and dental professions; the food producers; over the counter availability in some countries, combined with modern travel, means that these organisms can rapidly develop resistance to antibiotics and spread around the world. There is a very real risk that another great plague caused by antibiotic resistant organisms will hit humanity. In 2011, The World Health Organisation echoed this concern, and my illness has made me more acutely aware of the possibility of the danger.

Avoidance of people with obvious false selves is also high up on my list of reinforced objectives. The terms true self and false self were introduced into psychoanalysis by Donald Winnicott in 1960. The authentic self is the core of who you really are, not what people tell you you should be. The false self is a façade, a fictitious self. The individual may actually believe the lie and will present it to the world as if it is the true self, using it to hide the true self. I wish to spend my time with real people not façades. In this respect, a quote from John Ruskin, the British art critic, who was born in 1819, frequently comes to mind. It has been a guiding principle for my life and I suppose for my appraisal of others. He stated, "What we think or what we know or what we believe is, in the end, of little consequence. The only thing of consequence is what we do."

The past five years have really taught me not to worry about things that may never happen. I appreciate that it is far easier to say these words than to live life according to this principle. However, how much energy is lost, stress generated and probably ill health caused only to find that the very thing you were worrying about never occurred. Worrying about the outcome of the multitude of medical tests that I underwent would probably have done nothing other than make me more ill. It could also have been projected onto my family whom, in turn, would have their already high stress levels heightened. The life-and-death medical scenario is perhaps the ultimate regarding this but once the concept sinks in, it is remarkable how it applies to so many situations, both small and large. But, it would be disingenuous to say that I never succumb to this ill-advised thought process. Most of the time I do not worry about the prospects of further heart problems or of the kidney failing but there are odd occasions when something triggers negative thoughts. The one that is most likely to do this is when I meet other transplant patients and I ask how they are. Sometimes the response is, "OK, but as you know we all live with the prospect of something going wrong." I don't usually think that way but that can then trigger the question, "What happens if the kidney fails?" At my age, I presume that I would be very low down on the list for a cadaveric transplant and the possibility of a live donor is unknown. Not a pleasant thought, but I am happy to say it doesn't linger.

I have spent my adult life in a caring profession, helping people and frequently changing lives but I now feel an even greater desire to help other people if I am able to do so. This can range from small things, such as opening a door for someone to be on the Boards of the London and National Acute Kidney Injury Projects. Teaching has always been one of my first loves; it facilitates the passing-on of knowledge and certainly helps people. Its effect is similar to dropping a stone into a pond and watching the ripples. Satisfyingly, as an effective teacher, you will never see the distant ripples but you know that they will be there. By not having the pressures and distractions of running a practice, it has become possible to devote more quality time to teaching, a very positive outcome.

There are so many ways in which pebbles, sand and water, not the rocks, can fill the jug. Time is too precious to allow this to happen without a fight. Of this, I am certain.

31

THE ARTS

My love of music, classical in particular, has been rekindled with a deeper insight and appreciation of the rich and variable canvas of sound and emotion present in it. Very interestingly, I have developed a sheer joy of painted works. Prior to my illness, sculpture "did things" for me, but painted works of art rarely had this effect. This has changed dramatically after attending some wonderfully curated exhibitions that say much about human emotions and interactions. The beauty of Renoir's soft paintings of a little girl which remind me of my granddaughters; the Manets in dark colours depicting human life; the bursting out of colour and life from the impressionists, so beautifully displayed in an exhibition at the Royal Academy of Art in London and in the Museum of Modern Art in New York. More recently, an exhibition at the National Gallery in London of art in Vienna during the late 19th and early 20th centuries, tracing the changes and tensions of social and political life in that period: the Schieles and Klimts were literally leaping from the canvases; so much richness to be enjoyed and learned from, why had my eyes never been able to see this before my illness? I seem now to have an almost insatiable hunger to see more. In November

2014, Priscilla and I visited to an exhibition at the National Gallery in London. I gazed in awe at the magnificence of Rembrandt's later works and his ability to capture human emotion in faces. I felt a sadness when thinking about the cruel twists and turns of life. This genius reached the heights of acclaim and financial reward only to die as a pauper and no longer recognised for his genius, as has happened to many remarkable people. Yet even in his desperate days, nothing could entice him to compromise the quality of his work. He fought against the odds and today we can see that he was right. How grateful I am for these new experiences and insights. I realise that while illness can turn you in on yourself, art has the unique ability to allow you to see the universe, the world and human beings through the eyes of others, displacing self and giving life a greater meaning and depth.

I have experienced a rediscovery of the wonder of Shakespeare. For that, I am indebted in particular to Rory Kinnear for his depictions of Iago in Othello and as Hamlet in the National Theatre productions, both directed so masterfully by Nicholas Hytner. How these individuals have reopened my eyes to the wonders of Shakespeare, the language, the twists and turns of the meanings of words, the understanding of human relationships in all of their forms, from deep love to treachery, compassion and envy. Has any play that is really new in terms of human feelings, thoughts, relationships and intercourse been written since Shakespeare? How I now see this with fresh eyes and delight in its sheer existence. We have been given so many glories to experience, what a waste of life if we allow it to slip by without exposing ourselves to them.

A recent performance of Wagner's Parsifal further reminded me of the ability of art to expose and convey human emotions. In this opera, the theme is of salvation by the hands of "a pure fool, enlightened by compassion". Parsifal is that man. As I have said previously, compassion is vital for the care of the sick.

I reflected upon recent experiences with three groups of relatively young dentists. One of the slides I showed was of a sculpture, Rodin's Thinker, since the pose was improvised from another Rodin sculpture, The American Athlete. The model for this was an American athlete named Samuel S. White who was studying in Paris and, subsequently, went home to enlarge the family business and make it one of the largest dental supply companies in the world. I show this slide to demonstrate, somewhat tongue in cheek, a relationship between art and dentistry. To my amazement, when I asked how many of them knew who Rodin was, there were only one or two in each group. If this is a reflection of their exposure to art, it is very sad since, as Chochinov H. states in his paper Dignity and the Essence of Medicine, "Compassion may develop over time, and it may also be cultivated by exposure to the medical humanities, including the interdisciplinary field of humanities (literature, philosophy, ethics, history and religion), social sciences (anthropology, cultural studies, psychology, sociology) and the arts (literature, theatre, film and visual arts). Each of these will not speak to every healthcare provider but they can offer insight into the human condition and the pathos and ambiguity that accompany illness." I wonder if medical students with their crammed curricula have time to be exposed to what the arts may teach and offer about compassion.

Words in literature and the thoughts of great thinkers have become more profound for me, and reflection upon many of them during my darkest days gave me strength and comfort. The succour that they gave me has stimulated a thirst for more. Interestingly, I have not had any desire to explore poetry. I think that has something to do with the obscure and seemingly unfathomable poems we were made to read at school. I hunger for good literature, theatre (how privileged we are to have the National Theatre in London) and film, to hear music and experience opera in particular and, as said previously, painted art has taken on a new meaning.

I feel awe and wonder at the ability of art, in all its forms, to demonstrate that life has meaning beyond self and that in many instances it can only be imbibed by the co-operation of human beings. For example, I could not have viewed the Rembrandts without him painting them, and then others who framed, preserved and decided to exhibit them. In addition, people needed to arrange the lighting and security and more. In the case of opera, the composer and librettist must write, and then others must agree to produce it, arrange a venue, direct, produce scenery, find musicians (who must be trained and then perform together), organise lighting, marketing and all of the other requirements for staging an opera. All of this creation and co-operation is required, so that we ordinary human beings can delight in such wonders of human endeavour and creativity. It makes me feel, more than ever, that while the exploration of self is of great benefit, it should not be done to the exclusion of seeking out products of humanity which illuminate the spiritual in whatever form that may take for each individual.

That is not to say that I am now deadly serious. Sport, walking, having fun and socialising are all very much on the agenda, also quiet time with Priscilla just sitting by the fire, talking, reading and watching some television. I have piano lessons and practise more than ever before. Perhaps subconsciously I'm trying to get to the stage when the episode with my sedated patient and the Chopin Mazurka will be repeated. However, this time she will not be sedated and I truly will be as good as she thought. Ah, to have dreams that will never come true, but that won't stop me from dreaming and trying. But I am sure, on this occasion, I need to change my mantra to, "I can't and I won't!" One of the ways to enjoy life in the face of the inevitable effects of ageing or severe illness is to accept our limitations.

32

MUNICH

In September 2013, I had nearly completed the first draft of this story, and Priscilla and I travelled to Munich for me to deliver a dental lecture. Friends and colleagues, who were genuinely concerned about my health and were delighted to see us, greeted us so warmly. The night before my presentation, we went out for a lovely candlelit meal and ended the night with tender, loving physicality. Something that, at one time, I thought would never happen again. Before I went to the podium to give my lecture in the Munich Philharmonic Concert Hall, I emptied my bladder. I think that if I were religious, I would probably say a little prayer of thanks every time I do that. Instead, I look on with a kind of awe and great delight, never taking it for granted as I once did. It frequently reminds me of a story told to me by one of my patients. One day, when he was a young MP, he went to the men's toilets in the House of Commons. Winston Churchill was standing at a urinal. In walked Clement Atlee, the then Labour Prime Minister. He stood at the urinal next to Churchill. Churchill moved up two places. "Why did you do that?" Atlee asked. Churchill, renowned for his quick witted immediate responses replied, "Because the last time you saw something big in good working order, you nationalised it. I wasn't taking any chances."

When I entered the hall, there was a five-minute hiatus before I started. As I looked out at an anticipated audience of 1400 people, what were the thoughts going through my mind? No thought about anything to do with the content of my lecture, it was well rehearsed. However, there was an enormous, almost overwhelming, feeling of gratitude to all the people who had helped me. Without them, I would not be standing here with my mind working clearly. I thought about the huge difference that a kidney transplant had made to my family and me. I hoped that I could encourage people who do not carry donor cards to consider doing so. After death, donors have the ability to change the lives of others dramatically. If they have the courage and desire to become a live kidney donor, that gift will be truly momentous.

I was relishing the opportunity to pass on information to colleagues from fifty-six countries and to have a high-level discussion with three experts about the content of my presentation in front of the audience. No feelings of nausea from kidney failure, no fear of losing consciousness from hypotension, well balanced, despite the absence of toes. The particular location also made me think that had my grandfather made a different toss of the coin, I would not be here. How life had taken dramatic twists on the outcome of events beyond my control and how my life had been enriched by surviving them.

I hope that when I am no longer here, my grandchildren will read this account and they will think of all the good and loving times that we had together. Perhaps they will realise that only through the love, dedication and selflessness of the people I have referred to could those times have happened after January 2009, my "toss of the coin". I also hope that they and others who read this will realise that the real things that matter in this world relate to human interaction and not self-delusion. I needed to convert both good and bad situations into challenges, not all of which I could surmount but which I could measure, to be actively involved rather than a passive victim. It was also helpful to ask for and accept help without pride and, very importantly, to have a reason to live.

I reflect and think how amazingly fortunate I am to live in a society with such outstanding medical care available to all, free at the point of need. The NHS is a remarkable institution and is a sign of a civilised society. I hope that the politicians will not destroy it.

Prior to my illness, I was happy, felt fulfilled, loved life, my work and my family. Yet standing on the podium, I felt as if I had a deeper richness to life. My wellness score was, and currently is, about 80. Other than the side effects of the drugs and the residual debilitations of illness, in many respects life is better than before. Perhaps there is now a greater congruence between reality and expectation. Does it really require what I went through to experience these life enhancements? Was I missing something previously? If so, how could I have found it? One thought was that there is a difference between being aware of one's mortality and actually facing it. Can other people who have not had a critical illness or a close brush with death gain this insight and live more fulfilled lives? I sincerely hope so.

I conclude by saying that my life is truly reclaimed; I live again, back from the very edge, the grim reaper has withdrawn for now – someday he will return but for now I am happy, fulfilled and grateful for the life that I have but was so nearly lost. It is impossible to know if and when the "toss of the coin" might occur for me again – life must not be taken for granted nor wasted.

Michael Wise November 2014

If, by reading this account, any reader is stimulated to become a kidney donor, either after their demise or as a living donor, then the time, energy and passion that have been invested in this book will have been particularly worthwhile. In 2014, an eighty-five-year-old British woman donated a kidney altruistically (i.e. she will never know who received her kidney). She said, "I don't need two kidneys to sit at home knitting and watching television." What an amazing gift this was.

At the time of publication (2017) my medical condition remains stable and I continue to live a full and active life.

APPENDICES

Appendix I

MEMORIES OF INTENSIVE CARE – PRISCILLA, MY WIFE

I am Michael's wife, Priscilla. I am contributing to On The Toss of a Coin to describe the earliest stages of Michael's devastating, critical illness and how it unfolded for both our family and me during those very dark days. We had no idea that something that seemed as mundane as a "touch of flu" would turn out as it did. I am going back right to the beginning of the illness and will describe, from my perspective, what happened.

January 2009. Life meanders along quite busily but uneventfully, a good mix of work and pleasure, family and friends. Michael seems well, the weekend arrives and he does his usual six-mile jog, the family stay over. We all enjoy these good family times. The next day he reports feeling a little "under the weather" – nothing he can pinpoint and nothing that seems of any unusual concern. The following day, a Sunday, again he does not feel 100%, but once again nothing seems unduly worrying. He takes our eldest grandson, Noam, to a football match and although he's not feeling too much like doing this, we have arranged to meet friends for a Chinese meal that evening, he's keen to see them and doesn't want to let them down. We return home where he has a bad night's sleep, he must have a fever, he is very hot and we wonder if it was the food but again the symptoms are not extraordinary in any measure. Monday, he teaches all day and I return in the evening – he finished the teaching early and obviously has a fever but again there is no sense of anything really untoward. An early night will do the trick. Another night of sweating. And Tuesday, a day of work treating a patient and being able to function normally.

I suppose Tuesday night is a turning point, but again any sense of real alarm feels obscured. We are to take our staff out for a late Christmas celebration. We order in pizzas and then plan to go to the Albert Hall to see Cirque du Soleil. Michael now says he doesn't feel well enough to come with us but is insistent that I go. I don't feel overly concerned, although this is out of character for him; a touch of flu, I imagine. I get back late and I suppose this is when the real nightmare starts to unfold, although I still have a strange sense of disbelief that anything is really wrong. How misguided can you be?

It's a troubled night and he stumbles to reach the bathroom and is violently sick on the way. We get through the night fitfully. In the morning, he manages to get out of bed and says he's going to have a bath. He manages to get in but is unable to get out. I struggle to help him and manage to get him back to the bed. It is only now that I am beginning to feel some real concern and think that something might be seriously wrong and I am beginning to feel my anxiety rising.

I phone the consultant physician whom Michael works with on his medically compromised patients. He is in a meeting and he will phone back. When he phones back, I find myself being almost apologetic for bothering him; maybe this is just the flu? How, honestly, does one know how to distinguish something really serious from something more mundane? I feel almost guilty telling this doctor the symptoms – am I making a big issue about nothing? But, thankfully, and with enormous gratitude to an astute clinician, he tells me to phone for an ambulance immediately and he will have a team of people waiting to receive Michael in A&E at University College Hospital. I am suddenly plunged more deeply into the reality of this grave, horrific, unplanned and unwanted situation. I feel scared. Much later in Michael's recovery, this doctor told me, "He smelled a rat," and it turned out to be a very large and toxic one. Very fortunately, we were staying at our dental practice in the centre of London and so were within five minutes of UCH. I often ask myself what if we were far away ..., but I suppose there's not much point in thinking along those lines.

The ambulance arrives very quickly. Michael, by this time, is very unaware of what's going on. He gets stretchered out of the building. I notice with horror the frightened and disbelieving faces of his staff as he is carried off. I am now beginning to feel very concerned and frightened.

The ambulance is right outside. We are taken in. Michael by this time seems unconscious. I hear the paramedic say his blood pressure has dropped to 60/30 and I am begin to understand something about the nightmarish reality of what's happening. By some amazing fortitude, well, for me anyway, one of my daughters-in-law, Davina, was just arriving at the practice for a hygienist appointment. She noticed the ambulance outside on the way into the building. Of course, when she arrived upstairs, she was told the news. She came straight down, knocked on the door of the ambulance, climbed aboard and was another one of our family thrown into what was the beginning of a something that, four days before when we were all together enjoying good family times, was beyond our wildest imagination. Having her calm presence was an amazing support, no doubt incredibly difficult for her, but I am so grateful that she came along at exactly the right time.

We arrive at A&E where Michael is stretchered in and we wait in a corridor. By this time, more of the family have been alerted and have arrived: our three sons, Justin, David and Jon. We are beginning to feel really scared. We are sitting by a door which has a flashing light over it saying "Resuscitation". I clearly remember saying to myself, "Why would he be taken there?" I didn't want to believe it; I didn't know how to believe it. The nightmare was beginning to form into a shape.

The resuscitation team was working hard on him and they asked us if we knew if he had been complaining of pain anywhere, if he had a cut of any sort? Is this really happening? It feels so unbelievable.

We formed a strong support network for each other that I believe carried us through some very dark days. We held and supported each other in our horror, disbelief and grief. The bonds between us felt incredibly strong and steadfast and still do after our grim shared experience. On reflection, I feel grateful that something so good could come out of something so bad, although we have always been a close and loving family. These words somehow seem so inadequate to describe the dread and intensity of our feelings.

The medical team then told us that they were transferring Michael to the ICU. There was a lot of waiting around. A sense of disbelief and unreality still hovered over us like a suffocating darkness. Is this really happening?

A couple of hours later we have to scrub up and can visit Michael, but only two at a time. What a gamut of extraordinarily difficult feelings to see him lying there; the strong father figure of our family and now so helpless. It is very frightening. How can a fit, vital person be reduced to this so rapidly and without warning? He is unable to speak and he is wired up to so many machines. We are told he has toxic shock and is on life support. All his organs are failing. It is indeed shocking. We hold back our tears while we are with him. We leave to allow the next two to enter and as we pass each other in the corridor, we cling together feeling some comfort in our shared trauma, fighting back the tears.

We stay late into the evening. The ICU nurse is monitoring the machines, entering recordings but she still takes time to explain what is going on. It feels a huge relief to be included in this way. Over the forthcoming days, we begin to understand something of the meaning of all these flashing numbers and whirring machines. Sometimes an alarm goes off – it sets off an alarm reverberating within us and we stare blankly at each other wondering as to the meaning of this. Again, the nurse takes time to patiently explain and lets us ask questions. This is so helpful and feels surprising given the seriousness of the situation.

Eventually, we reluctantly leave, we have to tear ourselves away; the doctors suggest a night's sleep will be important for us all. A prescription for a big glass of wine before going to bed was good advice. It helped numb the pain, although it felt odd to be drinking wine in this way. There is a blur for me around these days – exactly where I stayed each night.

What I can remember is some nights it was at one of my sons' homes and I felt loved, supported, helped and held by their thoughtfulness and care and the presence of my beloved daughters-in-law and grandchildren, and some nights at our dental practice (we had a flat there and it was conveniently nearby). It seems my sons had decided I mustn't be alone and, in a way, I shall never forget and always be extremely grateful for this; it got me through some very dark days and if I wasn't at one of their houses, they were staying with me. We held hands through the night, comforted, and supported each other through our fear and grief. It was indeed a wonderful support and a terrible time in all our lives.

Sometimes at night, when I struggled to sleep, I would find my mind relentlessly planning Michael's funeral. I couldn't switch these frightening thoughts off and I found them hugely distressing. I would imagine standing by his coffin feeling distraught, trying to hold myself together but feeling in pieces. My mind would wander to the thought of life without him and to what it would be like to be a widow. I imagined the grieving faces of loved ones and friends. I even tried to plan what I might wear and worried if I had anything suitable in my wardrobe. These were horrifying and troubling thoughts that plagued my mind, I felt angry with myself for thinking this way. How could I think like this, and how could I even contemplate something so trivial as to what I would be wearing? But the dark, lonely nights filled with fear allowed my thoughts to play havoc with my mind.

I know that this grim trauma had bulldozed its way into my sons' young lives (they were all in their thirties). A very dear friend also told me I could phone her anytime day or night and she would come to be there with me. I felt held and contained by this generous and selfless offer. That strong sense of love and support helped carry me through and resides in me even in the present. I imagine it always will be there and I am grateful in a way that is too hard to tell.

I am aware that my family all formed a strong network for each other but their wider network of family and friends supported them. I don't know how it felt to them but for me it felt like a network of support, with our closest family holding hands forming one circle and friends and wider family making a wall of support in the next circle. Then friends and family of our children forming another wall of support for us all – it made an extraordinarily visual picture of concentric circles in my mind and left me with a sense that if I fell I would be held and looked after in a loving, caring way. I'm also aware that I needed to be the strong coping mother, isn't that what mothers do? Much of the time I sense that I was right on the edge of my emotions, bursting into tears so spontaneously. I have regrets that I couldn't contain my strong feelings more appropriately, to help and support them; I can't imagine how that was for my immediate family, probably not terribly helpful but I seemed unable to hold back the feelings. They "mothered" me and I let them – thank you to all of you for that. Sorry to all of you if I couldn't do that so well for you. Right in the middle of all this, David's wife Jo was six weeks from giving birth to their second child. How hard for them to hold in mind the prospect of bringing new life, a new baby, into the world alongside trauma, devastating, critical illness and uncertainty and possibly death. Also the challenges of finding some way to make sense of and explain to the grandchildren what was happening to their beloved Poppa, in a digestible way (they were eight, five and two aged two years at the time).

The next morning we congregated early at the hospital. It seems we had commandeered one of the Relatives' Rooms; just big enough to accommodate all of us: sons, wives, partners, relatives and friends at various times. Non-stop food began to arrive, whether it was all of us on our way in buying coffee and muffins to sustain ourselves and each other or friends sending in bags of comfort food. Offers of chicken soup were without limit! My mobile phone was working overtime with calls and messages from people trying to find out first-hand what was going on or just offers of love and support.

I feel extremely fortunate as through my work as a Psychodynamic Counsellor I had access to therapeutic help. What an enormous and valuable support this proved to be. I could go along and express my deepest fears and most extreme emotions with someone professional who would listen to me with respect, dignity and humanity and help me to process these indigestible feelings. I am so very grateful for that solid, dependable, caring, never-wavering source of support and comfort. I felt as if my hands were being held and it certainly helped me through those dark, despairing days. It makes me wonder how people get through such grim experiences without at least some of the type of support that I have described, or indeed without any support. I was fortunate enough to have dual support – that of my beloved family and loving friends and also professional help.

At the onset of Michael's illness, which tore so savagely into our lives, I had worked part-time for a number of years in a hospital psychotherapy service and in private practice. I was able to continue to see my patients for a short while but the anxiety, emotional and physical pressures took a huge toll on my resources. When I could see there would be a much longer term involvement to help, care for and support Michael through his illness to recovery (not that I even really knew at this time if there would be a recovery), the realisation that I could not give my patients the attention, care and professionalism required became a reality. I barely had emotional space for myself, let alone for anyone else. I resolved to say goodbye personally to as many people as I was able, giving a brief résumé of the reasons and referring on to colleagues where possible; some patients I just had to write to. I anguished over having to let people down in this abrupt manner, people struggling with their own internal conflicts, but I felt I had no choice. I found myself explaining it as something we wouldn't choose or plan but that sometimes "life gets in the way", and it certainly did. I tried to imagine how they might feel about me and what I had done, despite extenuating circumstances, and the word "anger" was very much in the forefront of my mind. That was incredibly difficult to come to terms with. An awareness of my own anger at this time became clear and it felt huge. It presented itself as a rage to see "ordinary people leading ordinary lives", people out on the street, people shopping in supermarkets, people enjoying their families when our lives felt like they had been brutally ripped apart. There was a feeling of rage and envy in an almost unbearable way.

The next morning, the time had come to go to the ICU again to see Michael. I had lost touch with reality and my defence mechanisms were firmly in place so that I convinced myself we would enter the room and find him sitting up on the bed drinking a cup of tea and the nightmare would have ended. Alas, this was not to be. He was pretty much as we had left him the previous night. There was a new nurse in place; just as friendly, helpful and accommodating as the previous one. The machines whirred away. The nurse made recordings. We took our turns to be with him and we talked to him and over him, despite his lack of response. We had no clue as to whether he was aware of us. We massaged his legs. Our sons set up a music system to play his beloved music – Mahler, Mozart, Beethoven. We so desperately wanted to reach him, maybe this was a way we could connect with him or he could connect with the outside world. The grandchildren got busy with artwork – painting and drawing things he liked – I remember especially a painting of mountains; Michael always loved mountains. It seemed he had an enormous mountain to climb to get through this and we had no idea if he would be able to. The pictures were displayed around the wall in the ICU. Alas, at this time, it seems that only we could appreciate them.

At this point, I'd like to recount something that occurred for two of our sons, Justin and David, while Michael was so critically ill in ICU on life support. It created a real challenge for them at the time, not the sort of challenge that's easy to face in such circumstances!

Their task was related to accessing his bank accounts so they could deal with any necessary financial issues. Michael has a tendency to allocate a rather bizarre coding system to passwords, using cryptic clues for their identification. It seems to be something that is perfectly straightforward to him but which has always baffled me completely! He had given the codes to me but, knowing my bemusement, he had also given half of each password, identified by cryptic clues, to two of our three sons. His intention was that if, for some reason, the entire password was deciphered by someone, neither of them could feel responsible because they each only had half of it. It now became vital to access these passwords in order to deal with the financial consequences of the illness.

I was of no use whatsoever! Two Cambridge graduate sons, in their stressed, traumatised states, needed somehow to crack the code. Not an easy task. A cunning plan by Michael to keep them occupied in the face of a catastrophe? They put their minds together and persevered with this despite their fragile state. Eventually, eureka! They cracked the code! We were, surprisingly, able to smile about it, it seemed so bizarre and over time it has certainly made for good story telling, but at the time they were near to a state of apoplexy.

We had contact with the professor of the department. He explained the position, the very grave nature of it. He told us they would "pull out all the stops" to help Michael; they were testing, but suspected a Strep A septicaemia which had led to toxic shock and multi-organ failure. They were searching for a cause. As the day progressed, we met various doctors and consultants who were kind and straightforward and we felt that they treated us with respect and dignity. The Relatives Room is on the third floor overlooking the rear entrance of the new UCH hospital. As I stared blankly out of the window, I noticed some sort of monument with an inscription on it in the middle of this area. I strained to read it; I could only read a part of it. Later driven by curiosity and maybe as some sort of distraction, I ventured downstairs. It was written by Hippocrates and read, "A wise man should consider that health is the greatest of human blessings." These words echoed through my mind relentlessly. How we had taken health for granted, feeling that maintaining a healthy lifestyle would give us "magic" protection in some way. I see now that this is patently magical thinking, although it does seem that Michael's health and fitness regime was a strong factor in determining as good an outcome as possible.

Something else that comes vividly to mind is that I found people I encountered in many different situations during this dreadful period, people who knew of Michael's sudden, devastating, critical illness, would make contact with me in some way, in the street, by phone, email, text, letter, etc. There seemed to be a universal message, "We are praying for Michael." Even the delivery man who used to deliver the pharmacy drug order to the practice would stop me in the street and say, "How's Dr Wise? I've been to my temple, I am praying for him." I was so touched by this and still am.

Michael was in the ICU unit for a total of two weeks, two long, agonising weeks. Agonising for us, his loving, frightened family. We had, at this time, no idea of how it was for him. I suppose he mostly seemed calm; he seemed to be in a coma and we only hoped he was shielded from the agony that we were experiencing or some worse agony of his own. On one of these early days, he suddenly became very agitated, he seemed to want to pull the pipes and tubes out; it was grim and extremely upsetting to witness. The medical team was considering intubation (inserting a tube through his larynx and artificially assisting his breathing) as the probable only option. We left in the evening, they said if they decided to intubate, they would call us. We wanted to be right there to hold his hand and help him through, even if he had no idea of our presence. I remember the call came at midnight – we needed to go the hospital; although we had just gone to bed. My youngest son, Jon, was staying with me and he expressed surprise when I got up to get ready to go and took a shower. We were in a hurry to leave. I cannot explain it myself – why would I have a shower? Maybe the routine everyday rituals give some sort of comforting structure to a world thrown into turmoil.

We went to the hospital and waited anxiously while the intubation was performed. We felt relieved that we had been allowed to be present. Only when Michael seemed calm again did we leave to try and get some sleep to help us through whatever the next day might bring. Again, we felt treated with respect by the doctors who allowed us to return in the middle of the night and we were hugely grateful for that.

Michael had been admitted on Wednesday and from then until Saturday our routine was pretty much the same. Go early to the hospital, spend the day in the Relatives' Room, visit Michael two by two. Support each other as best we could. Doctors would talk to us but they didn't know what the outcome might be; however, we knew they were pulling out all the stops. The professor remained "cautiously optimistic" which gave us some hope to cling to. Michael's kidneys had failed – he told us, "They are the cowardly organs, the first ones to shut down." He also told us that eight out of nine kidneys do return to normal function. How we clung onto that piece of information. We formed a good relationship with the Prof., who told us we were a lovely family. One of my sons replied by saying, "Well, you're a lovely Prof." We all smiled at this and it is surprising how humour at such a traumatic time can still be relished!

However, on Saturday morning, things suddenly took a turn for the worse as Michael seemed to stop responding; the machines showed that he was deteriorating and the Prof said they were going to do everything they could to save him but it was very uncertain. They had conference calls with other teams around the world; I found this quite amazing and very comforting. They were going to give him massive doses of noradrenaline plus another medication which could save or kill him. It was the only course of action they could take. The next twenty-four hours would be a waiting game and they seemed very unsure of the outcome.

We felt devastated, but tried to think of those words "cautious optimism". Maybe they were no longer relevant. We hung around, the weight of the information bearing down on us like a huge black and menacing cloud. At one point in that day, one of our sons, David, was with Michael in ICU and we were in the Relatives' Room. A doctor came in and told us that Michael had had a seizure that had set off the alarms and alerted the crash team. A minute later, an ashen-faced, trembling David appeared. He had been thrown out of the room very abruptly and shockingly to make way for the crash team; in the urgency of the moment, they hadn't explained to him what was happening, he was visibly shaken to the core. It was a very traumatic for him. I understand it was an experience that left him with terrifying nightmares for quite a while after the event. Suddenly, it seemed Michael was really going downhill; again, it all seemed so unreal, also like a terrifying nightmare from which you surely must eventually wake up. Only it became clearer that the nightmare seemed destined to continue.

Because of the gravity of the situation, we summoned our nearest relatives to come to the hospital. A close friend, who is also the anaesthetist who Michael works with, visited, he seemed to be saying that we might have to say goodbye to Michael. No, this can't be real, I felt myself thinking; I can't let it be real. Our family arrived in dribs and drabs and the mood in the Relatives' Room became very sad and sombre. A cousin of Michael's turned up, a senior consultant. He, again, was saying that we needed to think about saying goodbye one by one. I felt as if I had cotton wool in my ears, I suppose this was my attempt to block out this information but it became clear that this was what we needed to do. We filed in one by one, we had no idea if Michael had any awareness of our presence. We said our goodbyes in whatever way was appropriate to each of us. We comforted each other in our shared agony, there was not much we could say to each other that could help but the physical presence provided some solace.

I remember thinking about what I might want to say to Michael. I knew it couldn't be much as my strong emotions and incredible sadness would overtake me and, if he had any awareness of my distraught presence, that might be so unhelpful to him. I think it was a simple goodbye to my darling and the very deep and real gratitude for the wonderful life we had shared together and for all the things we had achieved over forty happy years of a strong, loving marriage. This was one of the most agonising parts of the whole trauma for me and the close family – our hopes felt dashed and we felt completely bereft.

However, it seems almost inconceivable that a few hours later, the machines stopped alarming, things quietened down and we moved into a very different scenario. Now the doctors were saying, it seemed to their own incredulity too, that Michael was not succumbing, things seemed to be turning around. Acute pessimism was turning to cautious optimism again. It was hard to believe and trust that this could be true. Our emotions were in shreds but with each piece of more positive information, we began to understand that something that felt almost miraculous was happening. I don't believe in miracles, magical thinking or a deity that's going to make things right, but when one of the consultants described it as "despite the most adverse prognosis, this man seems to be making a miraculous recovery" it did indeed at that moment feel miraculous!

I suppose this early turning point was the genesis of some sort of recovery process; we had absolutely no idea of what the outcome might be but at least something was changing for what could only seem to be better. We felt shattered physically and emotionally, we felt hopeful but also very scared.

The medical team began planning the next stage. They decided they would give it a few more days to stabilise him and then they would begin the process of attempting to bring him round from his coma. We could and should be there when they did this. We really had no idea how this would be for Michael or for us. We talked to each other about our fears and anxieties. Would he recognise us? Would he have brain damage? Would he be in pain? Would he be frightened? Would he be able to talk? Would he understand us talking to him? The list was lengthy. However, the outcome at this time was totally unknown and even the professionals couldn't be sure how it would be. The latter was somewhat disconcerting. We were very scared. I can best describe it as terrified anticipation and anxious excitement.

Interestingly, the next part of the saga, which may be one of the most important parts, remains rather blurred in my mind. Maybe I have unconsciously blocked some of it out as a coping mechanism to get through something that was so incredibly difficult. I will attempt to describe what I remember.

We waited anxiously at the hospital and were summoned into the ICU. Michael seemed peaceful but what did strike me was that his beard had grown in rather a wild fashion; he looked so dishevelled and this felt upsetting, and it was strange this hadn't registered with me before. I'm not clear who was there, I think it was our three sons and I. We waited quietly as they started to withdraw some of the tubes and I assume reduce the medication. We felt agonisingly tense. It took quite a while, or seemed to. How incredibly difficult this felt. The tension in the small room was almost suffocating. Slowly, slowly, his eyelids began to flicker and slowly, slowly, his eyes opened and then closed. I have no knowledge of how long this process took. There was no clue as to whether he could recognise us at this stage. When his eyes were a little more open, I gently touched his forehead and said to him, "Hello, my lovely." What might his response be, if any? After a few agonising minutes, some sort of recognition seemed to register in his brain. He certainly broke the tension for us in rather a dramatic way; it both shook us and made us smile, quite out of character for him. His first words to us were: "Fucking hell, where am I?" We gave him time and space, touched him and held his hands as he gradually seemed to become more aware. I seem to remember one of our sons asking him if he knew where he was or what had happened. This is where things become more blurred and I can't recall much more of what was said. I seem to remember there were questions on both sides. What I do remember is sitting there, feeling the warm and alive body of my darling, surrounded by his loving family, seeing that he was back with us. Feeling enormous gratitude to the medical team who'd pulled out all the stops for him, to the NHS and enormous admiration of, and gratitude for, this man; the rock of our family, who'd been so close to death and had somehow come back to us.

It might be helpful to put all this in some sort of time frame. Michael's admission to hospital was on Wednesday 21st January 2009. His symptoms, the flu-like ones, had been developing over the previous three days. He spent two weeks in the ICU at University College Hospital. Bringing him round from the coma took place at day ten. He was then stabilised for another couple of days before being taken by ambulance to a private hospital (we had private medical insurance) on 4th February, where he spent the next seven weeks. So he was hospitalised for nine weeks in total. He was still on the critical list when he was taken to the private hospital.

At this point, he was incredibly weak and emaciated. Not surprisingly, his tolerance of many things was very low and he could easily get frustrated and impatient. He was on oxygen and had a tube into his jugular vein protruding from his neck. He looked awful. His legs were swollen with fluid and had a yellow, crusty appearance. He wasn't well enough for visitors except closest family. Get well cards with caring and meaningful words began to flood in. I'm not sure how much of this Michael could take in but they certainly were a great source of comfort for me and the family. He was soon moved to a bigger, much quieter room and we decorated all the walls with the cards and with the wonderful artwork produced by our grandchildren.

Recovery was underway. Michael's kidneys had failed from the start and he was having dialysis three times a week which was exhausting. His strength began to return but very, very slowly. At first, he couldn't walk to the bathroom unaided or do anything for himself. Gradually, he mastered many things as his strength and confidence grew. Physiotherapy certainly helped. I stayed at our flat in Wimpole Street, near to where the hospital is situated. It was very convenient, albeit very lonely at times. It meant, however, that I could be at the hospital at 7.30 am each day and stay until 10.30 or 11 pm. I wanted to be there and was grateful that I was able to help in any way to make him feel looked after and cared for and to help in his recovery. Our sons and daughters-in-law were constant visitors which must have been incredibly difficult for them; working, looking after their families, and one waiting for a new baby to arrive. They were amazing.

The new baby did arrive on 5th March to Jo and David, five weeks from the onset of illness; a healthy, beautiful boy. It was hard to hold in mind the strong and conflicting emotions of new life, another grandson and near death. He was named Ethan, which means strong, and I couldn't think of a more appropriate name for this wonderful little boy who emerged into our world amid all the trauma. What a blessing for us all.

It seems worth mentioning that, not unexpectedly, the enormous stress of the events I have described have caused some longer-term damage to me. The brutal suddenness of what happened and the frightening uncertainty of those first two weeks and beyond had a huge impact on all the family. I cannot speak for them but I am aware that for me, one of the longer-term implications has been some symptoms of post-traumatic stress. It has eased a great deal over time but I am left with a realisation that I startle much more easily than ever before. When this happens, and it can be over something quite trivial, it feels as though my body is still "on alert" in an endeavour to deal with any unexpected, sudden, high impact event. I am hoping that, over time, this will dissipate even more.

An example of the lingering effect of this was an episode that occurred in March 2014, five years after the ICU period. We have an automatic defibrillator in our home. On this occasion the alarm had been triggered on the equipment indicating a fault. Unknown to me, Michael was dealing with this while I was in another room. All I could hear were the automatic instructions of how to defibrillate coming from the machine; these are very loud. My panic was enormous and quite overwhelming. I ran into the room expecting to find him collapsed but trying to resuscitate himself! This, of course, was a totally ridiculous assumption since the defibrillator would only be used on a person whose heart had stopped, he couldn't possibly be using it on himself. Even after five years, my immediate gut reaction told me that something terrible had happened and I felt absolutely terrified. It didn't feel very helpful when I arrived in this distraught state to be laughed at! The long-term impact of post-traumatic stress should not be underestimated.

Initially, I found it impossible to separate from Michael, feeling as though I needed to be with him constantly, and experiencing high levels of anxiety when I was away from him. Slowly, and with great effort, I managed to tolerate longer periods of separation but, even now, it is sometimes a struggle. No one in the medical profession raised this difficulty with me, which I assume is fairly common among relatives of patients in ICU.

Michael left the hospital at the end of March 2009. He had certainly started real recovery but the journey was still enormous. Dialysis three times a week. Eight months later, he returned to his work and teaching which, in addition to the family, was one of his great passions.

I want to end by saying an enormous thank you to all our family, friends and people, both professional and non-professional, who have helped us along the way and shared some of this rough journey with us. We feel enormous gratitude, love and appreciation towards you. Our wonderful sons, Justin, David and Jon and their partners, Davina, Jo and Jon have been steady, supportive, thoughtful, caring and loving in so many ways and continue to be. It struck me that each of our sons took on a slightly different role during this period but the roles seemed to complement each other in a very helpful way. Our closest friends who held our hands, nurtured us, cooked for us, supported us; even some who live in Canada took the trouble to visit us.

Then there are our five beloved grandchildren. Ethan, of course, has no memories of the initial illness. The two girls, Zalie and Maya, now eight, may have some vague recollections of something difficult happening in the family and maybe some sense of the huge anxiety we all carried in the early stages.

The two older boys, Noam and Lior, have stronger memories; how hard for them to witness their beloved Poppa nearly destroyed. They may remember visiting the hospital and getting busy with artwork to decorate the walls. Whether all this will leave any long-term scars for them, we cannot know of course. It was no doubt incredibly hard for them to make sense of events, to witness the shock and anxiety of their terrified family and to have it explained to them by their parents that their beloved Poppa might die. Of course, we all need to face the reality that death eventually visits us but I found it so difficult, imagining what might be going through their young minds.

Certainly all five of them are now aware of a Poppa who can really engage with them, be interested in them, play with them, spoil them and love them immensely. My hope is that this good outcome can be internalised by them to help mitigate the previous trauma. Thank you to all of you for the love and joy you bring to us. It has helped us through some very dark days.

Also enormous thanks to my incredible cousin Lorraine who later in the story so selflessly offered Michael one of her kidneys and gave his life back to him. Well, to both of us. There is no way of saying thank you to her that feels enough or ever can. You are truly amazing Lorraine.

Also, of course, to the NHS, including its great teaching hospitals at UCLH and The Royal Free and all the other professionals who looked after, cared for him and saved his life. How privileged we are to have such a wonderful resource. Let us never take it for granted.

And to Michael, "my lovely", your amazing courage and will to live astound me. You fought this illness against all the odds. You remained strong and purposeful, calm and determined. I have sat back and witnessed your return to us with amazement, gratitude, relief and enormous pleasure. You rarely complain – your zest for life seems to be bursting out of you – it is very infectious! I love you deeply, I am loving our life together and I hope that we may have many, many years in good health and fulfillment.

Appendix II

MY SON DAVID'S MEMORIES – AGED 35 IN JANUARY 2009

What follows are my reflections on the experience of being the son of a patient during a critical illness and the subsequent stages of recovery. I kept a diary at the time in the hope that I would one day be able to use it to tell my dad about what had happened to him and how he survived/was saved. Some of it may be too detailed and other bits too sketchy, but I hope it's useful.

Before the age of thirty, I had very little experience of the NHS. Our family had been lucky enough to grow up without major illness and, bar a few football injuries requiring a trip to A&E for stitches, I had virtually no experience of being in a hospital environment. My knowledge of hospitals came mostly from ER which I later discovered gives a fairly accurate portrayal of acute medical care and the family experience of it.

This real life hospital drama began in January 2009, when what seemed like a bout of flu rapidly turned into a life-threatening invasive bacterial infection. I was out with my two-year-old daughter when I received the call from my family that Dad had collapsed and was at UCLH in A&E. I took my daughter home and rushed to the hospital. When I got there at around 11.30 am, my family was clearly very anxious and my dad, who was being attended to in A&E was disorientated, distressed and deteriorating rapidly. He had a very low blood pressure (60/30), a spreading red rash, blue toes and was breathless. He was trying to reassure us but was clearly in a lot of trouble. He had collapsed during the night after a couple of days of what seemed like a bad bout of flu.

The A&E staff was racing around trying to assess him and identify the cause of his collapse and worsening condition. It was a panicky, stressful environment to be in but we wanted to be near Dad and no one asked us to stay away.

Within an hour or so, they had identified that his kidneys were failing and he had suspected toxic shock syndrome. We were taken to a private area and told that it was very serious and that if they could get him stable enough, they would move him to intensive care. I remember feeling alarmed that the doctors couldn't identify the cause of the problem, having previously thought that doctors would always have the answers. I had also seen an episode of ER in which a patient was admitted with toxic shock and went on to rapidly deteriorate and die so I wasn't feeling very calm.

Within a few hours of being admitted to A&E, Dad was transferred to intensive care on oxygen and a drip. For a while, this seemed reassuring, as he was in his own room, with all the care and attention of the unit and he seemed to have stabilised a bit. We were told that he was on high levels of oxygen, noradrenaline and general antibiotics to treat what was now thought to be an invasive infection and he was put on dialysis. A fantastically friendly and calm consultant explained to us what he suspected was going on and what the intended course of treatment would be. He was clear that the road ahead was uncertain but he was "cautiously optimistic" that things would be OK.

But, by the next day, Dad had deteriorated, becoming increasingly disorientated, irrational and distressed. I tried to help him put some music on an iPod to listen to and he wanted to choose his own music but couldn't co-ordinate his fingers to operate the iPod and was very upset by this.

The consultant continued to be an incredibly consistent, reassuring presence for Dad and for us. He was warm and chatty but clearly very dedicated and professional. Throughout our time at UCLH, we found his presence and bedside manner a great source of comfort and strength. We always felt he was being honest and positive but he wasn't allowing us to have false hope and was clear about the risks, which seemed to us like the best approach to take.

This contrasted with some other doctors we met during the time in ICU who seemed to be either overly optimistic or extremely negative. We were acutely sensitive to every mood and every bit of information that was given to us (even if we didn't understand it). We became slightly obsessed about finding out as much information as we could about what was happening and what the blood tests and readings meant. From a relative's point of view, I think that "cautious optimism", where justified, is a brilliant position to take for medical staff. The sudden change in approach and mood could be quite alarming and disconcerting for us as relatives.

The lead consultant was clearly very concerned and seemed to be turning to increasingly experimental treatment to try and get a positive outcome. On the second day in ICU, he suggested administering a ninety-six-hour dose of a drug called APC to try to fight the infection, to which Dad gave his consent.

By the evening, things had got worse and the registrar on duty told us that there was a chance he may have to intubate and sedate Dad if he became more distressed. He gave him some tramadol to help calm him and, late in the evening, we went home to try and get some sleep. We were called at midnight and told that he had become very distressed and had tried to get up and pull his wires out, shouting, "I'm fit. I'm a runner." So they had intubated him. This was terrifying for us, but we knew it made sense and were really struggling at seeing Dad so distressed.

The next few days were a deeply worrying, up and down experience for all of us as we spent long days in the ICU, spending as much time by Dad's bedside as we could, talking to the doctors to try and find out what was wrong and what they could do about it. It felt like the team was doing everything they possibly could to fight off the infection. We were aware that other experts were being called in to offer their opinions on what might be going on. We could hear that Dad's case was being discussed in team meetings. The doctors asked the family to try to identify a possible cause of infection and together we followed up on a number of possible leads, but none of them was conclusive.

With Dad's condition deteriorating further, the lead consultant decided that a full CT was required to try to identify a potential source of local infection. He made it clear that the problem was that Dad was very unstable and another doctor was very concerned about the risk of moving him. He came through it but the CT didn't show anything.

Two days after being admitted, we were told that Dad's

condition was getting worse and we should say goodbye as he was likely to die. We appreciated the honesty but this was obviously an incredibly difficult experience. It just didn't seem possible that a fit and healthy sixty-two year old had gone from being absolutely fine to the edge of life within a few days and that nothing could be done. We all went in to see him and said our piece. I remember telling him not to give up and I think we all spent a lot of time saying that. We also constantly played music in the room – Mahler, Beethoven, Bach and Mozart – music we knew he loved, in the hope it would engage him.

The next day, we arrived early and were exhilarated to discover that Dad had improved slightly during the night and was a bit more stable. But, by the evening, his blood pressure dropped suddenly and, at one point while I was in the room, the alarm sounded and the crash team arrived. I was ushered out and was sure that was it for him.

He responded to noradrenaline and his blood pressure started to improve. This was followed soon after by a (fairly consistently negative, but probably justly concerned) doctor observing a minor fit, which he thought could have been a stroke (possibly caused by blood-thinning drugs). Again, this was hugely worrying, especially as we knew that a stroke and brain damage were Dad's worst nightmare.

By Sunday, the doctor (who seemed to have warmed up a lot) said he was much more optimistic and was "pleased". He said progress had been made and he hoped it would become a plateau within a couple of days and if it did that could be very significant.

And that's what happened. By Tuesday, he was virtually off noradrenaline and the focus then became trying to get him off life support as soon as he was able to respond to commands. Before they did this, they decided to do a head CT to make sure there had been no bleed into the brain. Much to our relief, it didn't show any problems. As the sedation was reduced, Dad became more alert (with limb movements, head movements, partially open eyes), some colour returned to his fingers and feet (which had turned increasingly blue/black during his days in ICU).

It took another two days to bring him fully out of sedation. During this time, confirmation came from the infectious disease specialist that the toxic shock had been caused by an invasive Streptococcal A infection. He said it was very rare and could only find records of seventeen similar cases across the whole of Northern Europe over the previous four years. Having identified the type of infection, they could be sure he was being treated with the right antibiotics (initially he was administered broad-spectrum antibiotics).

Generally, we felt much more positive and that we were moving from absolute despair to some hope. Our focus was on trying to help the medical staff encourage Dad out of sedation and on what the next stage was going to involve. At last, we didn't feel like helpless bystanders and now had a role.

During the time we spent in ICU, we were constantly amazed and humbled by the quality of care, professionalism and humanity of the staff. The nurses who worked long shifts and whom we got to know during our time at the hospital genuinely cared about my dad and our family. This meant so much to us and gave us a lot of strength. They had extraordinary dedication, skill, stamina and knowledge. At times, it seemed like the nurses had the real knowledge about treatment and the doctors were merely there to check on progress and occasionally instruct a change of direction.

Our only negative experience with medical staff was during the time when my dad was beginning to come round from sedation. A vascular registrar came in to look at my dad's damaged toes and hands. He brusquely announced to the nurse that it was likely that his legs would need to be amputated because of vascular damage. We knew that there was damage and this could be serious but no one had mentioned amputation up until then, and my brother and I were furious that the doctor announced this in this way to us and in front of our dad, who we believed could hear everything. The last thing we wanted was for him to find out his legs would be amputated at the very point he was coming round from the sedation and needed to be calm and strong.

My brother and I complained to the registrar and asked for a consultant to come and offer his opinion. The consultant was amazing and completely contradicted the registrar, which gave us all more hope. I think doctors and nurses should be very careful about what they say around patients, and I'm sure my dad's account of this experience will confirm that.

The first attempt to bring Dad out of full sedation wasn't very successful. He was able to communicate through blinking but was struggling to breathe. The doctors wanted to proceed with a tracheotomy to help maintain an airway as they felt he would struggle off the ventilator.

But, on Friday, they tried again to bring him out of sedation and this time Dad woke quickly. He was put on oxygen through a mask and was able to shout a few expletives (very out of character) and said, "I don't believe you," when we told him what had happened (he was convinced he'd been in a car crash and that my mum was dead but that we wouldn't tell him).

By the next day, Dad was much clearer, calmer and more comfortable and, within another few days, was able to eat soup and chocolate and to talk to his grandchildren on the phone. Some amazing physiotherapists came and soon had him sitting up. The doctors' view was that his toes would not recover but would eventually "mummify" and fall off and that his kidney function would most likely return within six months. Unfortunately, this didn't turn out to be the case.

Dad was displaying quite a lot of (understandable) confusion about what had happened during this time and was clearly trying to make sense of it all. He was uncharacteristically intolerant at times and it was difficult to make sense of this.

Two weeks after first arriving at UCLH, Dad was moved to a private hospital for what was going to be a long period of recovery, dialysis, investigation and treatment. My feeling was that he was moved too soon, although I understood he couldn't stay in ICU long-term. He didn't feel ready to be transferred and the level of care and attention at the private hospital felt poor in comparison.

The next couple of months were very difficult for everyone. My mum was virtually living at the hospital. We all had to go back to work, and tried to come as often as we could to visit. This period felt like a waiting game to see if the kidney function would return, while Dad tried to get used to his new reality of regular dialysis, tests and recovery. I think he found it mentally very hard and was also experiencing post-traumatic shock of what had happened.

While most of the staff in the private hospital were professional and pleasant, some were noticeably impatient, rude and some, I would say, were even a little bit cruel. It made me think about the difference between levels of care, dedication, motivation and organisation in the NHS and the private sector. It's not fair to generalise from experiences at one NHS hospital and one private hospital but I strongly felt that the care and experience in the NHS hospital was consistently superior. The main difference in the private hospital was that my dad had his own room which, during a long period of recovery, was very much appreciated. He also had the consistent medical supervision from NHS consultants. Had he not been fortunate enough to have the medical cover to pay for the stay in the private hospital, I have no idea what would have happened or how it would have affected the outcome.

After he returned home, my dad had regular dialysis at satellite dialysis centres connected to the Royal Free Hospital. The level of care and professionalism varied enormously between centres. In one, the care, hygiene and overall patient experience was very poor indeed. This was a private company taking on dialysis services for the over-stretched NHS. We felt very concerned by the care offered there and, after a much appreciated tip off from a member of staff, managed to get dad transferred to a different, excellent unit, where he remained until the transplant.

Once again, from a relative's perspective, it made an enormous difference to all of us when nurses and doctors were attentive, honest and friendly.

The weekly routine of dialysis was interrupted a couple of times by medical setbacks.

The main one came when dad picked up another infection (thought to be from his dialysis line) which resulted in a week or so in hospital and intensive antibiotic treatment. This brought back many of the feelings of trauma from the original illness and it was hard to remain calm. The medical care during this time was, by virtue of the fact that it was not ICU, less intensive. It was hard to get answers and any explanation of what was going on. Dad was seen as a subject of fairly hurried ward rounds.

The anxiety was exacerbated by Dad having to be taken off dialysis for a week, as there was a concern that the line would simply reintroduce infection. And an outbreak of norovirus, resulting in a lock down on the ward, didn't help.

Eventually, the antibiotics did their work and his infection markers came down. He went home.

He returned to work for a number of months as he tried to keep his dental practice going. How he managed to do this, I have no idea. It seemed to me that dialysis allows people just about to function, through waves of nausea, exhaustion, light-headedness and discomfort.

The moment shortly after a working kidney has been plumbed into the body of someone whose own kidneys have packed in is truly remarkable. I remember my dad's exhilaration as he came round, still under the influence of the anaesthetic, but also high on the excitement of having a new kidney inside him. And I remember his joy in the recovery room at seeing the "new" kidney pass urine for the first time – not an event I had expected to find so joyful.

Now, nearly four years and seven months on from the transplant, it is remarkable to see how his life has been transformed from the desperate low points and immediate aftermath of the serious illness that had nearly killed him four years ago.

As the relative of a kidney transplant patient, there are two main protagonists who shaped the experience and the outcome, and I am hugely grateful to both. The first is the NHS and its doctors and nurses, without whom my dad would not be alive. The second is the donor, who is a cousin of my mum's, who chose to donate one of her kidneys in the knowledge that it involved risky invasive surgery, but also in the knowledge that if it went well, it would change my dad's life, which it has.

Appendix III

THE TRANSPLANT– MY DONOR'S EXPERIENCE

"I'm the donor." I never thought those words would apply to me! So, how did that come about? How did I become the person who would give Michael the best chance to get back the life he led before he became gravely ill and fought back to the stage where a kidney belonging to someone else was really his best, if not his only, option?

The subject of donating a kidney never came up, it was something I'd never even given a passing thought to – why would the majority of the population think to do so? Unless, that is, someone you know and love desperately needs a kidney and you have one going spare. I had tried to be supportive to Priscilla (as much as one can be in such a situation), I wanted to help and said, "If there's anything I can do, anything at all, please just let me know." Well, I guess ultimately donating your kidney is about as supportive as it gets. Michael's immediate family, as well as close friends, had been tested or considered as potential donors but, unfortunately, none was a match. Michael has a less common blood type and I didn't even know what my blood type was; we aren't even related by blood, as Priscilla is the one who is my cousin. But I thought I had to offer to be tested; how fantastic would that be if it turned out that I was a possible match but, to be honest, I never expected it to be so.

So, there I was, a forty-eight-year-old female going along to the Royal Free Hospital to meet the live donor nurses for the first time; as it turned out, the first of many appointments and tests. I had no idea what to expect when the process started but the nurses were great: kind, helpful and supportive. I guess in the beginning I didn't have many questions as each step in the process was taken one at a time. The first step was to check my blood type, and I didn't have to wait long for the call to tell me mine was the same blood type as Michael's! That was quite a shock in a way – almost took my breath away for a moment. I took the call from one of the nurses early in the morning before I left for work, and I immediately called Priscilla and Michael to tell them the news. I could hear the emotion in Priscilla's voice when I told her. "So, what are you going to do?" she asked. "Go ahead with the next step," I answered.

The next step was a glucose test to see if I had any early signs of diabetes or potential to develop it as both my mother and maternal grandmother had suffered with the disease. That was painless but not very pleasant. I drank one glass of Lucozade, followed by another and when the nurse said, "You have to drink the whole of this jug I'm holding," I said, "You're kidding, right?" "No, I'm afraid not," was the answer. I did finally manage to down it all. The result of that test was negative – right answer – and good news for both Michael and me, so another call to Priscilla, who again asked, "So, what are you going to do?" Same answer, "Go ahead with the next step."

There followed a series of tests and a number of visits, including a whole day at the Royal Free, going from one department to another, having X-rays, an ECG, various scans and dye injected into me, and at every appointment, blood and urine samples were taken. I soon got to know the routine! Priscilla came with me to every appointment which certainly made it easier for me. I was doing this for them but it can feel a lonely experience; after all, no one but me was actually going through this, although I also felt we were all in this together. At every stage, as each test came back with the desired result, just making me more and more anxious for it to work out, Priscilla asked me what I was going to do and the answer was always the same, "I'm going to keep going as long as the results allow me to."

The three of us also went along to listen to the experience of a kidney transplant patient and his donor. The donor hadn't had the easiest time of it but did it put me off at all or make me reconsider? Did any of the process, the numerous tests, etc. make me waiver? No, not one little bit. I guess for me, the decision was already made when the blood test came back as a match. There was nothing I could do to affect the test results; if they were all indicating things were looking good, then I was going to go ahead with this as far as I could.

Certainly, no one ever put any pressure on me. My friends and family were supportive, if a little concerned at what I would be putting myself through and how my life might be affected post-donation. Was I scared as things progressed and the donation was looking more likely to go ahead? Only a little at times. I'm sure Priscilla and Michael were worried that I might change my mind at any point but how could I possibly even consider doing that to them? I couldn't, and wouldn't. I had made that commitment to them. What kept me going was the knowledge that it would be a relatively short period of pain/discomfort/disruption to my life, in exchange for something that would, with hope, give them back their lives.

Towards the end of most of the tests, I met a surgeon (as it turned out, not the one who would be removing my kidney and sewing me back up) and a consultant. Between them they explained the procedure (the intention was to perform keyhole surgery, putting four little portholes in my stomach and one large slit at my bikini line to extract the kidney through, but it was explained that at the time it might not prove to be possible and a more invasive approach to remove my kidney might have to be undertaken). They went through the possible risks – short- and long-term – and gave me literature to take away to read and the opportunity to ask any questions. I guess at that point it brought it all home; one way or another they were going to cut into me! I certainly hoped the keyhole approach would work at the time. Later I would have to sign a consent form to agree to let them do whatever they needed to do on the day.

The final test was a psychological one – this one was harder in a way. The medical tests were beyond my control but this one was down to me. What if I said the wrong thing, or didn't say what the independent assessor was expecting to hear? Michael wasn't a blood relation but he had always been a regular part of my life since I was a small child and I loved him and Priscilla very much, so surely I could get across how much I wanted to do this for him, for Priscilla and for their kids and grandkids. I must have said the right things, as I passed this test too.

So, this was it, after several months of testing. Decision made and date booked for the operation(s). The transplant was booked for three months' time. This was a bit of a difficult time for me. I guess it would have been easier if it were to have happened sooner, leaving less time to think about what was to come, less time to have it hanging over me.

But time has a habit of passing quicker than you think, and the day of the transplant approached. I'm lucky to work for a healthcare company who were very supportive of the time I had already taken off for hospital visits (appointments were fairly straightforward to make and I was able to be flexible with timings to fit in with hospital routines) and also gave me time off for the operation and recovery period without question.

How did I feel the night before I went into hospital? Surprisingly calm under the circumstances. I did feel uncomfortable about whether it would be painful, would it hurt, how would I cope afterwards, and about actually being in hospital. The only time I'd ever been in hospital myself was to have my tonsils out when I was seven years old. I remember that quite clearly: well, the fact I was given cornflakes for breakfast the next day – how could they! I'd mentioned my worry to one of the nurses at one of my earlier visits and she took me up to show me the ward. I thought that was so kind of her. Did it help allay my concern? Yes, a bit.

The admission itself was a rather long, slow process, with much waiting around, during which a junior doctor inserted a cannula into the back of my hand. As it turned out, I was asked to be at the hospital several hours before I was to go up to the ward. I guess I did get a bit jittery at that stage but eventually up

334

I went and, once I'd settled in to my cubicle, I was then allowed to go out for the evening. That felt rather strange, as the whole family went out for a meal together, although I didn't feel much like eating at that point, I must admit. Back to the hospital, followed by the usual bedtime routine, it all felt a little surreal. During this time, the surgeon who would be performing my operation came up to see me and I had to sign the consent form. He was very kind but I guess it all came over me a bit at that point as I do remember getting a bit emotional.

Early next morning, 1 was taken down to theatre. I'd asked my sister to come with me until the point at which she wasn't allowed any further. I think perhaps it was harder for her than for me at that moment; maybe I had shut down a bit emotionally as I can't remember really feeling anything in particular. As I was being whisked through the hospital corridors on a trolley where I could only see the walls on either side, it felt rather like I was on a conveyor belt. We'd arrived outside the theatre and it was explained to me what would happen – intravenous drug into the cannula in my hand, count backwards from ten to one (don't think I even got beyond ten, actually), then – nothing. Next thing I knew, someone was calling my name. I opened my eyes and then closed them again and then I was back up on the ward, having lost several hours of my life!

I hadn't really known what to expect post-operation – yes, probably pain but beyond that, it was a blank. However, I was out of it really for the next couple of days (enough that the catheter they'd inserted during the op didn't bother me too much, nor the noises from the other patients in the ward); drifting in and out of consciousness, with little awareness of anything around me, although my dad was there by my bedside every time I opened my eyes during the day. The endless checking of my vital signs, every half hour initially, meant I got very little sleep the first night and I was also feeling quite sick – from the painkillers and morphine or the anaesthetic, I don't know (I had intravenous PCA – patient-controlled analgesia – my choice – but maybe it was all a bit too much). The on call doctor responded to my nausea problem but it took three different anti-emetics before I finally felt relief and, after two days, I said no to taking any more oral painkillers as I felt they were probably adding to my feeling unwell. I wasn't prepared for just how thirsty I would feel; my liquid intake was very restricted to begin with until they were sure my remaining kidney was functioning OK without its twin. How was Michael doing? That was what I wanted to know. Thankfully very well; in fact, initially a lot better than I was. I had read that this operation was actually physically harder on the donor than the recipient, and certainly Michael and my other kidney were up and walking around a while before I felt up to leaving my bed (two days later when they didn't give me a choice any longer). The other main effect, apart from abdominal discomfort along with some pain, was a total loss of appetite. How many times have I wished I could lose my appetite! For three days, I couldn't think of a single thing I fancied eating; one spoonful of soup or custard and that was about all I could manage. The third day after the operation I woke up and suddenly felt like having some breakfast (rice crispies), the curtains round my bed were opened and, finally, I was back in the land of the living, so to speak.

My surgeon had come to see how I was doing the morning after the operation but, other than that, I was in the hands of the nursing staff on the ward, and rarely the same one twice. As I began to feel a bit more myself, I did somewhat feel that I was just a number passing through – to them it was just routine – to me it wasn't. I'd gone into hospital feeling well, and suddenly this was no longer the case; were they just ticking a box when they did my observations, etc.? Did they really care how I was feeling or if I needed help with anything; just something simple like a bowl and some water to brush my teeth? I don't recall ever being asked.

Two days after the surgery, my left hand and forearm, the one with the cannula in, swelled up suddenly. The cannula was being used for fluids to hydrate me. A doctor came and removed the cannula and tried to replace it in the other arm but had great difficulty in doing so. After several attempts to find a vein and puncturing me, she had to call a phlebotomist who inserted the cannula without any difficulties. I must say that I did feel that from the patient's perspective it would have been much better if the phlebotomist had come up straight away, but I appreciate that there may have been limited resources.

On the fourth full day after the operation, I was allowed to go home. Again, a long day of waiting until someone was available to sign my release. I was dispatched with a whole lot of painkillers and, suddenly, there I was with no one checking my temperature, blood pressure, oxygen saturation, etc., and this felt a little worrying at first; the whole in-patient experience is in many ways such an artificial environment.

Back home, with a weekly visit back to the hospital for a progress check, the live donor nurses were again very supportive and understanding. I spent the next few weeks at home recovering and getting my strength back. To start with, I didn't feel like doing much; on my first walk outside, I managed to get a few hundred yards to the end of my road, and that felt like hard work, but, gradually, I increased the distance and tried to get out every day. I did lose my independence for a while, as I was unable to drive and had to rely on family and friends to help with the shopping. I can't say I was in much pain, and doses of paracetamol helped initially but I did find the tightness and discomfort in my abdomen was the main thing to cope with, and by early afternoon, I felt like I had to lie down and stretch out.

Following a final check-up with my surgeon, I was back at work six weeks later; phased-in for the first couple of weeks, and often feeling the need to stand up and type by the afternoon just to stretch out and relieve the abdominal tightness I was feeling. This probably looked a strange sight to my office colleagues! This gradually lessened over time, though it was still there from time to time many months after the operation.

So, where are we now? November 2014 – coming up to the fifth anniversary. It's amazing to see how well Michael is doing, and I know he's taking good care of the kidney – is it yours, mine or ours, we often joke when we meet up. It feels good – actually it feels terrific – he and Priscilla have their lives back and knowing I played a big part in that makes it all worthwhile, and it's definitely brought us all closer together. I now have an annual check-up at the hospital (yes, more blood and urine taken) and at each visit I make an appointment for the following year.

Once I'd fully recovered, I can't say donating a kidney has made any difference to my life. I rarely give it a thought and I've certainly never for a moment regretted giving such a gift.

To anyone reading this and thinking of donating one of

their kidneys, I'd say go ahead – you won't regret it! I don't think this is something I could have done altruistically, but having the chance to see the huge difference this has made to someone else's life and to the lives of their family makes it all worthwhile.

Appendix IV

MY COPING STRATEGIES

1. Do not reflect on what might have been.
2. Develop strategies to cope with each day.
3. Whatever the situation, it is how you react to it that really matters. You may not be able to change what has happened, but you do have the ability to take control of your mind and use it positively. You need to take responsibility for your reaction to the situation.
4. Take one step at a time up the mountain and only focus on doing that. Once that's passed, it doesn't have to be repeated.
5. Turn each situation into a challenge.
6. Divert your attention from unpleasant circumstances. I remembered stories from the past that related to what was happening.
7. Don't worry about things that may not happen.
8. Recognise that you have something to live for.
9. Don't be a passive victim. Be proactive, but not aggressive, if you feel something isn't right.
10. Ensure that as far as possible you are living your life today as you want to. If not, then do something about it because our time on this earth is finite. There is no point in spending the first part of your life looking to the future

and the second part looking back on the past but never enjoying today.

11. Remember that this life is not a rehearsal.
12. Exercise.
13. Avoid things that make you unhappy, but do not hurt other people.
14. Try to remain positive, but recognise that this may not always be possible and accept that reality.
15. Try and maintain a sense of humour.
16. Seek out situations that make you laugh.
17. Do not be embarrassed or afraid of revealing any part of your medical condition to your doctors/carers.
18. Seek and accept help when you need it.
19. In waiting rooms, try not to listen to other patients' interpretations of your illness.
20. Tell the people who you love that you love and value them.
21. Spend time with your family and friends.
22. Immerse yourself in music; for me it is remarkable therapy.
23. Have a project/hobby. Restarting piano lessons – which I stopped as a teenager; tennis; joining a rambling group; writing this book; helping with the NHS Think Kidneys Programme, London Acute Kidney Injury Network and UCL Partners Project all worked for me.
24. Do not be afraid to fail at something, but ensure that if you fall (physically and/or mentally), pick yourself up and try again. Otherwise, if you don't try, how can you reach your potential?

Appendix V

THE DIETARY RESTRICTIONS FOR DIALYSIS

Not all patients need to follow the same dietary advice, and the advice varies depending on blood test results, nutritional status, blood pressure and other medical problems which may be present.

Salt is present in many processed foods, such as: tomato ketchup; brown sauce and soy sauce; Bisto powder; bouillon cubes; gravy granules; guacamole; monosodium glutamate; mustard; Oxo cubes; oyster sauce; pesto; piccalilli; ready-made curry sauces; ready-made pasta sauces; ready-made tomato sauces; salad cream; shop-bought sour cream dips; stock cubes; taramasalata; Worcestershire sauce to name but a few, these all need to be restricted.

Dietary instructions from the Nutrition and Dietetics Services of the Royal Free Hospital London NHS Foundation are that fresh or frozen meats, fish and vegetables rather than pre-prepared, ready-made meals should be used wherever possible – this could be problematic for patients on very low incomes. If tinned vegetables are used, the ones with no added salt should be purchased, and tinned meats, sausages, beef burgers, meat pies, smoked fish, tinned fish in brine, olives in brine, tinned and packet soups, peanuts, crisps and poppadoms should be avoided, or eaten in small quantities on an occasional basis. Bacon and bread now contribute the most salt to UK diets, and just two rashers of bacon contains up to a whole day's recommended salt intake. The guidelines suggest that not more than six grams of salt should be consumed per day: that's about a teaspoon. Salt should not be used in cooking, but pepper, vinegar, herbs and spices can be used to add flavour. Marinating meat and fish in advance to give them more flavour by using, for example, garlic, onions and lemon can enhance flavour, as can adding small amounts of red wine to stews and casseroles, and white wine to risottos and sauces for chicken.

There are substantial restrictions on other types of foods that can be eaten, among these, in particular, are those containing potassium. The most serious side effect of the increased blood potassium levels is its effect on the heart. It can cause abnormal heart rhythms (cardiac arrhythmias) because of changes in electrical impulses in the heart muscles, a slow weak pulse, chest pain, heart palpitations, numbness or tingling and nausea. The more severe the raised potassium, the greater the effect. On the other hand, low potassium levels can also cause an abnormal heartbeat. Advice for limiting potassium is quite restrictive and the recommendations are as follows: coffee once-daily; any fruit twice-daily but completely exclude: avocado; banana; blackcurrants; rhubarb; dried fruits; melon. Vegetables twice-daily, which should be boiled for at least ten minutes, but there is a risk of reducing water-soluble vitamins, such as vitamins B and C, which may have to be supplemented. Baked beans, Brussels sprouts, mushrooms, parsnips and raw spinach should be completely excluded; potatoes once daily, but only after following the same boiling regime as for vegetables. Completely avoid: some starchy foods (e.g. baked potato, chips, fried plantain); some breakfast cereals (e.g. All Bran, muesli); instant porridge (e.g. Ready Brek, hot oat cereal); snacks (e.g. chocolate, crisps, liquorice, nuts); some drinks (e.g. cider, fruit juice, stout, strong ale); milk-based drinks (e.g. Build Up, Complan, Horlicks, Nurishment, Ovaltine); salt substitutes (e.g. Losalt, Solo); limit any food containing nuts, dried fruit or chocolate; and some miscellaneous foods (e.g. evaporated and condensed milk, tomato purée).

Foods that are allowed freely concerning potassium are meat and all types of fish, rice, pasta, noodles and bread, breakfast cereals except for those listed above, plain sponge and pastries, plain or cream filled biscuits. With regard to the latter, patients with diabetes need to continue to avoid sugary foods.

On long-term dialysis, there is an additional dietary problem since calcium levels can be low and phosphate high, increasing the risk of heart damage and bone problems (renal bone disease) which can ultimately result in bone pain and fractures. Sometimes phosphate in the diet needs to be reduced by eliminating the following from the diet: some types of meat and poultry (e.g. veal, hare, venison, goose, grouse, partridge, pheasant, pigeon); offal (e.g. liver, kidney, heart); some types of biscuits and cakes (e.g. oatcakes); cheese-filled crackers (e.g. Ritz, Tuck, rye and crispbreads, cereal bars and custard tarts); some types of dairy produce (e.g. evaporated milk, condensed milk, crème fraîche, single cream, soured cream, imitation cream, cheese triangles, processed cheese slices, cheese in tubes); certain snacks (e.g. chocolate, nuts, seeds, tahini, fudge, Indian sweets); fish and shellfish (e.g. anchovies, sprats, whitebait, monkfish, sea bass, prawns, scallops, lobster, crab, scampi, clams, fish paste, taramasalata, fish roe); breakfast cereals (e.g. All Bran, Bran Buds, muesli, wheat germ, Branflakes, instant porridge). No more than two thirds of a pint of milk should be drunk daily and if cheese is eaten, it should be changed to cream cheeses, cottage cheese and ricotta as often as possible as they are lower in phosphate. Rice, pasta, plain breakfast cereals, bread (although the latter may be problematic with regards to salt), plain or cream-filled biscuits can be eaten freely. In an attempt to reduce and control phosphate in the blood, a phosphate binder is prescribed: for me this was Calcichew.

Appendix VI

HISTORY OF DIALYSIS

Dr Willem Kolff is considered to be the father of modern dialysis, although the first time that dialysis is mentioned in scientific literature was by Thomas Graham, a Scottish chemist, who, in his 1854 Bakerian lecture, described dialysis and gave the word a new and still current meaning. Previously, dialysis meant dissolution of the strength or weakness of the limbs, coming from the Greek, to part asunder. Kolff was a Dutch physician and he constructed the first dialyser (artificial kidney) in 1943. It is salutary to consider The Renal Association report of 2013 which states that, "the survival of patients already on renal replacement therapy means that even without further increases in take-on rate, the number of dialysis places needed will continue to rise. In fact, take-on rates will need to rise because of the increasing number of elderly individuals in the population (there is a dramatic rise in risk of requiring renal replacement therapy with age) and because of the age structure of some high-risk groups (diabetes, some racial minorities)."

Dialysis treatment was shown to be viable in the Korean War (1950-1953) and, because of this, it was introduced as a short-term treatment to tide patients over acute renal failure. At the first meeting of the International Society of Nephrology in Evian, France in 1960, Belding Scribner from Seattle reported using dialysis to prolong the lives of patients with irreversible kidney disease, instead of simply for recoverable acute renal failure.

In 2013, the DaVita HealthCare Partners Inc. website (a private US provider of kidney care) published the following, "In 1962, Dr Belding Scribner started the world's first outpatient dialysis facility. Immediately the problem arose of who should receive dialysis, since demand far exceeded the capacity of the six dialysis machines at the centre. In another brilliant move, Scribner decided that he would not make the decision about who would receive dialysis and who wouldn't; a matter of life and death for the patients involved. Instead, the choices would be made by an anonymous committee composed of local residents from various walks of life plus two doctors who practiced outside of the kidney field. Although his decision caused controversy at the time, it was the creation of the first bioethics committee which changed the approach to accessibility of health care." What terrible decisions to have to make.

Dialysis was slow to be adopted in the UK, where conservative dietary management had been the norm. The first attempts to repeat the Seattle experience in the UK were both in London, at the Royal Free Hospital in 1961 and at Charing Cross Hospital in 1964. Although there continue to be intermittent severe stresses, particularly with adequate growth of haemodialysis provision in some regions, it is now generally true that long-term dialysis is available to all those who need it in the UK.

Appendix VII

ACUTE KIDNEY INJURY (AKI)

The following is reproduced with the permission of the NHS Think Kidneys Programme.

Acute kidney injury and what you need to know
Think Kidneys is the NHS's programme to increase awareness of the prevention, detection and treatment of acute kidney injury. We are working with health and care professionals.

What is acute kidney injury and what causes it?
Your kidneys are vital organs in your body and are responsible for keeping you healthy. Acute kidney injury is a sudden and recent reduction in a person's kidney function. It is often referred to as AKI. Kidney function is measured by blood tests, and acute kidney injury is identified in the same way. Acute kidney injury can be caused by a number of things. It might be because of stress on the kidneys, due to other illnesses or infection. It might be due to severe dehydration or it could be the result of the side effects of some drugs when you are unwell. Sometimes it's due to a combination of factors. Acute kidney injury can get better in a few days or weeks, but sometimes it causes ongoing problems. Although

called acute kidney injury, it is not caused as a result of a physical blow to the body. Nor is it caused by excessive intake of alcohol, yet it should be remembered that too much alcohol can damage your other organs and cause you to be dehydrated.

What are the symptoms of acute kidney injury?
Sometimes there are no real symptoms or signs. A blood test is needed to detect it. Acute kidney injury can have the following symptoms:

- Changes to urine output, particularly a major reduction in the amount of urine passed;
- Nausea, vomiting;
- Abdominal pains and feeling generally unwell, similar to a hangover;
- Dehydration or thirst;
- Confusion and drowsiness.

If you have concerns about your kidney function, you should seek advice from your GP. If you are concerned about acute kidney injury, there is a lot of helpful information online. Use these links to find out more about your kidneys and acute kidney injury, connect with others with acute kidney injury or get support. (These links can be found in Appendix IX.)

Facts about your kidneys
- Your kidneys are vital organs that filter your blood up to 30 times a day. They keep what is needed and get rid of what is not needed through urine.
- Each of your two kidneys is about the size and weight

of a mobile phone. Placed end to end, the filters in one kidney would stretch about five miles.

- Your kidneys help keep your bones healthy by activating vitamin D.
- Kidneys have some control over your red blood cells – if your kidneys are not getting enough oxygen they send a signal to your body to make more red blood cells and prevent you from becoming anaemic (deficiency of red blood cells). Your kidneys are responsible for keeping the components of your blood in balance.
- Your kidneys use one quarter of your body's energy. They work 24-hours-a-day, seven-days-a-week, for the whole of your life. They have a higher blood flow rate than your heart, brain or liver.
- Kidneys keep on working until they have lost up to 90% of their function. They are the unsung heroes of our bodies and don't stop working until they really can't cope.
- Your body can work with just one kidney so a kidney can be donated to someone who needs it with no detriment to the donor.

https://www.thinkkidneys.nhs.uk/information-for-the-public/

Appendix VIII

LIVING KIDNEY DONATION – QUESTIONS & ANSWERS

Provided by the NHS Blood and Transplant – NHS Blood and Transplant Service Organ Donation 2013.

Who can donate?

Donors are often a close relative, such as a parent, brother or sister, son or daughter, but may also be individuals who are not related but have an established emotional relationship with the recipient, such as a partner or close friend. Sometimes a donor and a recipient may be incompatible with each other because of blood group or tissue-type and, in this case, it may be possible for them to be paired with another donor and recipient in the same situation. This means that each recipient will benefit from a transplant that they would otherwise not have had (this is called paired donation). Where more than two pairs are involved in the swap, it is called pooled donation. Donors may also offer to give a kidney to someone who is on the waiting list for a transplant but whom they have never met before (this is called non-directed altruistic donation).

What is the age range for being a donor?

In England, Wales and Northern Ireland there is no minimum age limit specified within the Human Tissue Act 2004 for a person to be considered as a living kidney donor. However, the majority of donors will be over the age of eighteen years, and children would only be considered in very exceptional circumstances. In Scotland, only people over sixteen years of age can be legally considered as living kidney donors.

How will I know if I am suitable to donate?

You will have a thorough medical, surgical and psychological assessment to establish that you are fit and healthy to donate. A number of people who wish to donate find that they are not able to do so because health problems are discovered through the assessment process. Members of the healthcare team involved in your assessment include counsellors, co-ordinators and social workers.

Are there any risks to me?

All operations carry some risk and this is no different for living donation. Donors are at risk of infections (e.g. chest, wound or urine) and, more rarely, bleeding or blood clots. There is a very small risk of death for the donor: this is estimated at 1 in 3,000 for this operation.

Are there any long-term risks?

There is a small possibility of a slight rise in blood pressure and excess protein in your urine. However, studies have shown that there is no long-term effect on the health of the donor or your remaining kidney.

Am I at greater risk of developing kidney failure?

You are at no greater risk of developing kidney failure after donating than anyone in the general population.

Will it shorten my lifespan?

Studies have shown that donors live longer than the average population. This is because donors are selected on the basis of good health and are thoroughly screened prior to donation.

Will I have to change my lifestyle after donating?

No. You should lead a normal, healthy life as before.

Will donating my kidney affect a future pregnancy or fathering a child?

The small amount of data available shows that, having donated one kidney, there is no evidence to suggest an increased risk of complications during pregnancy. A man's fertility will not be affected.

Will I be covered by my health insurance?

You should check with your insurance company.

What if I live in a different part of the UK from the person I am donating to?

You can still donate. The transplant team can arrange for your donor assessment to take place at a hospital near you if that is more convenient for you. Usually the donation will take place in the hospital where the person you are donating to is cared for. However, different arrangements can be made depending upon individual circumstances for both the donor and recipient.

What if I live overseas?

You can still donate. Some preliminary tests can be arranged in your own country to see if you will be a suitable donor.

What are the religious views on living donation?

Most religions support living donation as they view it as a gift to a loved one. If you have any doubt, you should contact your religious leader.

How long does the donor assessment process take?

In general, this will take at least three months. There is variation depending upon where you live and what tests you may require. Wherever possible, the assessment is tailored to your needs and commitments.

How much time will I need to take off work?

Most transplant centres will try to arrange the tests and investigations before the operation around your work schedule to minimise disruption to your job. It is sometimes possible to arrange for some of this to be done locally if the donor lives a long way from the transplant centre. The operation and recovery period varies from 2 – 12 weeks depending on surgery, your individual recovery and the type of work you will be resuming.

How will I be able to afford time off work?

You should discuss this with your employer and find out what is available under your (their) terms of employment around Statutory Sick Pay. You may be eligible for reimbursement of loss of earnings and costs. However, reimbursement is at the discretion of the recipient's healthcare providers. You will need to discuss this with your transplant team.

What if I am in receipt of a benefit such as job seeker's allowance?
You should take advice about this by contacting your local Citizens Advice Bureau.

How is the kidney removed?
You will be given a general anaesthetic which means that you will be asleep during the operation. Traditionally in the UK, the kidney is removed by making an incision in the side or abdomen (tummy) that is known as the "open" technique. Increasingly, keyhole surgery is used to remove the kidney and this is also available in a number of transplant centres in the UK.

How long will the operation take?
The operation takes approximately two hours and you will have a urinary catheter and a drip when you return from theatre.

How long will I be in hospital?
This varies depending on your individual recovery. The average stay is four to ten days.

Will I experience a lot of pain?
Strong pain relief will be provided to help alleviate pain and discomfort after the operation.

Will I need to take any medication after donating?
You will need to take some painkillers immediately after the operation and during the recovery period. You may also be prescribed antibiotics for a short period if you need them.

However, you will not need any long-term medication as a result of kidney donation.

What about follow-up?
You would usually be seen by the transplant team between two and six weeks after donation. We recommend that you attend an annual follow-up appointment, if you wanted this, for the rest of your life.

Do some donors have trouble making the decision?
Some people make the decision easily. Others go through some soul-searching before deciding. Being afraid of donating a kidney or feeling guilty about not wanting to donate is quite normal. The only "right" decision is the one that makes you, the potential donor, feel comfortable. Finding out more information about living donation and what it involves may help you with this decision.

Can I speak to somebody who has donated?
Your co-ordinator at your local transplant centre should be able to arrange this for you.

Suppose I decide against being a donor?
You have the right to withdraw your offer at any time and you would be supported in your decision by the transplant team.

Who makes the final decision?
Once all the tests have been completed and found satisfactory by the transplant team, a date is set for the operation. The transplant will only take place if both the donor and recipient are willing to proceed.

Will the transplant be successful?

There is no guarantee that any kidney transplant will work. However, living kidney transplantation is overwhelmingly successful, with 90-95% of live donated kidneys working well at one year. This compares with a success rate of 85-90% for kidneys from deceased donors.

What is the first thing I should do if I am thinking about being a donor?

If you know the person who you are considering donating to, you will need to contact the hospital/transplant centre where the intended recipient is cared for. The first piece of information we would need to know is your blood group to see if it is compatible with your recipient. After this an appointment will be arranged for more detailed discussion and initial blood tests. If you do not know who the intended recipient might be, the best thing to do is to contact your local transplant centre for further advice.

What governs living organ donation in the UK?

In England, Wales and Northern Ireland, the Human Tissue Act 2004, and in Scotland the Human Tissue (Scotland) Act 2006, provide the legal framework for organ and tissue donation in the UK. The Human Tissue Authority is the regulatory body that is established under the Acts to ensure that there is no coercion, pressure or payment involved in the donation of organs, which is illegal in the UK. The Authority must approve all donations from living donors and all donors will be assessed by an Independent Assessor as a routine part of the evaluation process to ensure that all the legal requirements are met.

Sources:

UK Living Donor Kidney Transplantation, 2005; information about living donor transplants, Human Tissue Authority, 2006; Meier-Kreische, H-U, Kaplan, B. 2002.

Appendix IX

USEFUL LINKS

There are a number of charities that provide support and advice for people and their families with acute kidney injury in the UK. The below are reproduced from the Think Kidneys Website 2014.

The British Kidney Patient Association

The British Kidney Patient Association (BKPA) was established in 1975 and works to improve the quality of life for adults and children with kidney disease.

The BKPA provides information and advice. They also give grants to help patients and families with kidney disease for the purpose of covering the costs of domestic bills, hospital travel, education and holidays during times of financial hardship. The BKPA also gives financial support to kidney units throughout the UK to help improve kidney services and patient care.

The National Kidney Federation

The National Kidney Federation is unique because it is the only national kidney charity actually run by kidney patients for kidney patients.

Most renal units have a Kidney Patient Association (KPA) specifically attached to that unit but, in 1978, these independent charities realised that they needed a national organisation to fight their cause as renal provision was facing difficulties in many areas. There are 69 KPAs and they come together as the controlling Council of the National Kidney Federation, the KPAs are the ears and the eyes of the NKF. Patients are the officers and executive committee of the NKF and the workforce of the NKF.

Unlike other kidney charities, the NKF has only two roles: campaigning for improvements to renal provision and treatment; and national patient support services.

Kidney Research UK
Kidney Research UK is a national charity dedicated to research that will lead to better treatments and cures for kidney disease. It also provides information for patients and raises vital awareness of kidney-related issues among the general public.

Each year, KRUK works to raise immediate awareness of kidney-related issues among the general public, including people at higher risk. Their patient information service also provides advice and literature on how best to deal with each type of kidney condition, helping millions of people better understand the disease.

Kidney Research UK is the largest funder dedicated to research into the causes and prevention of kidney disease. Money raised goes directly into research to find better treatments and ultimately a cure.

Kidney Dialysis Information Centre
KDIC provides useful information about dialysis in straightforward language, but with enough medical terms to

help anyone understand what they are being told by medical staff about their care.

InfoKID
InfoKID provides information for parents and carers about kidney conditions in babies, children and young people. They provide information about conditions, tests, treatments and supporting information – on screen or in downloadable leaflets.

Links for patients
- British Kidney Patient Association – http://www. britishkidney-pa.co.uk/
- Diabetes UK – http://www.diabetes.org.uk/
- Kidney Alliance – http://www.infokid.org.uk/
- Kidney Dialysis Information Centre – http://www. kidneydialysis.org.uk/
- Kidney Patient Guide – http://www.kidneypatientguide. org.uk/support.php
- Kidney Research UK – www.kidneyresearchuk.org
- National Kidney Federation – http://www.kidney.org. uk/
- NHS England Think Kidneys. National programme of NHS England in partnership with the UK Renal Registry – www.thinkkidneys.nhs.uk
- NHS Choices – http://www.nhs.uk/conditions/acute-kidney-injury
- NICE – http://www.nice.org.uk/guidance/cg169/ documents/acute-kidney-injury-full-version2
- Patient.co.uk – http://www.patient.co.uk/doctor/acute-kidney-injury-pro

- PatientView – www.patientview.org
- Polycystic Kidney Disease Charity – http://pkdcharity.org.uk/
- Rare Renal – http://rarerenal.org/
- Welsh Kidney Patients Association – http://www.wkpa.org.uk/

Links for health and care professionals
- Advisory Committee on the Safety of Blood, Tissues and Organs (SaBTO) – http://www.worldkidneyday.co.uk/
- American Transplantation Society – www.myast.org
- Australia & New Zealand Dialysis and Transplant Registry (ANZ DATA) – http://www.anzdata.org.au/v1/
- British Association of Paediatric Nephrology – http://www.renal.org/BAPN#sthash.ySTfxadZ.dpbs
- British Renal Society – http://www.britishrenal.org/Home.aspx
- British Transplantation Society – http://www.bts.org.uk/
- Care Quality Commission – http://www.cqc.org.uk/
- Department of Health – www.gov.uk/government/organisations/department-of-health
- European Renal Association & European Dialysis & Transplant Association – http://www.era-edta.org/
- Health & Social Care Information Centre – http://content.digital.nhs.uk
- Healthcare Quality Improvement Partnership – http://www.hqip.org.uk/
- International Society for Peritoneal Dialysis – http://www.ispd.org/
- International Society of Nephrology – http://www.theisn.org/

- Japanese Society of Nephrology – http://www.jsn.or.jp/
- Kidney Disease | Improving Global Outcomes – http://kdigo.org/home/
- Latin American Society of Nephrology & Hypertension – http://www.slanh.org/
- List of all the European Societies of Nephrology – http://www.era-edta.org/page-13-80-0-80-
- europeansocietiesofnephrology.html
- Malaysian Society of Nephrology – http://www.msn.org.my/fwbPagePublic.jsp?fwbPageId=pIndex
- National Cardiovascular Intelligence Network – http://www.yhpho.org.uk/default.aspx?RID=185778
- National Kidney Foundation (USA) – https://www.kidney.org/
- National Kidney Foundation, Singapore (NKFS) – http://www.nkfs.org/
- NHS Blood & Transplant – http://www.nhsbt.nhs.uk/
- NHS England – http://www.england.nhs.uk/ourwork/patientsafety/akiprogramme/
- NICE – http://www.nice.org.uk/guidance/cg169/
- documents/acute-kidney-injury-full-version2
- RaDaR – https://www.radar.nhs.uk
- Renal Association – http://www.renal.org/#sthash.
- LayTniLY.dpbs
- Scottish Renal Registry – http://www.srr.scot.nhs.uk/
- Sociedade Brasiliera de Nefrologia – http://www.sbn.org.br/
- South African Renal Society – http://www.sa-
- renalsociety.org/
- The American Society of Nephrology – http://www.asn-
- online.org/

- The Canadian Society of Nephrology – www.csnscn.ca/new-website
- The Health Foundation – http://www.health.org.uk/
- The Renal Information Exchange Group – http://www.rixg.org.uk/j/index.php
- The Renal Society of Australasia – http://www.renalsociety.org/
- UK Renal Registry – https://www.renalreg.org/

Links to research and researchers
- British Renal Society – http://www.britishrenal.org/Research-for-Renal.aspx
- Health Research Authority – http://www.hra.nhs.uk/
- Epsom & St Helier University Hospitals NHS Trust – https://www.epsom-sthelier.nhs.uk/
- Keele University – http://www.keele.ac.uk/
- London School of Hygiene & Tropical Medicine – www.lshtm.ac.uk/
- National Institute for Health Research – http://www.nihr.ac.uk/research/
- Renal Association – http://www.renal.org/academic/research#sthash.5tUCZaQR.dpbs
- University of Aberdeen – www.abdn.ac.uk
- University of Bristol – www.bristol.ac.uk
- University of Sheffield – www.sheffield.ac.uk
- University of Southampton – www.southampton.ac.uk

NOTES ON SOURCES

Page

Introduction

xiii   Plan as if you will live forever and live each day as if it were your last: *Adapted from Gabriol S. 1021-1058. Source unknown*

Part 1: Intensive Care. 21st January 2009 – 4th February 2009

1: Darkness

6   Subsequently a diagnosis was made that I had a rare blood infection caused by bacteria: *The Management of Invasive Group A Streptococcal Infections in Ireland. Invasive Group A Streptococcus Sub-Committee. Health Protection Surveillance Centre*

7   Severe sepsis is a major cause of illness and death: Daniels R. *Surviving the first hours in sepsis: getting the basics right (an intensivist's perspective). Journal of Antimicrobial Chemotherapy 2011; 66 (suppl 2; 11-23)*

12   I wonder if this was perhaps the near-death experience: *van Lommel P et al. "Near-Death*

Experience in Survivors of Cardiac Arrest: A Prospective Study in the Netherlands," The Lancet, 2001; 358 (9298):2039-45

14   They listen to and trust their parents and significant adults: *Harris P and Corriveau K. Young children's selective trust in informants http://rstb.royalsocietypublishing.org/content/366/1567/1179.long*

18   My views were subsequently further reinforced by the cogent arguments of Steve Stewart-Williams in his book: *Darwin, God And The Meaning Of Life. How Evolutionary Theory Undermines Everything You Thought You Knew. Cambridge University Press: New York, 2010.352pp., ISBN #978-0-521-76278-6 (hardcover)*

18   In common with other human constructs such as nation states, political ideologies and limited companies, it also facilitates the cooperation of large numbers of strangers. "Large numbers of strangers can cooperate successfully by believing in common myths." This may have given the species sapiens the ability to dominate and annihilate other species of the genus Homo. "*Homo sapiens* conquered the world thanks above all to its unique language." *Harari Y N discusses this concept in his book Sapiens A Brief History of Humankind. Kinneret, Zmora-Bitan, Dvir 2011(Hebrew version), Vintage Books:2014 pp 21, 30 (English version).*

20   I recalled sections of a book by Steven Pinker, Professor of Psychology at MIT: How the Mind Works: *Pinker S. How the Mind Works. Penguin Books 1997*

22   Apparently, hallucinations are common among intensive care patients: *Skirrow P, Jones C, Griffiths D, Kaney S. Intensive care – easing the trauma. The Psychologist 2001;14:640-642*

31   There is growing evidence of poor mental health and quality of life among survivors of intensive care: In a group of 157 intensive care patients, it was found that those whose breathing was maintained mechanically by a machine for more than 24 hours or those who had two or more organs supported by a machine, (I had both) suffered considerable psychological distress both during and following the admission. Three months after discharge, 27% had probable post-traumatic stress disorder, 46% had probable depression and 44% had anxiety *Wade D M. et al. Investigating risk factors for psychological morbidity three months after intensive care: a prospective cohort study. Critical Care 2012, 16:R192 doi:10.1186/cc11677*

32   What proof you could give if anyone should ask us now: *Plato A. Theaetetus 158b-d 369 BCE*

2: Awakening

38   It can teach us about life, since as in life it...: *Barenboim D. Edward W. Said London Lecture 2015. Music in Life and Life in Music. Can be viewed at www.mosaicrooms.org*

38   It was a privilege to be part of rock group during my university years. The group was named Dave Douglas and the Vistas. The only online reference

is: *http://california-ballroom.info/bands/dave-Douglas-and-the-Vistas.htm*

45   The risk of love is loss, and the price of loss is grief: *Stanton Zunin H. Zunin L. Art of Condolence: What to Write, Say and Do at a Time of Loss.* Publ. HarperCollins.1992 page 11

Part 2: Out of Intensive Care. 4th February 2009 - 27th March 2009

3: One step at a time

50   Labour can be viewed as something that may get out of control or it can be viewed as climbing a mountain ....: *Parsons B 1915-2012.* Her books included *Understanding Childbirth Publ. Aurum Press Ltd. 1996, Preparing for Childbirth. Fisher Books 1997 and The Expectant Father Publ. Elliot Right Way Books 2004*

51   Our greatest glory is not in never falling, but in rising every time we fall: *Confucius. Chinese philosopher and reformer 551BC-479BC.* There is some dispute about the origin of this saying. For further information see *http://quoteinvestigator.com/2014/05/27/rising/*

51   We should never be afraid to go after something that we want for fear of failure: *Zamet S J. Consultant Periodontologist. Personal communication 1978*

4: Mental distraction

59   *Porter C 1944 Every Time We Say Goodbye Music and Lyrics by Cole Porter. New York: Chappell & Co., Inc. p. 205. ISBN 394-70794-X*

59 McVie Christine 1998 *Songbird on the 1977 album Rumours*

59 Cassidy E. 1998. *Songbird in Songbird compilation album.* She was virtually unknown outside her native Washington DC, when she died of melanoma in 1996. Songbird climbed to the top of the UK Albums Charts, almost three years after its initial release

5: Dialysis

72 Good quality standard haemodialysis: *O'Donoghue D. 2013 Personal communication*

75 I found three books very informative, all published by Class publishing: *Stein A. Wilde J. Kidney Failure Explained. Class Publ. London 2007; Stein A. Wilde J. Kidney Dialysis and Transplants. Class Publ. London 2008; Auer J. Living Well With Kidney Failure. Class Publ. London 2005*
The dietary restrictions can be quite daunting and these books were very helpful.

75 Dialysis: making the right choices for you. The Dialysis Decision Aid Booklet. *Bekker H. et al. www.kidneyresearchuk.org/health-information* E mail: *kidneyhealth@kidneyresearchuk.org*
This publication became available after my transplant so I didn't use it. However, it was highly commended at the BMA Patient Information Awards.

76 Despite representing just 0.1% of the population: In 2011, in a survey of fifty-two hospitals in England that offered dialysis services, remarkably, up to

50% of their patient transport service costs were accounted for by dialysis. From 2008 to 2009, there was a 3.5% growth of haemodialysis patients and, in 2011, 35,702 patients in the UK received NHS dialysis, an increase of 4% from 2010.

Green S. NHS Kidney Care. England Dialysis Capacity Survey as at October 2011. http://webarchive. nationalarchives.gov.uk/20130504185629//http:// kidneycare.nhs.uk/our_work_programmes/ commissioning/dialysis_capacity_survey//#

Wheeler D. The Renal Registry Report 2012. http:// www.renalreg.com/Reports/2012.html

76   The following section is reproduced with permission of: NHS Think Kidneys Programme 2014. Terms of reference. *https://www.thinkkidneys. nhs.uk/wp-content/uploads/2014/10/AKI-Terms- of-Reference-Final-October-2014.pdf*

77   It is estimated that one in five emergency admissions into hospital are associated with AKI: *Wang, H et al. Acute kidney injury and mortality in hospitalised patients. Am J Nephrol 2012;35:349-355; National Confidential Enquiry into Patient Outcome and Death 2009 Adding Insult to Injury (NCEPOD) http://www.ncepod.org. uk/2009report1/Downloads/AKI_report.pdf*

77   This is not just an issue for kidney specialists: *Selby NM, et al. Use of electronic results reporting to diagnose and monitor AKI in hospitalized patients. Clin J Am Soc Nephrol. 2012 Apr;7(4):533-40*

77   The older person with complex health issues and associated illnesses is most at risk: *National Institute*

for Care Effectiveness (NICE) 2013. Acute kidney injury. Prevention, detection and management up to the point of renal replacement therapy.

77   The complication of AKI to ongoing illness prolongs hospital stays and increases mortality: *NHS Think Kidneys programme 2014. Terms of reference. https://www.thinkkidneys.nhs.uk/wp-content/uploads/2014/10/AKI-Terms-of-Reference-Final-October-2014.pdf*

77   The financial burden upon the NHS is large: *NHS Programme Budgeting Data 2003/4-2012/13 Summarised Programme Budgeting Aggregate PCT Figures: https://www.networks.nhs.uk/nhs-networks/health-investment-network/;*

Kerr M, Bedford M, Matthews B and O'Donoghue D. The economic impact of acute kidney injury in England. Nephrol Dial Transplant 2014;29:1362-1368;

Kerr M. Economic Impact:Calculating The Cost. Health Service Journal 2011; Suppl 23 June;

National Institute for Care Effectiveness (NICE) 2013. Acute kidney injury. Prevention, detection and management up to the point of renal replacement therapy. http://www.nice.org.uk/guidance

NHS Think kidneys programme 2014. Terms of reference. https://www.thinkkidneys.nhs.uk/wp-content/uploads/2014/10/AKI-Terms-of-Reference-Final-October-2014.pdf

77   Thousands of deaths could be avoided through the provision of basic medical care: *O'Donoghue D.(a) British Journal of Renal Medicine 2013; Vol 18 No 1 – http://www.bjrm.co.uk; O'Donoghue D. (b)*

BBC News Health 2013. http://m.bbc.co.uk/news/ health-22891644

6: Misunderstandings

80   An Ipsos Morri survey in 2015 found that only 51% of the population ...: *ThinkKidneys/Ipsos MORI 2014*

7: Something to live for

83   Even in the degradation, torture and abject misery of a concentration camp: Viktor Emil Frankl was an Austrian neurologist and psychiatrist as well as a Holocaust survivor. He discovered the importance of finding meaning in all forms of existence, even the most brutal ones and, by extension, a reason to continue living. He became one of the key figures in existential therapy: *Frankl F. Man's Search for Meaning . Publ. Rider an imprint of Ebury Publishing. 2004. First published in 1946*

84   I prefer to be true to myself, even at the hazard of incurring the ridicule of others: *Douglas F. Narrative of the Life of Frederick Douglass, An American Slave Chapter 5 Boston: Published at the Anti-Slavery Office, 1845*

84   'This above all: to thine own self be true, And it must follow, as the night the day, Thou canst not then be false to any man': *Polonius. Hamlet Act 1 Scene 3. Shakespeare W. Uncertain date between 1599 and 1602*

8: Too Weak to Walk

86   Medication was given to control the nausea, (prochlorperazine – Stemetil; or domperidone 10-20mg four times a day, I think, as an inpatient, but I'm not sure; domperidone 10mg twice a day as an outpatient).

9: Progress

95   Of course, there may be a counter-effect. If they are praying for you, you're probably close to being on the "way out": *Benson H, Dusek JA, Sherwood JB, et al. Study of the Therapeutic Effects of Intercessory Prayer (STEP) in cardiac bypass patients: a multicenter randomized trial of uncertainty and certainty of receiving intercessory prayer. American Heart Journal 2006;151 (4): 934–42*

11: Visitors

108   Irvin Yalom addresses the inevitability of, and difficulties associated with, confronting one's own death: *Yalom I. Momma and the Meaning of Life. 2013;Page 134; Piatkus Publ.*

108   In this tale, which dates back four thousand years, Gilgamesh realised that the death of his friend Enkidu…: *Epic of Gilgamesh 13-10 BC http:// en.wikipedia.org/wiki/Epic_of _Gilgamesh*

12: Lesson learned

116   Yesterday: *McCartney P. Yesterday, originally recorded by the Beatles for their 1965 album Help! Credited to "Lennon-McCartney", but the song*

was written solely by Paul McCartney. *http://
en.wikipedia.org/wiki/Yesterday_(song)*

116   Keep a Goin' : *Gibson H 1976.* He adapted the lyrics
from a poem written by Frank L.Stanton. Stanton
was an American lyricist and was also the initial
columnist for the Atlanta Constitution and became
the first poet laureate of the State of Georgia, a
post to which he was appointed by Governor
Clifford Walker in 1925 and which he held until
his death. He was born in 1857 and died in 1927.
Gibson's adaptation changed the last verse to refer
to doctors being human and so they cannot always
predict your fate.
Nashville/KeepaGoin(1975)YouTube

13: Financial concerns

122   It's interesting to note that financial concerns are
common in patients who have been in critical care:
*Kmidtowicz Z .Critical care patients have major
health and financial problems 12 months after
discharge, finds study BMJ 2013;346:f3451*

124   A doctor's visit in 1930 would have cost thirty
pence: *Maggs. Jan.2014. http://maggs224.hubpages.
com/hub/Working-Class-Life-in-the-1930s*

125   Smile: *Composed by Charlie Chaplin for soundtrack
of his 1936 movie Modern Times. John Turner
and Geoffrey Parsons added the lyrics in 1954.
Wada Linda. "Smile". Edna Purviance, Charlie
Chaplin's Leading Lady – Welcome to Paradise.
Retrieved 2010-05-02.* Scans of the sheet music
clearly attribute authorship of the music and lyrics.

Part 3: Home and Outpatient Dialysis. 27th March 2009 – 28th February 2010

15: Much-needed support

140   Some people dream of success while others wake up and work hard at it: *Churchill W 1874-1965. http://www.searchquotes.com/quotation/Some_people_dream_of_success_while_others_wake_up_and_work_hard_at_it./458/*

140   An upbeat district nurse came to change the dressings on my feet three times a week. She used special dressings … : Aquacell silver on the wounds and Allevyn heel: *http://www.woundsinternational.com/media/issues/415/files/content_9845.pdf*

143   *Kahneman D. Desert Island Disc Radio 4. 16th Aug 2013 http://www.bbc.co.uk/iplayer/episode/b0381l2v/Desert_Island_Discs_Daniel_Kahneman/*

145   Anatole Broyard, essayist and former editor of the New York Times book review: *Broyard A. Intoxicated by my illness: and other writings on life and death. New York: Ballantine Books 1992. Pp 43:44*

149   This was a much happier scenario. I was privileged to know a world famous violinist: *Professional confidentiality regulations prevent me from naming him.*

16: Not a good experience

160   Restless legs syndrome: *Al-Jahdali HH et al. Restless leg syndrome in patients on dialysis. Saudi J Kidney Dis Transpl 2009;20:378-85*

19: Setback

179   My Favourite Things, sung by Julie Andrews in The Sound of Music: *Rogers Rogers R and Hammerstein O. 1959. The Sound of Music*

180   He described the essence of his loss-aversion theory: *Kahneman, D. and Tversky, A. "Choices, Values, and Frames". American Psychologist 1984;39 (4): 341–350*

20: What a difference

185   An organ could, however, be received from a donor with blood group type O which represent 44% of the population: *NHS blood and transplant service 2013(a) http://www.blood.co.uk/*

185   In a situation where there is a shortage of donor organs: *Kidney Research UK. 2013 http://www. kidneyresearchuk.org/health/factsheets/ckd-and-issues/kidney-transplantation.php*

186   I do not know the figures for 2009 (when I was put on the list) but at 1st April 2013, there were 9,224 patients on the kidney transplant list:
NHS Blood and transplant Annual Report on Kidney Transplantation. Report for 2013/14: http://www. odt.nhs.uk/pdf/organ_specific_report_kidney_2014. NHS Organ donation and transplantation activity report 2013/14: https://nhsbtmediaservices.blob.core. windows.net/organ-donation-assets/pdfs/activity_ report_2013_14.pdf
Personal communication Lisa Bradbury. *Dept. of Statistics and Clinical Studies, NHSBT*

187   In 2008, it was reported that the annual cost to

the NHS for haemodialysis of one patient for three sessions per week in a satellite unit: *Baboola K. et al. The cost of renal dialysis in a UK setting – a multi-centre study Nephrol. Dial. Transplant 2008;23:1982-1989*

188 The average cost to the NHS of a kidney transplant.....: *NHS Blood and Transplant Service 2009: http://www.organdonation.nhs. uk/newsroom/fact_sheets/cost_effectiveness_of_ transplantation.asp*

21: The word gets out

189 The figures for adults receiving their first living donor kidney transplant are an average of 97% graft: *https://nhsbtmediaservices.blob.core. windows.net/organ-donation-assets/pdfs/activity_ report_2012_13.pdf*

189 The figures for cadaveric donors, according to Kidney Research UK, are slightly different: *Kidney Research UK. 2013 http://www.kidneyresearchuk. org/health/factsheets/ckd-and-issues/kidney- transplantation.php*

190 There are, of course, risks for the donor which are very clearly explained to them. The information provided by the NHS is reproduced in Appendix VIII, with permission: *NHS Blood and Transplant Service Organ Donation 2013(b) http://www. organdonation.nhs.uk/how_to_become_a_donor/ living_kidney_donation/questions_and_answers. asp*

22: A heartbeat away from disaster

200   In the UK in 2004, following a court case in which Miss Chester sued Mr Afshar, a neurosurgeon. In the judgment, the following was stated: "Although the risk of the operation going wrong would not at all have been changed had Miss Chester been warned, it was the duty of the doctor to warn her. It is a basic principle of good medical practice that adults should consent on a fully informed basis to surgery, aware of all risks. Dr Afshar had therefore violated her right to choose." This raises a fundamental question and that is, what are all of the risks? How far should a doctor (or dentist) go in explaining the risks? Should, for example, the potential complications of local anaesthetic be given? What about the figures for success rates of junior doctors compared to experienced ones?

Chester v Afshar [2004] UKHL 41. http://www. publications.parliament.uk/pa/ld200304/ldjudgmt/ jd041014/cheste-1.htm

201   This is the approach adopted by the General Medical Council *GMC. Consent Guidance : Patients and Doctors Making Decisions Together. 2008. http://www.gmc-uk.org/guidance/ethical_guidance/ consent_guidance_index.asp*

202   Gawande A. *Complications. Metropolitan books. ISBN 978-1-84668-132 5*

202   Marsh H. *Do No Harm. Phoenix an imprint of Orion Books Ltd. ISBN 978-1-7802-2592-0*

Part 4: The Transplant and Subsequent Recovery.
1st March 2010 – November 2014

25: Things that are said

222   Receiving 25% of the blood from every heartbeat: *NHS Think kidneys programme 2014. Public Campaign: https://www.thinkkidneys.nhs.uk/wp*

26: Regaining what I had lost

228   When, at the end of their lives, most men look back they will find that they have lived throughout ad interim: *Schopenhauer A. Essays Chapter 4. The University of Adelaide eBooks 2012; http://ebooks.adelaide.edu.au/s/schopenhauer/arthur/controversy/complete.html*

228   To enjoy the present, and to make this the purpose of one's life …: *Schopenhauer A. Essays The Emptiness Of Existence; https://books.google.co.uk/books?id=Iif5CgAAQBAJ&pg=PT48&lpg=PT48&dq*

27: Medication

231   Currently, I am regularly taking a variety of medications, the immunosuppressants and various tablets for my heart, prostate, cholesterol, stomach and acidity of my blood: *lisinopril, bisoprosol, aspirin, tamsulosin, omeprazole, pravistatin, sodium bicarbonate, ezetamibe*

232   An American study reported that skin cancer was more common on the left arm and that driver-side automobile ultraviolet light exposure is a likely contributing factor: *Paulson K et al. Asymmetric lateral distribution of melanoma and Merkel cell*

carcinoma in the United States. *Journal of the American Academy of Dermatology 2011;65:35-39*
There is some evidence that laminated glass, as used in windscreens, may reduce UV penetration, but why take the chance?

233 Keeping hands clean through improved hand hygiene is one of the most important steps we can take to avoid getting sick and spreading germs to others: *CDC – Handwashing: Clean Hands Save Lives 11/01/2013; http://www.cdc.gov/handwashing/*

233 Eighty per cent of all infectious diseases are transmitted by contact both direct and indirect – direct such as kissing: *Tierno P. 2013 in: How germy is a handshake? http://ph.news.yahoo.com/germy-handshake-study-reports-172841530.html*

29: Getting on with life

250 A medical doctor had been a live kidney donor for his wife, unfortunately, subsequently, the marriage ended in divorce: *Guardian Newspaper. Wednesday 7th January 2009*

256 UK dentists are sued two or three times more often than UK medics: *Dental Protection Society. Report December 2014*

262 As a patient, I am delighted that the NHS is placing an emphasis on AKI: *NHS Think kidneys programme 2014. Terms of reference. https://www.thinkkidneys.nhs.uk/wp-content/uploads/2014/10/AKI-Terms-of-Reference-Final-October-2014.pdf*

Part 5: Reflections

30: What has the effect of the journey been?

272   In his book Thus Spake Zarathustra, Nietzsche introduces the question: *Nietzsche FW.1883. Thus Spake Zarathustra. Publ by Thrifty Books 2009; Nietzsche F W. 1882. The Gay Science, p. 341 (passage translated in Nietzsche as Philosopher by Danto A 1965, p. 210). Columbia University Press*

278   The best-laid schemes o' mice an' men/gang aft agley: *Burns R. poem, To a Mouse, on Turning Her Up in Her Nest with the Plough 1786. This is often paraphrased in English as "The best-laid plans of mice and men/Often go awry". John Steinbeck shortened the original phrase and used it as the title for a book Of Mice and Men. Publ. Covici, Friede Inc.1937.*

281   The World Health Organisation (Leung E 2011) echoed this concern: *Leung E et al. The WHO policy package to combat antimicrobial resistance. Bulletin of the World Health Organization 2011;89:390-392. doi: 10.2471/BLT.11.088435*

281   The terms true self and false self were introduced into psychoanalysis: *Winnicot D.W. "Ego distortion in terms of true and false self" in the Maturational Process and the Facilitating Environment: Studies in the Theory of Emotional Development. New York International UP Inc. 1965,pp 140-152*

281   What we think or what we know or what we believe is, in the end, of little consequence: *Ruskin J. The Crown of Wild Olive, lecture IV: The Future of England, 1866 section 151*

Appendices

Appendix I: Memories of Intensive Care – Priscilla, my wife

307 'A wise man should consider that health is the greatest of human blessings': *Hippocrates c 460-c 370 BC Regimen in Health*

Appendix V: Dietary restrictions for dialysis

342 Dietary instructions from the Nutrition and Dietetics Services, of the Royal Free Hospital NHS Trust 2009

343 The guidelines suggest that not more than six grams of salt should be consumed per day: *White E. Top healthy tips for 2013, Royal Free Hospital Dietician, RF HK PA newsletter April 2013: 12 – 13*

Appendix VI: History of dialysis

346 Previously, dialysis meant dissolution of the strength or weakness of the limbs, coming from the Greek, to part asunder: *Graham T. E. The Bakerian Lecture on Osmotic Force. Phil. Trans. R Soc. Lond. 1854;177-228*

346 'The survival of patients already on renal replacement therapy means that even without further increases in take-on rate.' In England there are now some clinical commissioning groups which are responsible for issuing contracts for dialysis services. It is difficult to see how groups of general practitioners, with very little training in dialysis will be in a position to make the choices:

Renal Association Report 2013. Levels of Renal Replacement Therapy (RRT) http://www.renal.org/whatwedo/UKNephrology.aspx

347   At the first meeting of the International Society of Nephrology in Evian, France, in 1960, Belding Scribner from Seattle: Scribner B. International Society of Nephrology 1960. *See Blagg CR. The first dialysis for chronic renal failure 50 years ago. Hemodialysis International 2010;14:1-2*

347   'In 1962, Dr Belding Scribner started the world's first outpatient dialysis facility. Immediately the problem arose of who should receive dialysis, since demand far exceeded the capacity of the six dialysis machines at the centre': DaVita Healthcare Partners Inc. 2013 *http://www.davita.com/kidney-disease/dialysis/motivational/the-history-of-dialysis/e/197*

Appendix VII: Acute Kidney Injury (AKI)

348   The following is reproduced with the permission of the NHS Think Kidneys Programme: *NHS Think kidneys programme 2014. Terms of reference. https://www.thinkkidneys.nhs.uk/wp-content/uploads/2014/10/AKI-Terms-of-Reference-Final-October-2014.pdf*

Appendix VIII: Living kidney donation – Questions & Answers

351   Living organ donation – Questions & Answers: *NHS Blood and Transplant http://www.organdonation.nhs.uk/*

357   What governs living organ donation in the UK?: *Human Tissue Act 2004 http://www.legislation.gov.uk/ukpga/2004/30/contents; Human tissue*

(*Scotland*) *Act 2006. http://www.legislation.gov.uk/ asp/2006/4/contents*

358   Sources: UK Living Donor Kidney Transplantation, BTS & Renal Association, 2nd Edition, April 2005. *Information about living donor transplants, Human Tissue Authority, 2006. http://www.hta.gov.uk/_ db/_documents/Information_on_living_donor_ transplants.pdf*

358   Meier-Kreische, H-U, Kaplan, B. *Waiting time on dialysis as the strongest modifiable risk factor for renal transplant outcomes. Transplantation, 2002;74: 1377-1381*

Appendix IX: Useful links

359   NHS Think Kidneys programme 2014. *Terms of reference.   https://www.thinkkidneys.nhs.uk/wp-content/uploads/2014/10/AKI-Terms-of-Reference-Final-October-2014.pdf*